STEVEN J. LEON

Linear Algebra

WITH APPLICATIONS

Custom Edition for the University of California, Irvine

Material selected from:
Linear Algebra with Applications, Sixth Edition
by Steven J. Leon

PEARSON
Custom
Publishing

PEARSON
Prentice
Hall

Cover Art: *Umeday1*, by Barry Cronin.

Taken from:

Linear Algebra with Applications, Sixth Edition
by Steven J. Leon
Copyright © 2002 by Prentice-Hall, Inc.
A Pearson Education Company
Upper Saddle River, New Jersey 07458

This special edition published in cooperation with Pearson Custom Publishing.

Printed in the United States of America

10 9 8 7 6 5 4 3 2 1

ISBN 0-536-74706-7

BA 998198

SS

Please visit our web site at *www.pearsoncustom.com*

PEARSON CUSTOM PUBLISHING
75 Arlington Street, Suite 300, Boston, MA 02116
A Pearson Education Company

Linear Algebra with Applications

Taken From: Linear Algebra with Applications, Sixth Edition by Steven J. Leon

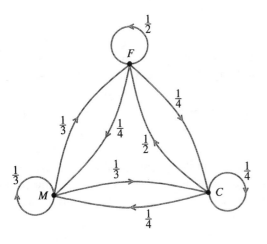

CHAPTER

1

MATRICES AND SYSTEMS OF EQUATIONS

Probably the most important problem in mathematics is that of solving a system of linear equations. Well over 75 percent of all mathematical problems encountered in scientific or industrial applications involve solving a linear system at some stage. By using the methods of modern mathematics, it is often possible to take a sophisticated problem and reduce it to a single system of linear equations. Linear systems arise in applications to such areas as business, economics, sociology, ecology, demography, genetics, electronics, engineering, and physics. Therefore, it seems appropriate to begin this book with a section on linear systems.

1 SYSTEMS OF LINEAR EQUATIONS

A *linear equation in n unknowns* is an equation of the form

$$a_1x_1 + a_2x_2 + \cdots + a_nx_n = b$$

where $a_1, a_2, \ldots, a_n$ and b are real numbers and $x_1, x_2, \ldots, x_n$ are variables. A *linear system* of m equations in n unknowns is then a system of the form

(1)
$$
\begin{aligned}
a_{11}x_1 + a_{12}x_2 + \cdots + a_{1n}x_n &= b_1 \\
a_{21}x_1 + a_{22}x_2 + \cdots + a_{2n}x_n &= b_2 \\
&\vdots \\
a_{m1}x_1 + a_{m2}x_2 + \cdots + a_{mn}x_n &= b_m
\end{aligned}
$$

where the a_{ij}'s and the b_i's are all real numbers. We will refer to systems of the form (1) as $m \times n$ linear systems. The following are examples of linear systems:

(a) $x_1 + 2x_2 = 5$
     $2x_1 + 3x_2 = 8$

(b) $x_1 - x_2 + x_3 = 2$
     $2x_1 + x_2 - x_3 = 4$

(c) $x_1 + x_2 = 2$
     $x_1 - x_2 = 1$
     $x_1\qquad = 4$

System (a) is a 2×2 system, (b) is a 2×3 system, and (c) is a 3×2 system.

By a solution to an $m \times n$ system, we mean an ordered n-tuple of numbers $(x_1, x_2, \ldots, x_n)$ that satisfies all the equations of the system. For example, the ordered pair $(1, 2)$ is a solution to system (a), since

$$1 \cdot (1) + 2 \cdot (2) = 5$$

$$2 \cdot (1) + 3 \cdot (2) = 8$$

The ordered triple $(2, 0, 0)$ is a solution to system (b), since

$$1 \cdot (2) - 1 \cdot (0) + 1 \cdot (0) = 2$$

$$2 \cdot (2) + 1 \cdot (0) - 1 \cdot (0) = 4$$

Actually, system (b) has many solutions. If α is any real number, it is easily seen that the ordered triple $(2, \alpha, \alpha)$ is a solution. However, system (c) has no solution. It follows from the third equation that the first coordinate of any solution would have to be 4. Using $x_1 = 4$ in the first two equations, we see that the second coordinate must satisfy

$$4 + x_2 = 2$$

$$4 - x_2 = 1$$

Since there is no real number that satisfies both of these equations, the system has no solution. If a linear system has no solution, we say that the system is *inconsistent*. If the system has at least one solution, we say that it is *consistent*. Thus system (c) is inconsistent, while systems (a) and (b) are both consistent.

The set of all solutions to a linear system is called the *solution set* of the system. If a system is inconsistent, its solution set is empty. A consistent system will have a nonempty solution set. To solve a consistent system, we must find its solution set.

2 × 2 Systems

Let us examine geometrically a system of the form

$$a_{11}x_1 + a_{12}x_2 = b_1$$

$$a_{21}x_1 + a_{22}x_2 = b_2$$

Each equation can be represented graphically as a line in the plane. The ordered pair (x_1, x_2) will be a solution to the system if and only if it lies on both lines. For example, consider the three systems

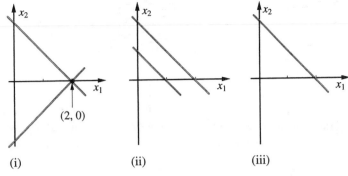

FIGURE 1.1.1

(i) $x_1 + x_2 = 2$
    $x_1 - x_2 = 2$

(ii) $x_1 + x_2 = 2$
     $x_1 + x_2 = 1$

(iii) $x_1 + x_2 = 2$
      $-x_1 - x_2 = -2$

The two lines in system (i) intersect at the point $(2, 0)$. Thus $\{(2, 0)\}$ is the solution set to (i). In system (ii) the two lines are parallel. Therefore, system (ii) is inconsistent and hence its solution set is empty. The two equations in system (iii) both represent the same line. Any point on that line will be a solution to the system (see Figure 1.1.1).

In general, there are three possibilities: the lines intersect at a point, they are parallel, or both equations represent the same line. The solution set then contains either one, zero, or infinitely many points.

The situation is similar for $m \times n$ systems. An $m \times n$ system may or may not be consistent. If it is consistent, it must either have exactly one solution or infinitely many solutions. These are the only possibilities. We will see why this is so in Section 2 when we study the row echelon form. Of more immediate concern is the problem of finding all solutions to a given system. To tackle this problem, we introduce the notion of *equivalent systems*.

Equivalent Systems

Consider the two systems

(a) $3x_1 + 2x_2 - x_3 = -2$
     $\phantom{3x_1 + {}} x_2 \phantom{{} - x_3} = 3$
     $\phantom{3x_1 + 2x_2 - {}} 2x_3 = 4$

(b) $3x_1 + 2x_2 - x_3 = -2$
     $-3x_1 - x_2 + x_3 = 5$
     $3x_1 + 2x_2 + x_3 = 2$

System (a) is easy to solve because it is clear from the last two equations that $x_2 = 3$ and $x_3 = 2$. Using these values in the first equation, we get

$$3x_1 + 2 \cdot 3 - 2 = -2$$

$$x_1 = -2$$

Thus the solution to the system is $(-2, 3, 2)$. System (b) seems to be more difficult to solve. Actually, system (b) has the same solution as system (a). To see this, add the first two equations of the system:

$$3x_1 + 2x_2 - x_3 = -2$$
$$\underline{-3x_1 - x_2 + x_3 = 5}$$
$$x_2 = 3$$

If (x_1, x_2, x_3) is any solution to (b), it must satisfy all the equations of the system. Thus it must satisfy any new equation formed by adding two of its equations. Therefore, x_2 must equal 3. Similarly, (x_1, x_2, x_3) must satisfy the new equation formed by subtracting the first equation from the third:

$$3x_1 + 2x_2 + x_3 = 2$$
$$\underline{3x_1 + 2x_2 - x_3 = -2}$$
$$2x_3 = 4$$

Therefore, any solution to system (b) must also be a solution to system (a). By a similar argument, it can be shown that any solution to (a) is also a solution to (b). This can be done by subtracting the first equation from the second:

$$x_2 = 3$$
$$\underline{3x_1 + 2x_2 - x_3 = -2}$$
$$-3x_1 - x_2 + x_3 = 5$$

Then add the first and third equations:

$$3x_1 + 2x_2 - x_3 = -2$$
$$\underline{2x_3 = 4}$$
$$3x_1 + 2x_2 + x_3 = 2$$

Thus (x_1, x_2, x_3) is a solution to system (b) if and only if it is a solution to system (a). Therefore, both systems have the same solution set, $\{(-2, 3, 2)\}$.

▶ **DEFINITION** Two systems of equations involving the same variables are said to be **equivalent** if they have the same solution set. ◀

Clearly, if we interchange the order in which two equations of a system are written, this will have no effect on the solution set. The reordered system will be equivalent to the original system. For example, the systems

$$\begin{array}{lll} x_1 + 2x_2 = 4 & & 4x_1 + x_2 = 6 \\ 3x_1 - x_2 = 2 & \text{and} & 3x_1 - x_2 = 2 \\ 4x_1 + x_2 = 6 & & x_1 + 2x_2 = 4 \end{array}$$

both involve the same three equations and, consequently, they must have the same solution set.

If one of the equations of a system is multiplied through by a nonzero real number, this will have no effect on the solution set, and the new system will be equivalent to the original system. For example, the systems

$$x_1 + x_2 + x_3 = 3$$
$$-2x_1 - x_2 + 4x_3 = 1$$

and

$$2x_1 + 2x_2 + 2x_3 = 6$$
$$-2x_1 - x_2 + 4x_3 = 1$$

are equivalent.

If a multiple of one equation is added to another equation, the new system will be equivalent to the original system. This follows since the n-tuple $(x_1, \ldots, x_n)$ will satisfy the two equations

$$a_{i1}x_1 + \cdots + a_{in}x_n = b_i$$
$$a_{j1}x_1 + \cdots + a_{jn}x_n = b_j$$

if and only if it satisfies the equations

$$a_{i1}x_1 + \cdots + a_{in}x_n = b_i$$
$$(a_{j1} + \alpha a_{i1})x_1 + \cdots + (a_{jn} + \alpha a_{in})x_n = b_j + \alpha b_i$$

To summarize, there are three operations that can be used on a system to obtain an equivalent system:

I. The order in which any two equations are written may be interchanged.
II. Both sides of an equation may be multiplied by the same nonzero real number.
III. A multiple of one equation may be added to another.

Given a system of equations, we may use these operations to obtain an equivalent system that is easier to solve.

$n \times n$ Systems

Let us restrict ourselves to $n \times n$ systems for the remainder of this section. We will show that if an $n \times n$ system has exactly one solution, operations I and III can be used to obtain an equivalent "triangular system."

▶ **DEFINITION** A system is said to be in **triangular form** if in the kth equation the coefficients of the first $k - 1$ variables are all zero and the coefficient of x_k is nonzero ($k = 1, \ldots, n$). ◀

EXAMPLE I. The system

$$3x_1 + 2x_2 + x_3 = 1$$
$$x_2 - x_3 = 2$$
$$2x_3 = 4$$

is in triangular form, since in the second equation the coefficients are 0, 1, -1, respectively, and in the third equation the coefficients are 0, 0, 2, respectively. Because of the triangular form, this system is easy to solve. It follows from the third equation that $x_3 = 2$. Using this value in the second equation, we obtain

$$x_2 - 2 = 2 \qquad \text{or} \qquad x_2 = 4$$

Using $x_2 = 4$, $x_3 = 2$ in the first equation, we end up with

$$3x_1 + 2 \cdot 4 + 2 = 1$$
$$x_1 = -3$$

Thus the solution to the system is $(-3, 4, 2)$.   ◀

Any $n \times n$ triangular system can be solved in the same manner as the last example. First, the nth equation is solved for the value of x_n. This value is used in the $(n-1)$st equation to solve for x_{n-1}. The values x_n and x_{n-1} are used in the $(n-2)$nd equation to solve for x_{n-2}, and so on. We will refer to this method of solving a triangular system as *back substitution*.

EXAMPLE 2.   Solve the system

$$2x_1 - x_2 + 3x_3 - 2x_4 = 1$$
$$x_2 - 2x_3 + 3x_4 = 2$$
$$4x_3 + 3x_4 = 3$$
$$4x_4 = 4$$

SOLUTION.   Using back substitution, we obtain

$$4x_4 = 4 \qquad x_4 = \quad 1$$
$$4x_3 + 3 \cdot 1 = 3 \qquad x_3 = \quad 0$$
$$x_2 - 2 \cdot 0 + 3 \cdot 1 = 2 \qquad x_2 = -1$$
$$2x_1 - (-1) + 3 \cdot 0 - 2 \cdot 1 = 1 \qquad x_1 = \quad 1$$

Thus the solution is $(1, -1, 0, 1)$.   ◀

If a system of equations is not triangular, we will use operations I and III to try to obtain an equivalent system that is in triangular form.

EXAMPLE 3.   Solve the system

$$x_1 + 2x_2 + x_3 = 3$$
$$3x_1 - x_2 - 3x_3 = -1$$
$$2x_1 + 3x_2 + x_3 = 4$$

SOLUTION. Subtracting 3 times the first row from the second yields

$$-7x_2 - 6x_3 = -10$$

Subtracting 2 times the first row from the third row yields

$$-x_2 - x_3 = -2$$

If the second and third equations of our system, respectively, are replaced by these new equations, we obtain the equivalent system

$$\begin{aligned}
x_1 + 2x_2 + x_3 &= 3 \\
-7x_2 - 6x_3 &= -10 \\
-x_2 - x_3 &= -2
\end{aligned}$$

If the third equation of this system is replaced by the sum of the third equation and $-\frac{1}{7}$ times the second equation, we end up with the following triangular system:

$$\begin{aligned}
x_1 + 2x_2 + x_3 &= 3 \\
-7x_2 - 6x_3 &= -10 \\
-\tfrac{1}{7}x_3 &= -\tfrac{4}{7}
\end{aligned}$$

Using back substitution, we get

$$x_3 = 4, \qquad x_2 = -2, \qquad x_1 = 3 \qquad \blacktriangleleft$$

Let us look back at the system of equations in the last example. We can associate with that system a 3×3 array of numbers whose entries are the coefficients of the x_i's.

$$\begin{bmatrix} 1 & 2 & 1 \\ 3 & -1 & -3 \\ 2 & 3 & 1 \end{bmatrix}$$

We will refer to this array as the *coefficient matrix* of the system. The term *matrix* means simply a rectangular array of numbers. A matrix having m rows and n columns is said to be $m \times n$.

If we attach to the coefficient matrix an additional column whose entries are the numbers on the right-hand side of the system, we obtain the new matrix

$$\left[\begin{array}{ccc|c} 1 & 2 & 1 & 3 \\ 3 & -1 & -3 & -1 \\ 2 & 3 & 1 & 4 \end{array}\right]$$

We will refer to this new matrix as the *augmented matrix*. In general, when an $m \times r$ matrix B is attached to an $m \times n$ matrix A in this way, the augmented matrix is denoted by $(A|B)$. Thus if

$$
A = \begin{bmatrix} a_{11} & a_{12} & \cdots & a_{1n} \\ a_{21} & a_{22} & \cdots & a_{2n} \\ \vdots & & & \\ a_{m1} & a_{m2} & \cdots & a_{mn} \end{bmatrix}, \qquad B = \begin{bmatrix} b_{11} & b_{12} & \cdots & b_{1r} \\ b_{21} & b_{22} & \cdots & b_{2r} \\ \vdots & & & \\ b_{m1} & b_{m2} & \cdots & b_{mr} \end{bmatrix}
$$

then

$$
(A|B) = \begin{bmatrix} a_{11} & \cdots & a_{1n} & b_{11} & \cdots & b_{1r} \\ \vdots & & & \vdots & & \\ a_{m1} & \cdots & a_{mn} & b_{m1} & \cdots & b_{mr} \end{bmatrix}
$$

With each system of equations we may associate an augmented matrix of the form

$$
\begin{bmatrix} a_{11} & \cdots & a_{1n} & b_{1} \\ \vdots & & & \vdots \\ a_{m1} & \cdots & a_{mn} & b_{m} \end{bmatrix}
$$

The system can be solved by performing operations on the augmented matrix. The x_i's are place holders that can be omitted until the end of the computation. Corresponding to the three operations used to obtain equivalent systems, the following row operations may be applied to the augmented matrix.

Elementary Row Operations

   I. Interchange two rows.
   II. Multiply a row by a nonzero real number.
   III. Replace a row by its sum with a multiple of another row.

Returning to the example, we find that the first row is used to eliminate the elements in the first column of the remaining rows. The entries to be eliminated are given in color in the matrix below. We refer to the first row as the *pivotal row*. For emphasis, the entries in the pivotal row are all in bold type and the entire row is color shaded. The first nonzero entry in the pivotal row is called the *pivot*.

$$
\left.\begin{array}{r} (\text{pivot } a_{11} = 1) \\[4pt] \text{entries to be eliminated} \\[4pt] a_{21} = 3 \text{ and } a_{31} = 2 \end{array}\right\} \;\rightarrow\; \begin{bmatrix} \mathbf{1} & \mathbf{2} & \mathbf{1} & \mathbf{3} \\ 3 & -1 & -3 & -1 \\ 2 & 3 & 1 & 4 \end{bmatrix} \;\leftarrow \text{pivotal row}
$$

By using row operation **III**, 3 times the first row is subtracted from the second row and 2 times the first row is subtracted from the third. When this is done, we end up with the matrix

$$\begin{bmatrix} 1 & 2 & 1 & | & 3 \\ 0 & -7 & -6 & | & -10 \\ 0 & -1 & -1 & | & -2 \end{bmatrix} \leftarrow \text{pivotal row}$$

At this step we choose the second row as our new pivotal row and apply row operation **III** to eliminate the last element in the second column. This time the pivot is -7 and the quotient $\frac{-1}{-7} = \frac{1}{7}$ is the multiple of the pivotal row that is subtracted from the third row. We end up with the matrix

$$\begin{bmatrix} 1 & 2 & 1 & | & 3 \\ 0 & -7 & -6 & | & -10 \\ 0 & 0 & -\frac{1}{7} & | & -\frac{4}{7} \end{bmatrix}$$

This is the augmented matrix for the triangular system, which is equivalent to the original system. The solution to the system is easily obtained using back substitution.

EXAMPLE 4.   Solve the system

$$\begin{aligned} - x_2 - x_3 + x_4 &= 0 \\ x_1 + x_2 + x_3 + x_4 &= 6 \\ 2x_1 + 4x_2 + x_3 - 2x_4 &= -1 \\ 3x_1 + x_2 - 2x_3 + 2x_4 &= 3 \end{aligned}$$

SOLUTION.   The augmented matrix for this system is

$$\begin{bmatrix} 0 & -1 & -1 & 1 & | & 0 \\ 1 & 1 & 1 & 1 & | & 6 \\ 2 & 4 & 1 & -2 & | & -1 \\ 3 & 1 & -2 & 2 & | & 3 \end{bmatrix}$$

Since it is not possible to eliminate any entries using 0 as a pivot element, we will use row operation **I** to interchange the first two rows of the augmented matrix. The new first row will be the pivotal row and the pivot element will be 1.

$$(\text{pivot } a_{11} = 1) \quad \begin{bmatrix} 1 & 1 & 1 & 1 & | & 6 \\ 0 & -1 & -1 & 1 & | & 0 \\ 2 & 4 & 1 & -2 & | & -1 \\ 3 & 1 & -2 & 2 & | & 3 \end{bmatrix} \leftarrow \text{pivotal row}$$

Row operation **III** is then used twice to eliminate the two nonzero entries in the first column.

$$\begin{bmatrix} 1 & 1 & 1 & 1 & 6 \\ 0 & -1 & -1 & 1 & 0 \\ 0 & 2 & -1 & -4 & -13 \\ 0 & -2 & -5 & -1 & -15 \end{bmatrix}$$

Next, the second row is used as the pivotal row to eliminate the entries in the second column below the pivot element -1.

$$\begin{bmatrix} 1 & 1 & 1 & 1 & 6 \\ 0 & -1 & -1 & 1 & 0 \\ 0 & 0 & -3 & -2 & -13 \\ 0 & 0 & -3 & -3 & -15 \end{bmatrix}$$

Finally, the third row is used as the pivotal row to eliminate the last element in the third column.

$$\begin{bmatrix} 1 & 1 & 1 & 1 & 6 \\ 0 & -1 & -1 & 1 & 0 \\ 0 & 0 & -3 & -2 & -13 \\ 0 & 0 & 0 & -1 & -2 \end{bmatrix}$$

This augmented matrix represents a triangular system. Solving by back substitution, we obtain the solution $(2, -1, 3, 2)$. ◀

In general, if an $n \times n$ linear system can be reduced to triangular form, then it will have a unique solution that can be obtained by performing back substitution on the triangular system. We can think of the reduction process as an algorithm involving $n - 1$ steps. At the first step, a pivot element is chosen from among the nonzero entries in the first column of the matrix. The row containing the pivot element is called the *pivotal row*. We interchange rows (if necessary) so that the pivotal row is the new first row. Multiples of the pivotal row are then subtracted from each of the remaining $n - 1$ rows so as to obtain 0's in the $(2, 1), \ldots, (n, 1)$ positions. At the second step, a pivot element is chosen from the nonzero entries in column 2, rows 2 through n of the matrix. The row containing the pivot is then interchanged with the second row of the matrix and is used as the new pivotal row. Multiples of the pivotal row are then subtracted from the remaining $n - 2$ rows so as to eliminate all entries below the pivot in the second column. The same procedure is repeated for columns 3 through $n - 1$. Note that at the second step row 1 and column 1 remain unchanged, at the third step the first two rows and first two columns remain unchanged, and

$$\text{Step 1}\quad
\begin{pmatrix}
x & x & x & x & x \\
x & x & x & x & x \\
x & x & x & x & x \\
x & x & x & x & x
\end{pmatrix}
\rightarrow
\begin{pmatrix}
x & x & x & x & x \\
0 & x & x & x & x \\
0 & x & x & x & x \\
0 & x & x & x & x
\end{pmatrix}$$

$$\text{Step 2}\quad
\begin{pmatrix}
x & x & x & x & x \\
0 & x & x & x & x \\
0 & x & x & x & x \\
0 & x & x & x & x
\end{pmatrix}
\rightarrow
\begin{pmatrix}
x & x & x & x & x \\
0 & x & x & x & x \\
0 & 0 & x & x & x \\
0 & 0 & x & x & x
\end{pmatrix}$$

$$\text{Step 3}\quad
\begin{pmatrix}
x & x & x & x & x \\
0 & x & x & x & x \\
0 & 0 & x & x & x \\
0 & 0 & x & x & x
\end{pmatrix}
\rightarrow
\begin{pmatrix}
x & x & x & x & x \\
0 & x & x & x & x \\
0 & 0 & x & x & x \\
0 & 0 & 0 & x & x
\end{pmatrix}$$

FIGURE I.I.2

so on. At each step the overall dimensions of the system are effectively reduced by 1 (see Figure 1.1.2).

If the elimination process can be carried out as described, we will arrive at an equivalent triangular system after $n - 1$ steps. However, the procedure will break down if, at any step, all possible choices for a pivot element are equal to 0. When this happens, the alternative is to reduce the system to certain special echelon or staircase-shaped forms. These echelon forms will be studied in the next section. They will also be used for $m \times n$ systems, where $m \neq n$.

EXERCISES

1. Use back substitution to solve each of the following systems of equations.

(a) $x_1 - 3x_2 = 2$
   $2x_2 = 6$

(b) $x_1 + x_2 + x_3 = 8$
   $2x_2 + x_3 = 5$
   $3x_3 = 9$

(c) $x_1 + 2x_2 + 2x_3 + x_4 = 5$
   $3x_2 + x_3 - 2x_4 = 1$
   $-x_3 + 2x_4 = -1$
   $4x_4 = 4$

(d) $x_1 + x_2 + x_3 + x_4 + x_5 = 5$
   $2x_2 + x_3 - 2x_4 + x_5 = 1$
   $4x_3 + x_4 - 2x_5 = 1$
   $x_4 - 3x_5 = 0$
   $2x_5 = 2$

2. Write out the coefficient matrix for each of the systems in Exercise 1.

3. In each of the following systems, interpret each equation as a line in the plane. For each system, graph the lines and determine geometrically the number of solutions.

(a) $x_1 + x_2 = 4$
$x_1 - x_2 = 2$

(b) $x_1 + 2x_2 = 4$
$-2x_1 - 4x_2 = 4$

(c) $2x_1 - x_2 = 3$
$-4x_1 + 2x_2 = -6$

(d) $x_1 + x_2 = 1$
$x_1 - x_2 = 1$
$-x_1 + 3x_2 = 3$

4. Write an augmented matrix for each of the systems in Exercise 3.

5. Write out the system of equations that corresponds to each of the following augmented matrices.

(a) $\begin{bmatrix} 3 & 2 & 8 \\ 1 & 5 & 7 \end{bmatrix}$

(b) $\begin{bmatrix} 5 & -2 & 1 & 3 \\ 2 & 3 & -4 & 0 \end{bmatrix}$

(c) $\begin{bmatrix} 2 & 1 & 4 & -1 \\ 4 & -2 & 3 & 4 \\ 5 & 2 & 6 & -1 \end{bmatrix}$

(d) $\begin{bmatrix} 4 & -3 & 1 & 2 & 4 \\ 3 & 1 & -5 & 6 & 5 \\ 1 & 1 & 2 & 4 & 8 \\ 5 & 1 & 3 & -2 & 7 \end{bmatrix}$

6. Solve each of the following systems.

(a) $x_1 - 2x_2 = 5$
$3x_1 + x_2 = 1$

(b) $2x_1 + x_2 = 8$
$4x_1 - 3x_2 = 6$

(c) $4x_1 + 3x_2 = 4$
$\frac{2}{3}x_1 + 4x_2 = 3$

(d) $x_1 + 2x_2 - x_3 = 1$
$2x_1 - x_2 + x_3 = 3$
$-x_1 + 2x_2 + 3x_3 = 7$

(e) $2x_1 + x_2 + 3x_3 = 1$
$4x_1 + 3x_2 + 5x_3 = 1$
$6x_1 + 5x_2 + 5x_3 = -3$

(f) $3x_1 + 2x_2 + x_3 = 0$
$-2x_1 + x_2 - x_3 = 2$
$2x_1 - x_2 + 2x_3 = -1$

(g) $\frac{1}{3}x_1 + \frac{2}{3}x_2 + 2x_3 = -1$
$x_1 + 2x_2 + \frac{3}{2}x_3 = \frac{3}{2}$
$\frac{1}{2}x_1 + 2x_2 + \frac{12}{5}x_3 = \frac{1}{10}$

(h) $x_2 + x_3 + x_4 = 0$
$3x_1 + 3x_3 - 4x_4 = 7$
$x_1 + x_2 + x_3 + 2x_4 = 6$
$2x_1 + 3x_2 + x_3 + 3x_4 = 6$

7. The two systems

$$2x_1 + x_2 = 3 \qquad \text{and} \qquad 2x_1 + x_2 = -1$$
$$4x_1 + 3x_2 = 5 \qquad\qquad\qquad 4x_1 + 3x_2 = 1$$

have the same coefficient matrix but different right-hand sides. Solve both systems simultaneously by eliminating the (2, 1) entry of the augmented matrix

$$\begin{bmatrix} 2 & 1 & 3 & -1 \\ 4 & 3 & 5 & 1 \end{bmatrix}$$

and then performing back substitutions for each of the columns corresponding to the right-hand sides.

8. Solve the two systems

$$
\begin{aligned}
x_1 + 2x_2 - 2x_3 &= 1 \\
2x_1 + 5x_2 + x_3 &= 9 \\
x_1 + 3x_2 + 4x_3 &= 9
\end{aligned}
\qquad
\begin{aligned}
x_1 + 2x_2 - 2x_3 &= 9 \\
2x_1 + 5x_2 + x_3 &= 9 \\
x_1 + 3x_2 + 4x_3 &= -2
\end{aligned}
$$

by doing elimination on a 3×5 augmented matrix and then performing two back substitutions.

9. Given a system of the form

$$
\begin{aligned}
-m_1 x_1 + x_2 &= b_1 \\
-m_2 x_1 + x_2 &= b_2
\end{aligned}
$$

where m_1, m_2, b_1, and b_2 are constants:

(a) Show that the system will have a unique solution if $m_1 \neq m_2$.
(b) If $m_1 = m_2$, show that the system will be consistent only if $b_1 = b_2$.
(c) Give a geometric interpretation to parts (a) and (b).

10. Consider a system of the form

$$
\begin{aligned}
a_{11} x_1 + a_{12} x_2 &= 0 \\
a_{21} x_1 + a_{22} x_2 &= 0
\end{aligned}
$$

where a_{11}, a_{12}, a_{21}, and a_{22} are constants. Explain why a system of this form must be consistent.

11. Give a geometrical interpretation of a linear equation in three unknowns. Give a geometrical description of the possible solution sets for a 3×3 linear system.

2 ROW ECHELON FORM

In Section 1 we learned a method for reducing an $n \times n$ linear system to triangular form. However, this method will fail if at any stage of the reduction process all the possible choices for a pivot element in a given column are 0.

EXAMPLE I. Consider the system represented by the augmented matrix

$$\left[\begin{array}{ccccc|c} \mathbf{1} & \mathbf{1} & \mathbf{1} & \mathbf{1} & \mathbf{1} & \mathbf{1} \\ -1 & -1 & 0 & 0 & 1 & -1 \\ -2 & -2 & 0 & 0 & 3 & 1 \\ 0 & 0 & 1 & 1 & 3 & -1 \\ 1 & 1 & 2 & 2 & 4 & 1 \end{array} \right] \leftarrow \text{pivotal row}$$

If row operation **III** is used to eliminate the nonzero entries in the last four rows of the first column, the resulting matrix will be

$$\left[\begin{array}{ccccc|c} 1 & 1 & 1 & 1 & 1 & 1 \\ \mathbf{0} & \mathbf{0} & \mathbf{1} & \mathbf{1} & \mathbf{2} & \mathbf{0} \\ 0 & 0 & 2 & 2 & 5 & 3 \\ 0 & 0 & 1 & 1 & 3 & -1 \\ 0 & 0 & 1 & 1 & 3 & 0 \end{array} \right] \leftarrow \text{pivotal row}$$

At this stage the reduction to triangular form breaks down. All four possible choices for the pivot element in the second column are 0. How do we proceed from here? Since our goal is to simplify the system as much as possible, it seems natural to move over to the third column and eliminate the last three entries.

$$\left[\begin{array}{ccccc|c} 1 & 1 & 1 & 1 & 1 & 1 \\ 0 & 0 & 1 & 1 & 2 & 0 \\ \mathbf{0} & \mathbf{0} & \mathbf{0} & \mathbf{0} & \mathbf{1} & \mathbf{3} \\ 0 & 0 & 0 & 0 & 1 & -1 \\ 0 & 0 & 0 & 0 & 1 & 0 \end{array} \right]$$

In the fourth column, all the choices for a pivot element are 0; so again we move on to the next column. If we use the third row as the pivotal row, the last two entries in the fifth column are eliminated.

$$\left[\begin{array}{ccccc|c} 1 & 1 & 1 & 1 & 1 & 1 \\ 0 & 0 & 1 & 1 & 2 & 0 \\ 0 & 0 & 0 & 0 & 1 & 3 \\ 0 & 0 & 0 & 0 & 0 & -4 \\ 0 & 0 & 0 & 0 & 0 & -3 \end{array} \right]$$

The equations represented by the last two rows are

$$0x_1 + 0x_2 + 0x_3 + 0x_4 + 0x_5 = -4$$
$$0x_1 + 0x_2 + 0x_3 + 0x_4 + 0x_5 = -3$$

Since there are no 5-tuples that could possibly satisfy these equations, the system is inconsistent. Note that the coefficient matrix that we end up with is not in triangular form; it is in staircase or echelon form.   ◀

Suppose now that we change the right-hand side of the system in the last example so as to obtain a consistent system. For example, if we start with

$$\begin{bmatrix} 1 & 1 & 1 & 1 & 1 & 1 \\ -1 & -1 & 0 & 0 & 1 & -1 \\ -2 & -2 & 0 & 0 & 3 & 1 \\ 0 & 0 & 1 & 1 & 3 & 3 \\ 1 & 1 & 2 & 2 & 4 & 4 \end{bmatrix}$$

then the reduction process will yield the augmented matrix

$$\begin{bmatrix} 1 & 1 & 1 & 1 & 1 & 1 \\ 0 & 0 & 1 & 1 & 2 & 0 \\ 0 & 0 & 0 & 0 & 1 & 3 \\ 0 & 0 & 0 & 0 & 0 & 0 \\ 0 & 0 & 0 & 0 & 0 & 0 \end{bmatrix}$$

The last two equations of the reduced system will be satisfied for any 5-tuple. Thus the solution set will be the set of all 5-tuples satisfying the first three equations.

(1)
$$\begin{aligned} x_1 + x_2 + x_3 + x_4 + x_5 &= 1 \\ x_3 + x_4 + 2x_5 &= 0 \\ x_5 &= 3 \end{aligned}$$

The variables corresponding to the first nonzero elements in each row of the augmented matrix will be referred to as *lead variables*. Thus x_1, x_3, and x_5 are the lead variables. The remaining variables corresponding to the columns skipped in the reduction process will be referred to as *free variables*. Thus x_2 and x_4 are the free variables. If we transfer the free variables over to the right-hand side in (1), we obtain the system

(2)
$$\begin{aligned} x_1 + x_3 + x_5 &= 1 - x_2 - x_4 \\ x_3 + 2x_5 &= -x_4 \\ x_5 &= 3 \end{aligned}$$

System (2) is triangular in the unknowns x_1, x_3, x_5. Thus, for each pair of values assigned to x_2 and x_4, there will be a unique solution. For example, if $x_2 = x_4 = 0$, then $x_5 = 3$, $x_3 = -6$, $x_1 = 4$, and hence $(4, 0, -6, 0, 3)$ is a solution to the system.

▶ **DEFINITION** A matrix is said to be in **row echelon form** if

   (i) The first nonzero entry in each row is 1.

   (ii) If row k does not consist entirely of zeros, the number of leading zero entries in row $k + 1$ is greater than the number of leading zero entries in row k.

   (iii) If there are rows whose entries are all zero, they are below the rows having nonzero entries. ◀

EXAMPLE 2. The following matrices are in row echelon form.

$$\begin{bmatrix} 1 & 4 & 2 \\ 0 & 1 & 3 \\ 0 & 0 & 1 \end{bmatrix}, \quad \begin{bmatrix} 1 & 2 & 3 \\ 0 & 0 & 1 \\ 0 & 0 & 0 \end{bmatrix}, \quad \begin{bmatrix} 1 & 3 & 1 & 0 \\ 0 & 0 & 1 & 3 \\ 0 & 0 & 0 & 0 \end{bmatrix}$$ ◀

EXAMPLE 3. The following matrices are not in row echelon form.

$$\begin{bmatrix} 2 & 4 & 6 \\ 0 & 3 & 5 \\ 0 & 0 & 4 \end{bmatrix}, \quad \begin{bmatrix} 0 & 0 & 0 \\ 0 & 1 & 0 \end{bmatrix}, \quad \begin{bmatrix} 0 & 1 \\ 1 & 0 \end{bmatrix}$$

The first matrix does not satisfy condition (i). The second matrix fails to satisfy condition (iii), and the third matrix fails to satisfy the condition (ii). ◀

▶ **DEFINITION** The process of using row operations **I**, **II**, and **III** to transform a linear system into one whose augmented matrix is in row echelon form is called **Gaussian elimination**. ◀

Note that row operation **II** is necessary in order to scale the rows so that the lead coefficients are all 1. If the row echelon form of the augmented matrix contains a row of the form

$$\begin{bmatrix} 0 & 0 & \cdots & 0 & | & 1 \end{bmatrix}$$

the system is inconsistent. Otherwise, the system will be consistent. If the system is consistent and the nonzero rows of the row echelon of the matrix form a triangular system, the system will have a unique solution.

Overdetermined Systems

A linear system is said to be *overdetermined* if there are more equations than unknowns. Overdetermined systems are usually (but not always) inconsistent.

EXAMPLE 4.

(a) $\begin{aligned} x_1 + x_2 &= 1 \\ x_1 - x_2 &= 3 \\ -x_1 + 2x_2 &= -2 \end{aligned}$

(b) $\begin{aligned} x_1 + 2x_2 + x_3 &= 1 \\ 2x_1 - x_2 + x_3 &= 2 \\ 4x_1 + 3x_2 + 3x_3 &= 4 \\ 2x_1 - x_2 + 3x_3 &= 5 \end{aligned}$

(c) $\begin{aligned} x_1 + 2x_2 + x_3 &= 1 \\ 2x_1 - x_2 + x_3 &= 2 \\ 4x_1 + 3x_2 + 3x_3 &= 4 \\ 3x_1 + x_2 + 2x_3 &= 3 \end{aligned}$

SOLUTION. By now the reader should be familiar enough with the elimination process that we can omit the intermediate steps in reducing each of these systems.

$$\text{System (a):} \quad \left[\begin{array}{rr|r} 1 & 1 & 1 \\ 1 & -1 & 3 \\ -1 & 2 & -2 \end{array}\right] \rightarrow \left[\begin{array}{rr|r} 1 & 1 & 1 \\ 0 & 1 & -1 \\ 0 & 0 & 1 \end{array}\right]$$

It follows from the last row of the reduced matrix that the system is inconsistent. The three equations in system (a) represent lines in the plane. The first two lines intersect at the point $(2, -1)$. However, the third line does not pass through this point. Thus there are no points that lie on all three lines (see Figure 1.2.1).

FIGURE 1.2.1

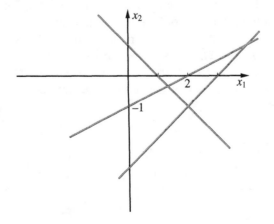

$$\text{System (b):} \quad \begin{bmatrix} 1 & 2 & 1 & | & 1 \\ 2 & -1 & 1 & | & 2 \\ 4 & 3 & 3 & | & 4 \\ 2 & -1 & 3 & | & 5 \end{bmatrix} \rightarrow \begin{bmatrix} 1 & 2 & 1 & | & 1 \\ 0 & 1 & \frac{1}{5} & | & 0 \\ 0 & 0 & 1 & | & \frac{3}{2} \\ 0 & 0 & 0 & | & 0 \end{bmatrix}$$

Using back substitution, we see that system (b) has exactly one solution $(0.1, -0.3, 1.5)$. The solution is unique because the nonzero rows of the reduced matrix form a triangular system.

$$\text{System (c):} \quad \begin{bmatrix} 1 & 2 & 1 & | & 1 \\ 2 & -1 & 1 & | & 2 \\ 4 & 3 & 3 & | & 4 \\ 3 & 1 & 2 & | & 3 \end{bmatrix} \rightarrow \begin{bmatrix} 1 & 2 & 1 & | & 1 \\ 0 & 1 & \frac{1}{5} & | & 0 \\ 0 & 0 & 0 & | & 0 \\ 0 & 0 & 0 & | & 0 \end{bmatrix}$$

Solving for x_2 and x_1 in terms of x_3, we obtain

$$x_2 = -0.2x_3$$
$$x_1 = 1 - 2x_2 - x_3 = 1 - 0.6x_3$$

It follows that the solution set is the set of all ordered triples of the form $(1 - 0.6\alpha, -0.2\alpha, \alpha)$, where α is a real number. This system is consistent and has infinitely many solutions because of the free variable x_3. ◀

Underdetermined Systems

A system of m linear equations in n unknowns is said to be *underdetermined* if there are fewer equations than unknowns ($m < n$). Although it is possible for underdetermined systems to be inconsistent, they are usually consistent with infinitely many solutions. It is not possible for an underdetermined system to have only one solution. The reason for this is that any row echelon form of the coefficient matrix will involve $r \le m$ nonzero rows. Thus there will be r lead variables and $n - r$ free variables, where $n - r \ge n - m > 0$. If the system is consistent, we can assign the free variables arbitrary values and solve for the lead variables. Therefore, a consistent underdetermined system will have infinitely many solutions.

EXAMPLE 5.

(a) $\begin{aligned} x_1 + 2x_2 + x_3 &= 1 \\ 2x_1 + 4x_2 + 2x_3 &= 3 \end{aligned}$

(b) $\begin{aligned} x_1 + x_2 + x_3 + x_4 + x_5 &= 2 \\ x_1 + x_2 + x_3 + 2x_4 + 2x_5 &= 3 \\ x_1 + x_2 + x_3 + 2x_4 + 3x_5 &= 2 \end{aligned}$

SOLUTION.

System (a):
$$\left[\begin{array}{ccc|c} 1 & 2 & 1 & 1 \\ 2 & 4 & 2 & 3 \end{array}\right] \rightarrow \left[\begin{array}{ccc|c} 1 & 2 & 1 & 1 \\ 0 & 0 & 0 & 1 \end{array}\right]$$

Clearly, system (a) is inconsistent. We can think of the two equations in system (a) as representing planes in 3-space. Usually, two planes intersect in a line; however, in this case the planes are parallel.

System (b):
$$\left[\begin{array}{ccccc|c} 1 & 1 & 1 & 1 & 1 & 2 \\ 1 & 1 & 1 & 2 & 2 & 3 \\ 1 & 1 & 1 & 2 & 3 & 2 \end{array}\right] \rightarrow \left[\begin{array}{ccccc|c} 1 & 1 & 1 & 1 & 1 & 2 \\ 0 & 0 & 0 & 1 & 1 & 1 \\ 0 & 0 & 0 & 0 & 1 & -1 \end{array}\right]$$

System (b) is consistent, and since there are two free variables, the system will have infinitely many solutions. Often with systems like this it is convenient to continue with the elimination process until all the terms above each leading 1 are eliminated. (These entries are printed in color.) Thus, for system (b), we will continue and eliminate the first two entries in the fifth column and then the first element in the fourth column.

$$\left[\begin{array}{ccccc|c} 1 & 1 & 1 & 1 & 1 & 2 \\ 0 & 0 & 0 & 1 & 1 & 1 \\ 0 & 0 & 0 & 0 & 1 & -1 \end{array}\right] \rightarrow \left[\begin{array}{ccccc|c} 1 & 1 & 1 & 1 & 0 & 3 \\ 0 & 0 & 0 & 1 & 0 & 2 \\ 0 & 0 & 0 & 0 & 1 & -1 \end{array}\right]$$

$$\rightarrow \left[\begin{array}{ccccc|c} 1 & 1 & 1 & 0 & 0 & 1 \\ 0 & 0 & 0 & 1 & 0 & 2 \\ 0 & 0 & 0 & 0 & 1 & -1 \end{array}\right]$$

If we put the free variables over on the right-hand side, it follows that

$$x_1 = 1 - x_2 - x_3$$
$$x_4 = 2$$
$$x_5 = -1$$

Thus, for any real numbers α and β, the 5-tuple

$$(1 - \alpha - \beta, \alpha, \beta, 2, -1)$$

is a solution to the system.

In the case where the row echelon form of a consistent system has free variables, it is convenient to continue the elimination process until all the entries above each lead 1 have been eliminated, as in system (b) of the previous example. The resulting reduced matrix is said to be in *reduced row echelon form*.

Reduced Row Echelon Form

▶ **DEFINITION** A matrix is said to be in **reduced row echelon form** if:

(i) The matrix is in row echelon form.

(ii) The first nonzero entry in each row is the only nonzero entry in its column.   ◀

The following matrices are in reduced row echelon form:

$$\begin{bmatrix} 1 & 0 \\ 0 & 1 \end{bmatrix}, \quad \begin{bmatrix} 1 & 0 & 0 & 3 \\ 0 & 1 & 0 & 2 \\ 0 & 0 & 1 & 1 \end{bmatrix}, \quad \begin{bmatrix} 0 & 1 & 2 & 0 \\ 0 & 0 & 0 & 1 \\ 0 & 0 & 0 & 0 \end{bmatrix}, \quad \begin{bmatrix} 1 & 2 & 0 & 1 \\ 0 & 0 & 1 & 3 \\ 0 & 0 & 0 & 0 \end{bmatrix}$$

The process of using elementary row operations to transform a matrix into reduced row echelon form is called *Gauss–Jordan reduction*.

EXAMPLE 6. Use Gauss–Jordan reduction to solve the system

$$\begin{array}{rcl} -x_1 + x_2 - x_3 + 3x_4 &=& 0 \\ 3x_1 + x_2 - x_3 - x_4 &=& 0 \\ 2x_1 - x_2 - 2x_3 - x_4 &=& 0 \end{array}$$

SOLUTION.

$$\begin{bmatrix} -1 & 1 & -1 & 3 & | & 0 \\ 3 & 1 & -1 & -1 & | & 0 \\ 2 & -1 & -2 & -1 & | & 0 \end{bmatrix} \rightarrow \begin{bmatrix} -1 & 1 & -1 & 3 & | & 0 \\ 0 & 4 & -4 & 8 & | & 0 \\ 0 & 1 & -4 & 5 & | & 0 \end{bmatrix}$$

$$\rightarrow \begin{bmatrix} -1 & 1 & -1 & 3 & | & 0 \\ 0 & 4 & -4 & 8 & | & 0 \\ 0 & 0 & -3 & 3 & | & 0 \end{bmatrix} \rightarrow \begin{bmatrix} 1 & -1 & 1 & -3 & | & 0 \\ 0 & 1 & -1 & 2 & | & 0 \\ 0 & 0 & 1 & -1 & | & 0 \end{bmatrix} \begin{array}{l} \text{row} \\ \text{echelon} \\ \text{form} \end{array}$$

$$\rightarrow \begin{bmatrix} 1 & -1 & 0 & -2 & | & 0 \\ 0 & 1 & 0 & 1 & | & 0 \\ 0 & 0 & 1 & -1 & | & 0 \end{bmatrix} \rightarrow \begin{bmatrix} 1 & 0 & 0 & -1 & | & 0 \\ 0 & 1 & 0 & 1 & | & 0 \\ 0 & 0 & 1 & -1 & | & 0 \end{bmatrix} \begin{array}{l} \text{reduced} \\ \text{row echelon} \\ \text{form} \end{array}$$

If we set x_4 equal to any real number α, then $x_1 = \alpha$, $x_2 = -\alpha$, and $x_3 = \alpha$. Thus all ordered 4-tuples of the form $(\alpha, -\alpha, \alpha, \alpha)$ are solutions to the system.　　◀

APPLICATION 1: TRAFFIC FLOW

In the downtown section of a certain city, two sets of one-way streets intersect as shown in Figure 1.2.2. The average hourly volume of traffic entering and leaving this section during rush hour is given in the diagram. Determine the amount of traffic between each of the four intersections.

SOLUTION. At each intersection the number of automobiles entering must be the same as the number leaving. For example, at intersection A, the number of automobiles entering is $x_1 + 450$ and the number leaving is $x_2 + 610$. Thus

$$x_1 + 450 = x_2 + 610 \qquad \text{(intersection } A\text{)}$$

Similarly,

$$x_2 + 520 = x_3 + 480 \qquad \text{(intersection } B\text{)}$$

$$x_3 + 390 = x_4 + 600 \qquad \text{(intersection } C\text{)}$$

$$x_4 + 640 = x_1 + 310 \qquad \text{(intersection } D\text{)}$$

FIGURE 1.2.2

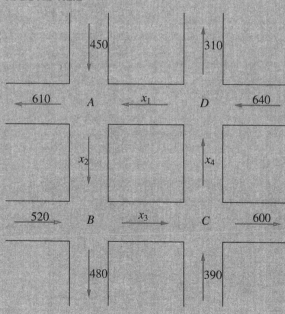

The augmented matrix for the system is

$$\begin{bmatrix} 1 & -1 & 0 & 0 & | & 160 \\ 0 & 1 & -1 & 0 & | & -40 \\ 0 & 0 & 1 & -1 & | & 210 \\ -1 & 0 & 0 & 1 & | & -330 \end{bmatrix}$$

The reduced row echelon form for this matrix is

$$\begin{bmatrix} 1 & 0 & 0 & -1 & | & 330 \\ 0 & 1 & 0 & -1 & | & 170 \\ 0 & 0 & 1 & -1 & | & 210 \\ 0 & 0 & 0 & 0 & | & 0 \end{bmatrix}$$

The system is consistent, and since there is a free variable, there are many possible solutions. The traffic flow diagram does not give enough information to determine x_1, x_2, x_3, x_4 uniquely. If the amount of traffic were known between any pair of intersections, the traffic on the remaining arteries could easily be calculated. For example, if the amount of traffic between intersections C and D averages 200 automobiles per hour, then $x_4 = 200$. Using this value, we can then solve for x_1, x_2, x_3.

$$x_1 = x_4 + 330 = 530$$
$$x_2 = x_4 + 170 = 370$$
$$x_3 = x_4 + 210 = 410$$ ◀

APPLICATION 2: ELECTRICAL NETWORKS

In an electrical network it is possible to determine the amount of current in each branch in terms of the resistances and the voltages. An example of a typical circuit is given in Figure 1.2.3.

FIGURE 1.2.3

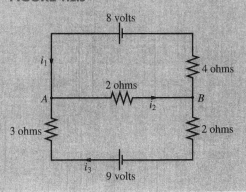

The symbols in the figure have the following meanings:

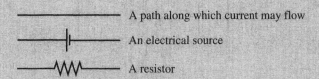

A path along which current may flow

An electrical source

A resistor

The electrical source is usually a battery (measured in volts) that drives a charge and produces a current. The current will flow out of the terminal of the battery represented by the longer vertical line. The resistances are measured in ohms. The letters represent nodes and the i's represent the currents between the nodes. The currents are measured in amperes. The arrows show the direction of the currents. If, however, one of the currents, say i_2, turns out to be negative, this would mean that the current along that branch is in the opposite direction of the arrow.

To determine the currents, the following rules are used:

Kirchhoff's Laws

1. At every node the sum of the incoming currents equals the sum of the outgoing currents.

2. Around every closed loop the algebraic sum of the voltage must equal the algebraic sum of the voltage drops.

The voltage drops E for each resistor are given by *Ohm's law*:

$$E = iR$$

where i represents the current in amperes and R the resistance in ohms.

Let us find the currents in the network pictured in Figure 1.2.3. From the first law, we have

$$i_1 - i_2 + i_3 = 0 \qquad \text{(node } A\text{)}$$
$$-i_1 + i_2 - i_3 = 0 \qquad \text{(node } B\text{)}$$

By the second law,

$$4i_1 + 2i_2 = 8 \qquad \text{(top loop)}$$
$$2i_2 + 5i_3 = 9 \qquad \text{(bottom loop)}$$

The network can be represented by the augmented matrix

$$\left[\begin{array}{rrr|r} 1 & -1 & 1 & 0 \\ -1 & 1 & -1 & 0 \\ 4 & 2 & 0 & 8 \\ 0 & 2 & 5 & 9 \end{array}\right]$$

This matrix is easily reduced to row echelon form

$$\left[\begin{array}{rrr|r} 1 & -1 & 1 & 0 \\ 0 & 1 & -\frac{2}{3} & \frac{4}{3} \\ 0 & 0 & 1 & 1 \\ 0 & 0 & 0 & 0 \end{array}\right]$$

Solving by back substitution, we see that $i_1 = 1$, $i_2 = 2$, and $i_3 = 1$.

Homogeneous Systems

A system of linear equations is said to be *homogeneous* if the constants on the right-hand side are all zero. Homogeneous systems are always consistent. It is a trivial matter to find a solution; just set all the variables equal to zero. Thus, if an $m \times n$ homogeneous system has a unique solution, it must be the trivial solution $(0, 0, \ldots, 0)$. The homogeneous system in Example 6 consisted of $m = 3$ equations in $n = 4$ unknowns. In the case that $n > m$, there will always be free variables and, consequently, additional nontrivial solutions. This result has essentially been proved in our discussion of underdetermined systems, but, because of its importance, we state it as a theorem.

▶ **THEOREM I.2.I** *An $m \times n$ homogeneous system of linear equations has a nontrivial solution if $n > m$.*

▶*Proof.* A homogeneous system is always consistent. The row echelon form of the matrix can have at most m nonzero rows. Thus there are at most m lead variables. Since there are n variables altogether and $n > m$, there must be some free variables. The free variables can be assigned arbitrary values. For each assignment of values to the free variables, there is a solution to the system.   ◀

APPLICATION 3: CHEMICAL EQUATIONS

In the process of photosynthesis, plants use radiant energy from sunlight to convert carbon dioxide (CO_2) and water (H_2O) into glucose ($C_6H_{12}O_6$) and oxygen (O_2).

The chemical equation of the reaction is of the form

$$x_1 CO_2 + x_2 H_2O \rightarrow x_3 O_2 + x_4 C_6 H_{12} O_6$$

In order to balance the equation we must choose x_1, x_2, x_3, and x_4 so that the number of carbon, hydrogen, and oxygen atoms are the same on each side of the equation. Since carbon dioxide contains one carbon atom and glucose contains six, then to balance the carbon atoms we require that

$$x_1 = 6x_4$$

Similarly, to balance the oxygen we need

$$2x_1 + x_2 = 2x_3 + 6x_4$$

and finally to balance the hydrogen we need

$$2x_2 = 12x_4$$

If we move all the unknowns to the left-hand sides of the three equations, we end up with the homogeneous linear system

$$
\begin{aligned}
x_1 \qquad\qquad\qquad - 6x_4 &= 0 \\
2x_1 + x_2 - 2x_3 - 6x_4 &= 0 \\
2x_2 \qquad\quad - 12x_4 &= 0
\end{aligned}
$$

By Theorem 1.2.1, the system has nontrivial solutions. To balance the equation, we must find solutions (x_1, x_2, x_3, x_4) whose entries are nonnegative integers. If we solve the system in the usual way, we see that x_4 is a free variable and

$$x_1 = x_2 = x_3 = 6x_4$$

In particular, if we take $x_4 = 1$, then $x_1 = x_2 = x_3 = 6$ and the equation takes the form

$$6CO_2 + 6H_2O \rightarrow 6O_2 + C_6H_{12}O_6$$

APPLICATION 4: ECONOMIC MODELS FOR EXCHANGE OF GOODS

Suppose that in a primitive society, the members of a tribe are engaged in three occupations: farming, manufacturing of tools and utensils, and weaving and sewing of clothing. Assume that initially the tribe has no monetary system and that all goods and services are bartered. Let us denote the three groups by F, M, and C, and suppose that the directed graph in Figure 1.2.4 indicates how the bartering system works in practice.

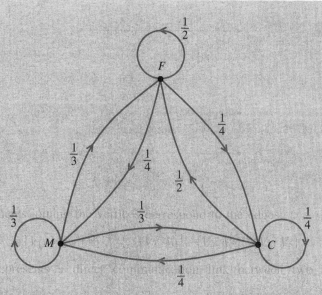

FIGURE 1.2.4

The figure indicates that the farmers keep half of their produce and give one-fourth of their produce to the manufacturers and one-fourth to the clothing producers. The manufacturers divide the goods evenly among the three groups, one-third going to each group. The group producing clothes gives half of the clothes to the farmers and divides the other half evenly between the manufacturers and themselves. The result is summarized in the following table.

	F	M	C
F	$\frac{1}{2}$	$\frac{1}{3}$	$\frac{1}{2}$
M	$\frac{1}{4}$	$\frac{1}{3}$	$\frac{1}{4}$
C	$\frac{1}{4}$	$\frac{1}{3}$	$\frac{1}{4}$

The first column of the table indicates the distribution of the goods produced by the farmers, the second column indicates the distribution of the manufactured goods, and the third column indicates the distribution of the clothing.

As the size of the tribe grows, the system of bartering becomes too cumbersome and, consequently, the tribe decides to institute a monetary system of exchange. For this simple economic system, we assume that there will be no accumulation of capital or debt and that the prices for each of the three types of goods will reflect the values of the existing bartering system. The question is how to assign values to the three types of goods that fairly represent the current bartering system.

The problem can be turned into a linear system of equations using an economic model that was originally developed by the Nobel prize winning economist Wassily

Leontief. For this model we will let x_1 be the monetary value of the goods produced by the farmers, x_2 be the value of the manufactured goods, and x_3 be the value of all the clothing produced. According to the first row of the table, the value of the goods received by the farmers amounts to half the value of the farm goods produced plus one-third the value of the manufactured products and half the value of the clothing goods. Thus the total value of goods received by the farmer is $\frac{1}{2}x_1 + \frac{1}{3}x_2 + \frac{1}{2}x_3$. If the system is fair, the total value of goods received by the farmers should equal x_1, the total value of the farm goods produced. Thus we have the linear equation

$$\frac{1}{2}x_1 + \frac{1}{3}x_2 + \frac{1}{2}x_3 = x_1$$

Using the second row of the table and equating the value of the goods produced and received by the manufacturers, we obtain a second equation:

$$\frac{1}{4}x_1 + \frac{1}{3}x_2 + \frac{1}{4}x_3 = x_2$$

Finally, using the third row of the table, we get

$$\frac{1}{4}x_1 + \frac{1}{3}x_2 + \frac{1}{4}x_3 = x_3$$

These equations can be rewritten as a homogeneous system:

$$-\tfrac{1}{2}x_1 + \tfrac{1}{3}x_2 + \tfrac{1}{2}x_3 = 0$$
$$\tfrac{1}{4}x_1 - \tfrac{2}{3}x_2 + \tfrac{1}{4}x_3 = 0$$
$$\tfrac{1}{4}x_1 + \tfrac{1}{3}x_2 - \tfrac{3}{4}x_3 = 0$$

The reduced row echelon form of the augmented matrix for this system is

$$\begin{bmatrix} 1 & 0 & -\frac{5}{3} & 0 \\ 0 & 1 & -1 & 0 \\ 0 & 0 & 0 & 0 \end{bmatrix}$$

There is one free variable x_3. Setting $x_3 = 3$, we obtain the solution $(5, 3, 3)$, and the general solution consists of all multiples of $(5, 3, 3)$. It follows that the variables x_1, x_2, x_3 should be assigned values in the ratio

$$x_1 : x_2 : x_3 = 5 : 3 : 3$$

 This simple system is an example of the closed Leontief input-output model. Leontief's models are fundamental to our understanding of economic systems. Modern applications would involve thousands of industries and lead to very large linear systems. The Leontief models will be studied in greater detail later in Section 7 of Chapter 6.

1. Which of the following matrices are in row echelon form? Which are in reduced row echelon form?

(a) $\begin{bmatrix} 1 & 2 & 3 & 4 \\ 0 & 0 & 1 & 2 \end{bmatrix}$

(b) $\begin{bmatrix} 1 & 0 & 0 \\ 0 & 0 & 0 \\ 0 & 0 & 1 \end{bmatrix}$

(c) $\begin{bmatrix} 1 & 3 & 0 \\ 0 & 0 & 1 \\ 0 & 0 & 0 \end{bmatrix}$

(d) $\begin{bmatrix} 0 & 1 \\ 0 & 0 \\ 0 & 0 \end{bmatrix}$

(e) $\begin{bmatrix} 1 & 1 & 1 \\ 0 & 1 & 2 \\ 0 & 0 & 3 \end{bmatrix}$

(f) $\begin{bmatrix} 1 & 4 & 6 \\ 0 & 0 & 1 \\ 0 & 1 & 3 \end{bmatrix}$

(g) $\begin{bmatrix} 1 & 0 & 0 & 1 & 2 \\ 0 & 1 & 0 & 2 & 4 \\ 0 & 0 & 1 & 3 & 6 \end{bmatrix}$

(h) $\begin{bmatrix} 0 & 1 & 3 & 4 \\ 0 & 0 & 1 & 3 \\ 0 & 0 & 0 & 0 \end{bmatrix}$

2. In each of the following, the augmented matrix is in row echelon form. For each case, indicate whether the corresponding linear system is consistent. If the system has a unique solution, find it.

(a) $\left[\begin{array}{cc|c} 1 & 2 & 4 \\ 0 & 1 & 3 \\ 0 & 0 & 1 \end{array}\right]$

(b) $\left[\begin{array}{cc|c} 1 & 3 & 1 \\ 0 & 1 & -1 \\ 0 & 0 & 0 \end{array}\right]$

(c) $\left[\begin{array}{ccc|c} 1 & -2 & 4 & 1 \\ 0 & 0 & 1 & 3 \\ 0 & 0 & 0 & 0 \end{array}\right]$

(d) $\left[\begin{array}{ccc|c} 1 & -2 & 2 & -2 \\ 0 & 1 & -1 & 3 \\ 0 & 0 & 1 & 2 \end{array}\right]$

(e) $\left[\begin{array}{ccc|c} 1 & 3 & 2 & -2 \\ 0 & 0 & 1 & 4 \\ 0 & 0 & 0 & 1 \end{array}\right]$

(f) $\left[\begin{array}{ccc|c} 1 & -1 & 3 & 8 \\ 0 & 1 & 2 & 7 \\ 0 & 0 & 1 & 2 \\ 0 & 0 & 0 & 0 \end{array}\right]$

3. In each of the following, the augmented matrix is in reduced row echelon form. In each case, find the solution set to the corresponding linear system.

(a) $\left[\begin{array}{ccc|c} 1 & 0 & 0 & -2 \\ 0 & 1 & 0 & 5 \\ 0 & 0 & 1 & 3 \end{array}\right]$

(b) $\left[\begin{array}{ccc|c} 1 & 4 & 0 & 2 \\ 0 & 0 & 1 & 3 \\ 0 & 0 & 0 & 1 \end{array}\right]$

(c) $\left[\begin{array}{ccc|c} 1 & -3 & 0 & 2 \\ 0 & 0 & 1 & -2 \\ 0 & 0 & 0 & 0 \end{array}\right]$

(d) $\left[\begin{array}{cccc|c} 1 & 2 & 0 & 1 & 5 \\ 0 & 0 & 1 & 3 & 4 \end{array}\right]$

(e) $\begin{bmatrix} 1 & 5 & -2 & 0 & 3 \\ 0 & 0 & 0 & 1 & 6 \\ 0 & 0 & 0 & 0 & 0 \\ 0 & 0 & 0 & 0 & 0 \end{bmatrix}$ (f) $\begin{bmatrix} 0 & 1 & 0 & 2 \\ 0 & 0 & 1 & -1 \\ 0 & 0 & 0 & 0 \end{bmatrix}$

4. For each of the systems in Exercise 3, make a list of the lead variables and a second list of the free variables.

5. For each of the following systems of equations, use Gaussian elimination to obtain an equivalent system whose coefficient matrix is in row echelon form. Indicate whether the system is consistent. If the system is consistent and involves no free variables, use back substitution to find the unique solution. If the system is consistent and there are free variables, transform it to reduced row echelon form and find all solutions.

(a) $\begin{aligned} x_1 - 2x_2 &= 3 \\ 2x_1 - x_2 &= 9 \end{aligned}$ (b) $\begin{aligned} 2x_1 - 3x_2 &= 5 \\ -4x_1 + 6x_2 &= 8 \end{aligned}$

(c) $\begin{aligned} x_1 + x_2 &= 0 \\ 2x_1 + 3x_2 &= 0 \\ 3x_1 - 2x_2 &= 0 \end{aligned}$ (d) $\begin{aligned} 3x_1 + 2x_2 - x_3 &= 4 \\ x_1 - 2x_2 + 2x_3 &= 1 \\ 11x_1 + 2x_2 + x_3 &= 14 \end{aligned}$

(e) $\begin{aligned} 2x_1 + 3x_2 + x_3 &= 1 \\ x_1 + x_2 + x_3 &= 3 \\ 3x_1 + 4x_2 + 2x_3 &= 4 \end{aligned}$ (f) $\begin{aligned} x_1 - x_2 + 2x_3 &= 4 \\ 2x_1 + 3x_2 - x_3 &= 1 \\ 7x_1 + 3x_2 + 4x_3 &= 7 \end{aligned}$

(g) $\begin{aligned} x_1 + x_2 + x_3 + x_4 &= 0 \\ 2x_1 + 3x_2 - x_3 - x_4 &= 2 \\ 3x_1 + 2x_2 + x_3 + x_4 &= 5 \\ 3x_1 + 6x_2 - x_3 - x_4 &= 4 \end{aligned}$ (h) $\begin{aligned} x_1 - 2x_2 &= 3 \\ 2x_1 + x_2 &= 1 \\ -5x_1 + 8x_2 &= 4 \end{aligned}$

(i) $\begin{aligned} -x_1 + 2x_2 - x_3 &= 2 \\ -2x_1 + 2x_2 + x_3 &= 4 \\ 3x_1 + 2x_2 + 2x_3 &= 5 \\ -3x_1 + 8x_2 + 5x_3 &= 17 \end{aligned}$ (j) $\begin{aligned} x_1 + 2x_2 - 3x_3 + x_4 &= 1 \\ -x_1 - x_2 + 4x_3 - x_4 &= 6 \\ -2x_1 - 4x_2 + 7x_3 - x_4 &= 1 \end{aligned}$

(k) $\begin{aligned} x_1 + 3x_2 + x_3 + x_4 &= 3 \\ 2x_1 - 2x_2 + x_3 + 2x_4 &= 8 \\ x_1 - 5x_2 + x_4 &= 5 \end{aligned}$ (l) $\begin{aligned} x_1 - 3x_2 + x_3 &= 1 \\ 2x_1 + x_2 - x_3 &= 2 \\ x_1 + 4x_2 - 2x_3 &= 1 \\ 5x_1 - 8x_2 + 2x_3 &= 5 \end{aligned}$

6. Use Gauss–Jordan reduction to solve each of the following systems.

(a) $\begin{aligned} x_1 + x_2 &= -1 \\ 4x_1 - 3x_2 &= 3 \end{aligned}$ (b) $\begin{aligned} x_1 + 3x_2 + x_3 + x_4 &= 3 \\ 2x_1 - 2x_2 + x_3 + 2x_4 &= 8 \\ 3x_1 + x_2 + 2x_3 - x_4 &= -1 \end{aligned}$

(c) $\begin{aligned} x_1 + x_2 + x_3 &= 0 \\ x_1 - x_2 - x_3 &= 0 \end{aligned}$ (d) $\begin{aligned} x_1 + x_2 + x_3 + x_4 &= 0 \\ 2x_1 + x_2 - x_3 + 3x_4 &= 0 \\ x_1 - 2x_2 + x_3 + x_4 &= 0 \end{aligned}$

7. Give a geometric explanation of why a homogeneous linear system consisting of two equations in three unknowns must have infinitely many solutions. What are

the possible numbers of solutions for a nonhomogeneous 2×3 linear system? Give a geometric explanation of your answer.

8. Consider a linear system whose augmented matrix is of the form

$$\left[\begin{array}{ccc|c} 1 & 2 & 1 & 1 \\ -1 & 4 & 3 & 2 \\ 2 & -2 & a & 3 \end{array}\right]$$

For what values of a will the system have a unique solution?

9. Consider a linear system whose augmented matrix is of the form

$$\left[\begin{array}{ccc|c} 1 & 2 & 1 & 0 \\ 2 & 5 & 3 & 0 \\ -1 & 1 & \beta & 0 \end{array}\right]$$

(a) Is it possible for the system to be inconsistent? Explain.
(b) For what values of β will the system have infinitely many solutions?

10. Consider a linear system whose augmented matrix is of the form

$$\left[\begin{array}{ccc|c} 1 & 1 & 3 & 2 \\ 1 & 2 & 4 & 3 \\ 1 & 3 & a & b \end{array}\right]$$

(a) For what values of a and b will the system have infinitely many solutions?
(b) For what values of a and b will the system be inconsistent?

11. Given the linear systems

(a) $x_1 + 2x_2 = 2$
    $3x_1 + 7x_2 = 8$

(b) $x_1 + 2x_2 = 1$
    $3x_1 + 7x_2 = 7$

Solve both systems by incorporating the right-hand sides into a 2×2 matrix B and computing the reduced row echelon form of

$$(A|B) = \left[\begin{array}{cc|cc} 1 & 2 & 2 & 1 \\ 3 & 7 & 8 & 7 \end{array}\right]$$

12. Given the linear systems

(a) $x_1 + 2x_2 + x_3 = 2$
    $-x_1 - x_2 + 2x_3 = 3$
    $2x_1 + 3x_2 = 0$

(b) $x_1 + 2x_2 + x_3 = -1$
    $-x_1 - x_2 + 2x_3 = 2$
    $2x_1 + 3x_2 = -2$

Solve both systems by computing the row echelon form of an augmented matrix $(A|B)$ and performing back substitution twice.

13. Determine the values of x_1, x_2, x_3, x_4 for the following traffic flow diagram.

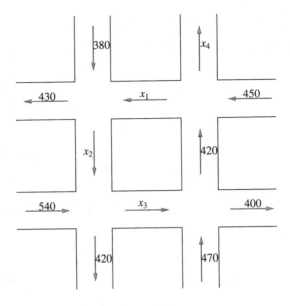

14. Consider the following traffic flow diagram, where a_1, a_2, a_3, a_4, b_1, b_2, b_3, b_4 are fixed positive integers. Set up a linear system in the unknowns x_1, x_2, x_3, x_4 and show that the system will be consistent if and only if

$$a_1 + a_2 + a_3 + a_4 = b_1 + b_2 + b_3 + b_4$$

What can you conclude about the number of automobiles entering and leaving the traffic network?

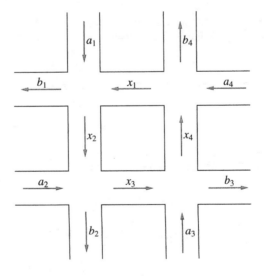

15. Let (c_1, c_2) be a solution to the 2×2 system

$$a_{11}x_1 + a_{12}x_2 = 0$$
$$a_{21}x_1 + a_{22}x_2 = 0$$

Show that for any real number α the ordered pair $(\alpha c_1, \alpha c_2)$ is also a solution.

16. In Application 3 the solution $(6, 6, 6, 1)$ was obtained by setting the free variable $x_4 = 1$.

  (a) Determine the solution corresponding to $x_4 = 0$. What information, if any, does this solution give about the chemical reaction? Is the term "trivial solution" appropriate in this case?

  (b) Choose some other values of x_4, such as 2, 4, or 5, and determine the corresponding solutions. How are these nontrivial solutions related?

17. Liquid benzene burns in the atmosphere. If a cold object is placed directly over the benzene, water will condense on the object and a deposit of soot (carbon) will also form on the object. The chemical equation for this reaction is of the form

$$x_1 C_6 H_6 + x_2 O_2 \rightarrow x_3 C + x_4 H_2 O$$

Determine values of x_1, x_2, x_3, and x_4 to balance the equation.

18. Nitric acid is prepared commercially by a series of three chemical reactions. In the first reaction, nitrogen (N_2) is combined with hydrogen (H_2) to form ammonia (NH_3). Next the ammonia is combined with oxygen (O_2) to form nitrogen dioxide (NO_2) and water. Finally, the NO_2 reacts with some of the water to form nitric acid (HNO_3) and nitrogen oxide (NO). The amounts of each of the components of these reactions are measured in moles (a standard unit of measurement for chemical reactions). How many moles of nitrogen, hydrogen, and oxygen are necessary in order to produce eight moles of nitric acid?

19. In Application 4, determine the relative values of x_1, x_2, and x_3 if the distribution of goods is as described in the following table.

	F	M	C
F	$\frac{1}{3}$	$\frac{1}{3}$	$\frac{1}{3}$
M	$\frac{1}{3}$	$\frac{1}{2}$	$\frac{1}{6}$
C	$\frac{1}{3}$	$\frac{1}{6}$	$\frac{1}{2}$

20. Determine the amount of each current for the following networks.

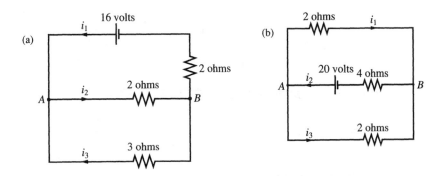

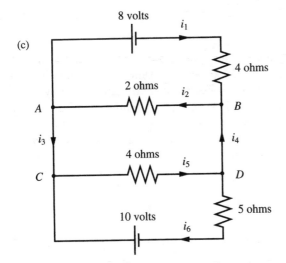

(c)

3 MATRIX ALGEBRA

In this section we define arithmetic operations with matrices and look at some of their algebraic properties. Matrices are one of the most powerful tools in mathematics. To use matrices effectively, we must be adept at matrix arithmetic.

The entries of a matrix are called *scalars*. They are usually either real or complex numbers. For the most part we will be working with matrices whose entries are real numbers. Throughout the first five chapters of the book the reader may assume that the term *scalar* refers to a real number. However, in Chapter 6 there will be occasions when we will use the set of complex numbers as our scalar field.

Matrix Notation

If we wish to refer to matrices without specifically writing out all their entries, we will use capital letters A, B, C, and so on. In general, a_{ij} will denote the entry of the matrix A that is in the ith row and the jth column. Thus, if A is an $m \times n$ matrix, then

$$A = \begin{pmatrix} a_{11} & a_{12} & \cdots & a_{1n} \\ a_{21} & a_{22} & \cdots & a_{2n} \\ \vdots & & & \\ a_{m1} & a_{m2} & \cdots & a_{mn} \end{pmatrix}$$

We will sometimes shorten this to $A = (a_{ij})$. Similarly, a matrix B may be referred to as (b_{ij}), a matrix C as (c_{ij}), and so on.

Vectors

Matrices that have only one row or one column are of special interest since they are used to represent solutions to linear systems. A solution to a system of m linear equations in n unknowns is an n-tuple of real numbers. We will refer to an n-tuple of real numbers as a *vector*. If an n-tuple is represented in terms of a $1 \times n$ matrix, then we will refer to it as a *row vector*. Alternatively, if the n-tuple is represented by an $n \times 1$ matrix, then we will refer to it as a *column vector*. For example, the solution to the linear system

$$x_1 + x_2 = 3$$
$$x_1 - x_2 = 1$$

can be represented by the row vector $(2, 1)$ or the column vector $\begin{bmatrix} 2 \\ 1 \end{bmatrix}$.

In working with matrix equations, it is generally more convenient to represent the solutions in terms of column vectors ($n \times 1$ matrices). The set of all $n \times 1$ matrices of real numbers is called *Euclidean n-space* and is usually denoted by R^n. Since we will be working almost exclusively with column vectors in the future, we will generally omit the word "column" and refer to the elements of R^n as simply *vectors*, rather than as column vectors.

The standard notation for a column vector is a boldface lowercase letter.

$$\mathbf{x} = \begin{bmatrix} x_1 \\ x_2 \\ \vdots \\ x_n \end{bmatrix}$$

Given an $m \times n$ matrix A, it is often necessary to refer to a particular row or column. The ith row vector of A will be denoted by $\mathbf{a}(i, :)$ and the jth column vector will be denoted by $\mathbf{a}(:, j)$. Since we will be working primarily with column vectors, it is convenient to have a shorthand notation for the jth column vector. We will use $\mathbf{a}_j$ in place of $\mathbf{a}(:, j)$. References to row vectors are far less frequent, so we will not use any shorthand notation to represent them.

If A is an $m \times n$ matrix, then the row vectors of A are given by

$$\mathbf{a}(i, :) = (a_{i1}, a_{i2}, \ldots, a_{in}) \qquad i = 1, \ldots, m$$

and the column vectors are given by

$$\mathbf{a}_j = \mathbf{a}(:, j) = \begin{bmatrix} a_{1j} \\ a_{2j} \\ \vdots \\ a_{mj} \end{bmatrix} \qquad j = 1, \ldots, n$$

The matrix A can be represented either in terms of its column vectors or in terms of its row vectors.

$$A = (\mathbf{a}_1, \mathbf{a}_2, \ldots, \mathbf{a}_n) \quad \text{or} \quad A = \begin{pmatrix} \mathbf{a}(1, :) \\ \mathbf{a}(2, :) \\ \vdots \\ \mathbf{a}(m, :) \end{pmatrix}$$

Similarly, if B is an $n \times r$ matrix, then $B = (\mathbf{b}_1, \mathbf{b}_2, \ldots, \mathbf{b}_r)$.

Equality

In order for two matrices to be equal, they must have the same dimensions and their corresponding entries must agree.

▶ **DEFINITION** Two $m \times n$ matrices A and B are said to be **equal** if $a_{ij} = b_{ij}$ for each i and j. ◀

Scalar Multiplication

If A is a matrix and α is a scalar, then αA is the matrix formed by multiplying each of the entries of A by α.

▶ **DEFINITION** If A is an $m \times n$ matrix and α is a scalar, then αA is the $m \times n$ matrix whose (i, j) entry is αa_{ij}. ◀

For example, if

$$A = \begin{pmatrix} 4 & 8 & 2 \\ 6 & 8 & 10 \end{pmatrix}$$

then

$$\frac{1}{2}A = \begin{pmatrix} 2 & 4 & 1 \\ 3 & 4 & 5 \end{pmatrix} \quad \text{and} \quad 3A = \begin{pmatrix} 12 & 24 & 6 \\ 18 & 24 & 30 \end{pmatrix}$$

Matrix Addition

Two matrices with the same dimensions can be added by adding their corresponding entries.

▶ **DEFINITION** If $A = (a_{ij})$ and $B = (b_{ij})$ are both $m \times n$ matrices, then the **sum** $A + B$ is the $m \times n$ matrix whose (i, j) entry is $a_{ij} + b_{ij}$ for each ordered pair (i, j). ◀

For example,

$$\begin{pmatrix} 3 & 2 & 1 \\ 4 & 5 & 6 \end{pmatrix} + \begin{pmatrix} 2 & 2 & 2 \\ 1 & 2 & 3 \end{pmatrix} = \begin{pmatrix} 5 & 4 & 3 \\ 5 & 7 & 9 \end{pmatrix}$$

$$\begin{bmatrix} 2 \\ 1 \\ 8 \end{bmatrix} + \begin{bmatrix} -8 \\ 3 \\ 2 \end{bmatrix} = \begin{bmatrix} -6 \\ 4 \\ 10 \end{bmatrix}$$

If we define $A - B$ to be $A + (-1)B$, then it turns out that $A - B$ is formed by subtracting the corresponding entry of B from each entry of A. Thus

$$\begin{bmatrix} 2 & 4 \\ 3 & 1 \end{bmatrix} - \begin{bmatrix} 4 & 5 \\ 2 & 3 \end{bmatrix} = \begin{bmatrix} 2 & 4 \\ 3 & 1 \end{bmatrix} + (-1)\begin{bmatrix} 4 & 5 \\ 2 & 3 \end{bmatrix}$$

$$= \begin{bmatrix} 2 & 4 \\ 3 & 1 \end{bmatrix} + \begin{bmatrix} -4 & -5 \\ -2 & -3 \end{bmatrix}$$

$$= \begin{bmatrix} 2-4 & 4-5 \\ 3-2 & 1-3 \end{bmatrix}$$

$$= \begin{bmatrix} -2 & -1 \\ 1 & -2 \end{bmatrix}$$

If O represents a matrix, with the same dimensions as A, whose entries are all 0, then

$$A + O = O + A = A$$

That is, the zero matrix acts as an additive identity on the set of all $m \times n$ matrices. Furthermore, each $m \times n$ matrix A has an additive inverse. Indeed,

$$A + (-1)A = O = (-1)A + A$$

It is customary to denote the additive inverse by $-A$. Thus

$$-A = (-1)A$$

Matrix Multiplication and Linear Systems

We have yet to define the most important operation, the multiplication of two matrices. Much of the motivation behind the definition comes from the applications to linear systems of equations. If we have a system of one linear equation in one unknown, it can be written in the form

(1) $$ax = b$$

We generally think of a, x, and b as being scalars; however, they could also be treated as 1×1 matrices. Our goal now is to generalize equation (1) so that we can represent an $m \times n$ linear system by a single matrix equation

$$A\mathbf{x} = \mathbf{b}$$

where A is an $m \times n$ matrix, $\mathbf{x}$ is in R^n, and $\mathbf{b}$ is in R^m. We consider first the case of one equation in several unknowns.

CASE I One Equation in Several Unknowns

Let us begin by examining the case of one equation in several variables. Consider for example the equation

$$3x_1 + 2x_2 + 5x_3 = 4$$

If we set

$$A = \begin{bmatrix} 3 & 2 & 5 \end{bmatrix} \qquad \text{and} \qquad \mathbf{x} = \begin{bmatrix} x_1 \\ x_2 \\ x_3 \end{bmatrix}$$

and define the product $A\mathbf{x}$ by

$$A\mathbf{x} = \begin{bmatrix} 3 & 2 & 5 \end{bmatrix} \begin{bmatrix} x_1 \\ x_2 \\ x_3 \end{bmatrix} = 3x_1 + 2x_2 + 5x_3$$

then the equation $3x_1 + 2x_2 + 5x_3 = 4$ can be written as the matrix equation

$$A\mathbf{x} = 4$$

In general, if

$$A = \begin{bmatrix} a_1 & a_2 & \dots & a_n \end{bmatrix}$$

and $\mathbf{x}$ is a column vector with n entries, then the product $A\mathbf{x}$ is defined by

$$A\mathbf{x} = a_1 x_1 + a_2 x_2 + \cdots + a_n x_n$$

For example, if

$$A = \begin{bmatrix} 2 & 1 & -3 & 4 \end{bmatrix} \qquad \text{and} \qquad \mathbf{x} = \begin{bmatrix} 3 \\ 2 \\ 1 \\ -2 \end{bmatrix}$$

then

$$A\mathbf{x} = 2 \cdot 3 + 1 \cdot 2 + (-3) \cdot 1 + 4 \cdot (-2) = -3$$

Note that the result of multiplying a row vector on the left times a column vector on the right is a scalar. Consequently, this type of multiplication is often referred to as a *scalar product*.

CASE 2 *M* Equations in *N* Unknowns

Consider now an $m \times n$ linear system

(2)
$$a_{11}x_1 + a_{12}x_2 + \cdots + a_{1n}x_n = b_1$$
$$a_{21}x_1 + a_{22}x_2 + \cdots + a_{2n}x_n = b_2$$
$$\vdots$$
$$a_{m1}x_1 + a_{m2}x_2 + \cdots + a_{mn}x_n = b_m$$

It is desirable to write the system in a form similar to (1), that is, as a matrix equation

(3)
$$A\mathbf{x} = \mathbf{b}$$

where $A = (a_{ij})$ is known, $\mathbf{x}$ is an $n \times 1$ matrix of unknowns, and $\mathbf{b}$ is an $m \times 1$ matrix representing the right-hand side of the system. Thus, if we set

$$A = \begin{bmatrix} a_{11} & a_{12} & \cdots & a_{1n} \\ a_{21} & a_{22} & \cdots & a_{2n} \\ \vdots & & & \\ a_{m1} & a_{m2} & \cdots & a_{mn} \end{bmatrix}, \qquad \mathbf{x} = \begin{bmatrix} x_1 \\ x_2 \\ \vdots \\ x_n \end{bmatrix}, \qquad \mathbf{b} = \begin{bmatrix} b_1 \\ b_2 \\ \vdots \\ b_m \end{bmatrix}$$

and define the product $A\mathbf{x}$ by

(4)
$$A\mathbf{x} = \begin{bmatrix} a_{11}x_1 + a_{12}x_2 + \cdots + a_{1n}x_n \\ a_{21}x_1 + a_{22}x_2 + \cdots + a_{2n}x_n \\ \vdots \\ a_{m1}x_1 + a_{m2}x_2 + \cdots + a_{mn}x_n \end{bmatrix}$$

then the linear system of equations (2) is equivalent to the matrix equation (3).

Given an $m \times n$ matrix A and a vector $\mathbf{x}$ in R^n, it is possible to compute a product $A\mathbf{x}$ by (4). The product $A\mathbf{x}$ will be an $m \times 1$ matrix, that is, a vector in R^m. The rule for determining the ith entry of $A\mathbf{x}$ is

$$a_{i1}x_1 + a_{i2}x_2 + \cdots + a_{in}x_n$$

which is equal to $\mathbf{a}(i, :)\mathbf{x}$, the scalar product of the ith row vector of A times the column vector $\mathbf{x}$. Thus

$$A\mathbf{x} = \begin{bmatrix} \mathbf{a}(1, :)\mathbf{x} \\ \mathbf{a}(2, :)\mathbf{x} \\ \vdots \\ \mathbf{a}(n, :)\mathbf{x} \end{bmatrix}$$

EXAMPLE 1.

$$A = \begin{bmatrix} 4 & 2 & 1 \\ 5 & 3 & 7 \end{bmatrix}, \quad \mathbf{x} = \begin{bmatrix} x_1 \\ x_2 \\ x_3 \end{bmatrix}$$

$$A\mathbf{x} = \begin{bmatrix} 4x_1 + 2x_2 + x_3 \\ 5x_1 + 3x_2 + 7x_3 \end{bmatrix} \qquad \blacktriangleleft$$

EXAMPLE 2.

$$A = \begin{bmatrix} -3 & 1 \\ 2 & 5 \\ 4 & 2 \end{bmatrix}, \quad \mathbf{x} = \begin{bmatrix} 2 \\ 4 \end{bmatrix}$$

$$A\mathbf{x} = \begin{bmatrix} -3 \cdot 2 + 1 \cdot 4 \\ 2 \cdot 2 + 5 \cdot 4 \\ 4 \cdot 2 + 2 \cdot 4 \end{bmatrix} = \begin{bmatrix} -2 \\ 24 \\ 16 \end{bmatrix} \qquad \blacktriangleleft$$

EXAMPLE 3. Write the following system of equations as a matrix equation $A\mathbf{x} = \mathbf{b}$.

$$\begin{aligned} 3x_1 + 2x_2 + x_3 &= 5 \\ x_1 - 2x_2 + 5x_3 &= -2 \\ 2x_1 + x_2 - 3x_3 &= 1 \end{aligned}$$

SOLUTION.

$$\begin{bmatrix} 3 & 2 & 1 \\ 1 & -2 & 5 \\ 2 & 1 & -3 \end{bmatrix} \begin{bmatrix} x_1 \\ x_2 \\ x_3 \end{bmatrix} = \begin{bmatrix} 5 \\ -2 \\ 1 \end{bmatrix} \qquad \blacktriangleleft$$

APPLICATION 1: WEIGHT REDUCTION

Bob weighs 178 pounds. He wishes to lose weight through a program of dieting and exercise. After consulting Table 1, he sets up the exercise schedule in Table 2. How many calories will he burn up exercising each day if he follows this program?

TABLE I

CALORIES BURNED PER HOUR

	Weight in lb			
Exercise Activity	**152**	**161**	**170**	**178**
Walking 2 mph	213	225	237	249
Running 5.5 mph	651	688	726	764
Bicycling 5.5 mph	304	321	338	356
Tennis (moderate)	420	441	468	492

TABLE 2

HOURS PER DAY FOR EACH ACTIVITY

	Exercise Schedule			
	Walking	**Running**	**Bicycling**	**Tennis**
Monday	1.0	0.0	1.0	0.0
Tuesday	0.0	0.0	0.0	2.0
Wednesday	0.4	0.5	0.0	0.0
Thursday	0.0	0.0	0.5	2.0
Friday	0.4	0.5	0.0	0.0

SOLUTION. The information pertaining to Bob is located in column four of Table 1. This information can be represented by a column vector **x**. The information in Table 2 can be represented by a 5×4 matrix A. To answer the question, we simply calculate $A\mathbf{x}$.

$$
\begin{bmatrix}
1.0 & 0.0 & 1.0 & 0.0 \\
0.0 & 0.0 & 0.0 & 2.0 \\
0.4 & 0.5 & 0.0 & 0.0 \\
0.0 & 0.0 & 0.5 & 2.0 \\
0.4 & 0.5 & 0.0 & 0.0
\end{bmatrix}
\begin{bmatrix}
249 \\
764 \\
356 \\
492
\end{bmatrix}
=
\begin{bmatrix}
605.0 \\
984.0 \\
481.6 \\
1162.0 \\
481.6
\end{bmatrix}
\begin{matrix}
Monday \\
Tuesday \\
Wednesday \\
Thursday \\
Friday
\end{matrix}
\qquad \triangleleft
$$

An alternative way to represent the linear system (2) as a matrix equation is to express the product $A\mathbf{x}$ as a sum of column vectors:

$$
A\mathbf{x} =
\begin{bmatrix}
a_{11}x_1 + a_{12}x_2 + \cdots + a_{1n}x_n \\
a_{21}x_1 + a_{22}x_2 + \cdots + a_{2n}x_n \\
\vdots \\
a_{m1}x_1 + a_{m2}x_2 + \cdots + a_{mn}x_n
\end{bmatrix}
$$

$$= x_1 \begin{bmatrix} a_{11} \\ a_{21} \\ \vdots \\ a_{m1} \end{bmatrix} + x_2 \begin{bmatrix} a_{12} \\ a_{22} \\ \vdots \\ a_{m2} \end{bmatrix} + \cdots + x_n \begin{bmatrix} a_{1n} \\ a_{2n} \\ \vdots \\ a_{mn} \end{bmatrix}$$

Thus we have

(5) $$A\mathbf{x} = x_1\mathbf{a}_1 + x_2\mathbf{a}_2 + \cdots + x_n\mathbf{a}_n$$

Using this formula we can represent the system of equations (2) as a matrix equation of the form

(6) $$x_1\mathbf{a}_1 + x_2\mathbf{a}_2 + \cdots + x_n\mathbf{a}_n = \mathbf{b}$$

EXAMPLE 4. The linear system

$$2x_1 + 3x_2 - 2x_3 = 5$$
$$5x_1 - 4x_2 + 2x_3 = 6$$

can be written as a matrix equation

$$x_1 \begin{bmatrix} 2 \\ 5 \end{bmatrix} + x_2 \begin{bmatrix} 3 \\ -4 \end{bmatrix} + x_3 \begin{bmatrix} -2 \\ 2 \end{bmatrix} = \begin{bmatrix} 5 \\ 6 \end{bmatrix}$$ ◀

▷ **DEFINITION** If $\mathbf{a}_1, \mathbf{a}_2, \ldots, \mathbf{a}_n$ are vectors in R^m and $c_1, c_2, \ldots, c_n$ are scalars, then a sum of the form

$$c_1\mathbf{a}_1 + c_2\mathbf{a}_2 + \cdots + c_n\mathbf{a}_n$$

is said to be a **linear combination** of the vectors $\mathbf{a}_1, \mathbf{a}_2, \ldots, \mathbf{a}_n$.   ◀

It follows from equation (5) that the product $A\mathbf{x}$ is a linear combination of the columns vectors of A. Some books even use this linear combination representation as the definition of matrix vector multiplication.

If A is an $m \times n$ matrix and $\mathbf{x}$ is a vector in R^n, then

$$A\mathbf{x} = x_1\mathbf{a}_1 + x_2\mathbf{a}_2 + \cdots + x_n\mathbf{a}_n$$

EXAMPLE 5. If we choose $x_1 = 2$, $x_2 = 3$, $x_3 = 4$ in Example 4, then

$$\begin{bmatrix} 5 \\ 6 \end{bmatrix} = 2 \begin{bmatrix} 2 \\ 5 \end{bmatrix} + 3 \begin{bmatrix} 3 \\ -4 \end{bmatrix} + 4 \begin{bmatrix} -2 \\ 2 \end{bmatrix}$$

Thus the vector $\begin{bmatrix} 5 \\ 6 \end{bmatrix}$ is a linear combination of the three column vectors of the coefficient matrix. It follows that the linear system in Example 4 is consistent and

$$\mathbf{x} = \begin{bmatrix} 2 \\ 3 \\ 4 \end{bmatrix}$$

is a solution to the system.   ◀

The matrix equation (6) provides a nice way of characterizing whether a linear system of equations is consistent. Indeed, the following theorem is a direct consequence of (6).

▶ **THEOREM 1.3.1 (Consistency Theorem for Linear Systems)** *A linear system $A\mathbf{x} = \mathbf{b}$ is consistent if and only if $\mathbf{b}$ can be written as a linear combination of the column vectors of A.*   ◀

EXAMPLE 6.   The linear system

$$x_1 + 2x_2 = 1$$
$$2x_1 + 4x_2 = 1$$

is inconsistent since the vector $\begin{bmatrix} 1 \\ 1 \end{bmatrix}$ cannot be written as a linear combination of the column vectors $\begin{bmatrix} 1 \\ 2 \end{bmatrix}$ and $\begin{bmatrix} 2 \\ 4 \end{bmatrix}$. Note that any linear combination of these vectors would be of the form

$$x_1 \begin{bmatrix} 1 \\ 2 \end{bmatrix} + x_2 \begin{bmatrix} 2 \\ 4 \end{bmatrix} = \begin{bmatrix} x_1 + 2x_2 \\ 2x_1 + 4x_2 \end{bmatrix}$$

and hence the second entry of the vector must be double the first entry.   ◀

Matrix Multiplication

More generally, it is possible to multiply a matrix A times a matrix B if the number of columns of A equals the number of rows of B. The first column of the product is determined by the first column of B; that is, the first column of AB is $A\mathbf{b}_1$, the second column of AB is $A\mathbf{b}_2$, and so on. Thus the product AB is the matrix whose columns are $A\mathbf{b}_1, A\mathbf{b}_2, \ldots, A\mathbf{b}_n$.

$$AB = (A\mathbf{b}_1, A\mathbf{b}_2, \ldots, A\mathbf{b}_n)$$

The (i, j) entry of AB is the ith entry of the column vector $A\mathbf{b}_j$. It is determined by multiplying the ith row vector of A times the jth column vector of B.

▶ **DEFINITION**   If $A = (a_{ij})$ is an $m \times n$ matrix and $B = (b_{ij})$ is an $n \times r$ matrix, then the product $AB = C = (c_{ij})$ is the $m \times r$ matrix whose entries are defined by

$$c_{ij} = \mathbf{a}(i, :)\mathbf{b}_j = \sum_{k=1}^{n} a_{ik}b_{kj} \qquad \triangleleft$$

EXAMPLE 7. If

$$A = \begin{bmatrix} 3 & -2 \\ 2 & 4 \\ 1 & -3 \end{bmatrix} \qquad \text{and} \qquad B = \begin{bmatrix} -2 & 1 & 3 \\ 4 & 1 & 6 \end{bmatrix}$$

then

$$AB = \begin{bmatrix} 3 & -2 \\ 2 & 4 \\ 1 & -3 \end{bmatrix} \begin{bmatrix} -2 & 1 & 3 \\ 4 & 1 & 6 \end{bmatrix}$$

$$= \begin{bmatrix} 3 \cdot (-2) - 2 \cdot 4 & 3 \cdot 1 - 2 \cdot 1 & 3 \cdot 3 - 2 \cdot 6 \\ 2 \cdot (-2) + 4 \cdot 4 & 2 \cdot 1 + 4 \cdot 1 & 2 \cdot 3 + 4 \cdot 6 \\ 1 \cdot (-2) - 3 \cdot 4 & 1 \cdot 1 - 3 \cdot 1 & 1 \cdot 3 - 3 \cdot 6 \end{bmatrix}$$

$$= \begin{bmatrix} -14 & 1 & -3 \\ 12 & 6 & 30 \\ -14 & -2 & -15 \end{bmatrix}$$

The shading indicates how the $(2, 3)$ entry of the product is computed using the second row of A and the third column of B. It is also possible to multiply BA; however, the resulting matrix is not equal to AB. In fact, AB and BA do not even have the same dimensions.

$$BA = \begin{bmatrix} -2 \cdot 3 + 1 \cdot 2 + 3 \cdot 1 & -2 \cdot (-2) + 1 \cdot 4 + 3 \cdot (-3) \\ 4 \cdot 3 + 1 \cdot 2 + 6 \cdot 1 & 4 \cdot (-2) + 1 \cdot 4 + 6 \cdot (-3) \end{bmatrix}$$

$$= \begin{bmatrix} -1 & -1 \\ 20 & -22 \end{bmatrix} \qquad \triangleleft$$

EXAMPLE 8. If

$$A = \begin{bmatrix} 3 & 4 \\ 1 & 2 \end{bmatrix} \qquad \text{and} \qquad B = \begin{bmatrix} 1 & 2 \\ 4 & 5 \\ 3 & 6 \end{bmatrix}$$

then it is impossible to multiply A times B, since the number of columns of A does not equal the number of rows of B. However, it is possible to multiply B times A.

$$BA = \begin{bmatrix} 1 & 2 \\ 4 & 5 \\ 3 & 6 \end{bmatrix} \begin{bmatrix} 3 & 4 \\ 1 & 2 \end{bmatrix} = \begin{bmatrix} 5 & 8 \\ 17 & 26 \\ 15 & 24 \end{bmatrix} \qquad \triangleleft$$

If A and B are both $n \times n$ matrices, then AB and BA will also be $n \times n$ matrices, but in general they will not be equal. *Multiplication of matrices is not commutative.*

EXAMPLE 9. If

$$A = \begin{bmatrix} 1 & 1 \\ 0 & 0 \end{bmatrix} \qquad \text{and} \qquad B = \begin{bmatrix} 1 & 1 \\ 2 & 2 \end{bmatrix}$$

then

$$AB = \begin{bmatrix} 1 & 1 \\ 0 & 0 \end{bmatrix} \begin{bmatrix} 1 & 1 \\ 2 & 2 \end{bmatrix} = \begin{bmatrix} 3 & 3 \\ 0 & 0 \end{bmatrix}$$

and

$$BA = \begin{bmatrix} 1 & 1 \\ 2 & 2 \end{bmatrix} \begin{bmatrix} 1 & 1 \\ 0 & 0 \end{bmatrix} = \begin{bmatrix} 1 & 1 \\ 2 & 2 \end{bmatrix}$$

and hence $AB \neq BA$. $\qquad \triangleleft$

APPLICATION 2: PRODUCTION COSTS

A company manufactures three products. Its production expenses are divided into three categories. In each category, an estimate is given for the cost of producing a single item of each product. An estimate is also made of the amount of each product to be produced per quarter. These estimates are given in Tables 3 and 4. The company would like to present at their stockholders' meeting a single table showing the total costs for each quarter in each of the three categories: raw materials, labor, and overhead.

TABLE 3

PRODUCTION COSTS PER ITEM (dollars)

Expenses	Product A	B	C
Raw materials	0.10	0.30	0.15
Labor	0.30	0.40	0.25
Overhead and miscellaneous	0.10	0.20	0.15

TABLE 4

AMOUNT PRODUCED PER QUARTER

Product	Season			
	Summer	Fall	Winter	Spring
A	4000	4500	4500	4000
B	2000	2600	2400	2200
C	5800	6200	6000	6000

SOLUTION. Let us consider the problem in terms of matrices. Each of the two tables can be represented by a matrix.

$$M = \begin{bmatrix} 0.10 & 0.30 & 0.15 \\ 0.30 & 0.40 & 0.25 \\ 0.10 & 0.20 & 0.15 \end{bmatrix}$$

and

$$P = \begin{bmatrix} 4000 & 4500 & 4500 & 4000 \\ 2000 & 2600 & 2400 & 2200 \\ 5800 & 6200 & 6000 & 6000 \end{bmatrix}$$

If we form the product MP, the first column of MP will represent the costs for the summer quarter.

Raw materials: $(0.10)(4000) + (0.30)(2000) + (0.15)(5800) = 1870$
Labor: $(0.30)(4000) + (0.40)(2000) + (0.25)(5800) = 3450$
Overhead and
miscellaneous: $(0.10)(4000) + (0.20)(2000) + (0.15)(5800) = 1670$

The costs for the fall quarter are given in the second column of MP.

Raw materials: $(0.10)(4500) + (0.30)(2600) + (0.15)(6200) = 2160$
Labor: $(0.30)(4500) + (0.40)(2600) + (0.25)(6200) = 3940$
Overhead and
miscellaneous: $(0.10)(4500) + (0.20)(2600) + (0.15)(6200) = 1900$

Columns 3 and 4 of MP represent the costs for the winter and spring quarters.

$$MP = \begin{bmatrix} 1870 & 2160 & 2070 & 1960 \\ 3450 & 3940 & 3810 & 3580 \\ 1670 & 1900 & 1830 & 1740 \end{bmatrix}$$

	Season				
	Summer	Fall	Winter	Spring	Year
Raw materials	1,870	2,160	2,070	1,960	8,060
Labor	3,450	3,940	3,810	3,580	14,780
Overhead and miscellaneous	1,670	1,900	1,830	1,740	7,140
Total production costs	6,990	8,000	7,710	7,280	29,980

TABLE 5

The entries in row 1 of *MP* represent the total cost of raw materials for each of the four quarters. The entries in rows 2 and 3 represent total cost for labor and overhead, respectively, for each of the four quarters. The yearly expenses in each category may be obtained by adding the entries in each row. The numbers in each of the columns may be added to obtain the total production costs for each quarter. Table 5 summarizes the total production costs. ◁

Notational Rules

Just as in ordinary algebra, if an expression involves both multiplication and addition and there are no parentheses to indicate the order of the operations, multiplications are carried out before additions. This is true for both scalar and matrix multiplications. For example, if

$$A = \begin{bmatrix} 3 & 4 \\ 1 & 2 \end{bmatrix}, \qquad B = \begin{bmatrix} 1 & 3 \\ 2 & 1 \end{bmatrix}, \qquad C = \begin{bmatrix} -2 & 1 \\ 3 & 2 \end{bmatrix}$$

then

$$A + BC = \begin{bmatrix} 3 & 4 \\ 1 & 2 \end{bmatrix} + \begin{bmatrix} 7 & 7 \\ -1 & 4 \end{bmatrix} = \begin{bmatrix} 10 & 11 \\ 0 & 6 \end{bmatrix}$$

and

$$3A + B = \begin{bmatrix} 9 & 12 \\ 3 & 6 \end{bmatrix} + \begin{bmatrix} 1 & 3 \\ 2 & 1 \end{bmatrix} = \begin{bmatrix} 10 & 15 \\ 5 & 7 \end{bmatrix}$$

Algebraic Rules

The following theorem provides some useful rules for doing matrix arithmetic.

▶ **THEOREM 1.3.2** *Each of the following statements is valid for any scalars α and β and for any matrices A, B, and C for which the indicated operations are defined.*

1. $A + B = B + A$
2. $(A + B) + C = A + (B + C)$

3. $(AB)C = A(BC)$
4. $A(B + C) = AB + AC$
5. $(A + B)C = AC + BC$
6. $(\alpha\beta)A = \alpha(\beta A)$
7. $\alpha(AB) = (\alpha A)B = A(\alpha B)$
8. $(\alpha + \beta)A = \alpha A + \beta A$
9. $\alpha(A + B) = \alpha A + \alpha B$

◀

We will prove two of the rules and leave the rest for the reader to verify.

▶**Proof of (4).** Assume that $A = (a_{ij})$ is an $m \times n$ matrix and $B = (b_{ij})$ and $C = (c_{ij})$ are both $n \times r$ matrices. Let $D = A(B + C)$ and $E = AB + AC$. It follows that

$$d_{ij} = \sum_{k=1}^{n} a_{ik}(b_{kj} + c_{kj})$$

and

$$e_{ij} = \sum_{k=1}^{n} a_{ik}b_{kj} + \sum_{k=1}^{n} a_{ik}c_{kj}$$

But

$$\sum_{k=1}^{n} a_{ik}(b_{kj} + c_{kj}) = \sum_{k=1}^{n} a_{ik}b_{kj} + \sum_{k=1}^{n} a_{ik}c_{kj}$$

so that $d_{ij} = e_{ij}$ and hence $A(B + C) = AB + AC$.

◀

▶**Proof of (3).** Let A be an $m \times n$ matrix, B an $n \times r$ matrix, and C an $r \times s$ matrix. Let $D = AB$ and $E = BC$. We must show that $DC = AE$. By the definition of matrix multiplication,

$$d_{il} = \sum_{k=1}^{n} a_{ik}b_{kl} \qquad \text{and} \qquad e_{kj} = \sum_{l=1}^{r} b_{kl}c_{lj}$$

The ijth term of DC is

$$\sum_{l=1}^{r} d_{il}c_{lj} = \sum_{l=1}^{r} \left(\sum_{k=1}^{n} a_{ik}b_{kl} \right) c_{lj}$$

and the (i, j) entry of AE is

$$\sum_{k=1}^{n} a_{ik}e_{kj} = \sum_{k=1}^{n} a_{ik} \left(\sum_{l=1}^{r} b_{kl}c_{lj} \right)$$

Since

$$\sum_{l=1}^{r} \left(\sum_{k=1}^{n} a_{ik}b_{kl} \right) c_{lj} = \sum_{l=1}^{r} \left(\sum_{k=1}^{n} a_{ik}b_{kl}c_{lj} \right) = \sum_{k=1}^{n} a_{ik} \left(\sum_{l=1}^{r} b_{kl}c_{lj} \right)$$

it follows that

$$(AB)C = DC = AE = A(BC)$$

◀

The arithmetic rules given in Theorem 1.3.2 seem quite natural since they are similar to the rules that we use with real numbers. However, there are some important differences between the rules for matrix arithmetic and those for real number arithmetic. In particular, multiplication of real numbers is commutative; however, we saw in Example 6 that matrix multiplication is not commutative. This difference warrants special emphasis.

WARNING: In general, $AB \neq BA$. Matrix multiplication is *not* commutative.

Some of the other differences between matrix arithmetic and real number arithmetic are illustrated in Exercises 19 through 22.

EXAMPLE 10. If

$$A = \begin{bmatrix} 1 & 2 \\ 3 & 4 \end{bmatrix}, \qquad B = \begin{bmatrix} 2 & 1 \\ -3 & 2 \end{bmatrix}, \qquad \text{and} \qquad C = \begin{bmatrix} 1 & 0 \\ 2 & 1 \end{bmatrix}$$

verify that $A(BC) = (AB)C$ and $A(B + C) = AB + AC$.

SOLUTION.

$$A(BC) = \begin{bmatrix} 1 & 2 \\ 3 & 4 \end{bmatrix} \begin{bmatrix} 4 & 1 \\ 1 & 2 \end{bmatrix} = \begin{bmatrix} 6 & 5 \\ 16 & 11 \end{bmatrix}$$

$$(AB)C = \begin{bmatrix} -4 & 5 \\ -6 & 11 \end{bmatrix} \begin{bmatrix} 1 & 0 \\ 2 & 1 \end{bmatrix} = \begin{bmatrix} 6 & 5 \\ 16 & 11 \end{bmatrix}$$

Thus

$$A(BC) = \begin{bmatrix} 6 & 5 \\ 16 & 11 \end{bmatrix} = (AB)C$$

$$A(B + C) = \begin{bmatrix} 1 & 2 \\ 3 & 4 \end{bmatrix} \begin{bmatrix} 3 & 1 \\ -1 & 3 \end{bmatrix} = \begin{bmatrix} 1 & 7 \\ 5 & 15 \end{bmatrix}$$

$$AB + AC = \begin{bmatrix} -4 & 5 \\ -6 & 11 \end{bmatrix} + \begin{bmatrix} 5 & 2 \\ 11 & 4 \end{bmatrix} = \begin{bmatrix} 1 & 7 \\ 5 & 15 \end{bmatrix}$$

Therefore,

$$A(B + C) = AB + AC \qquad \blacktriangleleft$$

Notation   Since $(AB)C = A(BC)$, we may simply omit the parentheses and write ABC. The same is true for a product of four or more matrices. In the case where an $n \times n$ matrix is multiplied by itself a number of times, it is convenient to use exponential notation. Thus, if k is a positive integer, then

$$A^k = \underbrace{AA \cdots A}_{k \text{ times}}$$

EXAMPLE 11. If

$$A = \begin{bmatrix} 1 & 1 \\ 1 & 1 \end{bmatrix}$$

then

$$A^2 = \begin{bmatrix} 1 & 1 \\ 1 & 1 \end{bmatrix} \begin{bmatrix} 1 & 1 \\ 1 & 1 \end{bmatrix} = \begin{bmatrix} 2 & 2 \\ 2 & 2 \end{bmatrix}$$

$$A^3 = AAA = AA^2 = \begin{bmatrix} 1 & 1 \\ 1 & 1 \end{bmatrix} \begin{bmatrix} 2 & 2 \\ 2 & 2 \end{bmatrix} = \begin{bmatrix} 4 & 4 \\ 4 & 4 \end{bmatrix}$$

and in general

$$A^n = \begin{bmatrix} 2^{n-1} & 2^{n-1} \\ 2^{n-1} & 2^{n-1} \end{bmatrix} \qquad \triangleleft$$

APPLICATION 3: A SIMPLE MODEL FOR MARITAL STATUS COMPUTATIONS

In a certain town, 30 percent of the married women get divorced each year and 20 percent of the single women get married each year. There are 8000 married women and 2000 single women. Assuming that the total population of women remains constant, how many married women and how many single women will there be after 1 year? After 2 years?

SOLUTION. Form a matrix A as follows. The entries in the first row of A will be the percent of married and single women, respectively, that are married after 1 year. The entries in the second row will be the percent of women who are single after 1 year. Thus

$$A = \begin{bmatrix} 0.70 & 0.20 \\ 0.30 & 0.80 \end{bmatrix}$$

If we let $\mathbf{x} = \begin{bmatrix} 8000 \\ 2000 \end{bmatrix}$, the number of married and single women after 1 year can be computed by multiplying A times $\mathbf{x}$.

$$A\mathbf{x} = \begin{bmatrix} 0.70 & 0.20 \\ 0.30 & 0.80 \end{bmatrix} \begin{bmatrix} 8000 \\ 2000 \end{bmatrix} = \begin{bmatrix} 6000 \\ 4000 \end{bmatrix}$$

After 1 year there will be 6000 married women and 4000 single women. To find the number of married and single women after 2 years, compute

$$A^2\mathbf{x} = A(A\mathbf{x}) = \begin{bmatrix} 0.70 & 0.20 \\ 0.30 & 0.80 \end{bmatrix} \begin{bmatrix} 6000 \\ 4000 \end{bmatrix} = \begin{bmatrix} 5000 \\ 5000 \end{bmatrix}$$

After 2 years, half of the women will be married and half will be single. In general, the number of married and single women after n years can be determined by computing $A^n\mathbf{x}$. ◄

APPLICATION 4: ECOLOGY: DEMOGRAPHICS OF THE LOGGERHEAD SEA TURTLE

Management and preservation of many wildlife species depend on our ability to model population dynamics. A standard modeling technique is to divide the life cycle of a species into a number of stages. The models assume that the population sizes for each stage depend only on the female population and that the probability of survival of an individual female from one year to the next depends only on the stage of the life cycle and not on the actual age of an individual. For example, let us consider a four-stage model for analyzing the population dynamics of the loggerhead turtle. At each stage we estimate the probability of survival over a 1 year period. We also estimate the ability to reproduce in terms of the expected number of eggs laid in a given year. The results are summarized in Table 6. The approximate ages for each stage are listed in parentheses next to the stage description.

If d_i represents the duration of the ith stage, and s_i is the annual survivorship rate for that stage, then it can be shown that the proportion remaining in stage i the

FIGURE 1.3.1

TABLE 6			
FOUR-STAGE MODEL FOR LOGGERHEAD TURTLE DEMOGRAPHICS			
Stage number	Description (age in years)	Annual survivorship	Eggs laid per year
1	Eggs, hatchlings (<1)	0.67	0
2	Juveniles and subadults (1–21)	0.74	0
3	Novice breeders (22)	0.81	127
4	Mature breeders (23–54)	0.81	79

following year will be

(7)
$$p_i = \left(\frac{1 - s_i^{d_i-1}}{1 - s_i^{d_i}} \right) s_i$$

and the proportion of the population that will survive and move into stage $i + 1$ the following year will be

(8)
$$q_i = \frac{s_i^{d_i}(1 - s_i)}{1 - s_i^{d_i}}$$

If we let e_i denote the average number of eggs laid by a member of stage i ($i = 2, 3, 4$) in 1 year and form the matrix

(9)
$$L = \begin{bmatrix} p_1 & e_2 & e_3 & e_4 \\ q_1 & p_2 & 0 & 0 \\ 0 & q_2 & p_3 & 0 \\ 0 & 0 & q_3 & p_4 \end{bmatrix}$$

then L can be used to predict the turtle populations for each stage in future years. A matrix of the form (9) is called a *Leslie matrix*, and the corresponding population model is sometimes referred to as a *Leslie population model*. Using the figures from Table 6, the Leslie matrix for our model is

$$L = \begin{bmatrix} 0 & 0 & 127 & 79 \\ 0.67 & 0.7394 & 0 & 0 \\ 0 & 0.0006 & 0 & 0 \\ 0 & 0 & 0.81 & 0.8077 \end{bmatrix}$$

Suppose that the initial populations at each stage were 200,000, 300,000, 500, and 1500, respectively. If we represent these initial populations by a vector $\mathbf{x}_0$, the

TABLE 7

LOGGERHEAD TURTLE POPULATION PROJECTIONS

Stage number	Initial population	10 years	25 years	50 years
1	200,000	114,264	74,039	35,966
2	300,000	329,212	213,669	103,795
3	500	214	139	68
4	1,500	1,061	687	334

populations at each stage after 1 year are determined by computing

$$\mathbf{x}_1 = L\mathbf{x}_0 = \begin{bmatrix} 0 & 0 & 127 & 79 \\ 0.67 & 0.7394 & 0 & 0 \\ 0 & 0.0006 & 0 & 0 \\ 0 & 0 & 0.81 & 0.8077 \end{bmatrix} \begin{bmatrix} 200,000 \\ 300,000 \\ 500 \\ 1,500 \end{bmatrix} = \begin{bmatrix} 182,000 \\ 355,820 \\ 180 \\ 1,617 \end{bmatrix}$$

(The computations have been rounded to the nearest integer.) To determine the population vector after 2 years, we multiply again by the matrix L.

$$\mathbf{x}_2 = L\mathbf{x}_1 = L^2\mathbf{x}_0$$

In general, the population after k years is determined by computing $\mathbf{x}_k = L^k\mathbf{x}_0$. To see longer-range trends, we compute $\mathbf{x}_{10}, \mathbf{x}_{25}, \mathbf{x}_{50}$. The results are summarized in Table 7. The model predicts that the total number of breeding-age turtles will decrease by 80 percent over a 50-year period.

A seven-stage model describing the population dynamics is presented in reference [1] below. We will use the seven-stage model in the computer exercises at the end of this chapter. Reference [2] is the original paper by Leslie.

REFERENCES

1. Crouse, Deborah T., Larry B. Crowder, and Hal Caswell, "A Stage-Based Population Model for Loggerhead Sea Turtles and Implications for Conservation," *Ecology*, 68(5), 1987.
2. Leslie, P. H., "On the Use of Matrices in Certain Population Mathematics," *Biometrika*, 33, 1945.

The Identity Matrix

Just as the number 1 acts as an identity for the multiplication of real numbers, there is a special matrix I that acts as an identity for matrix multiplication, that is,

(10) $$IA = AI = A$$

for any $n \times n$ matrix A. It is easy to verify that, if we define I to be an $n \times n$ matrix with 1's on the main diagonal and 0's elsewhere, then I satisfies equation (10) for any $n \times n$ matrix A. More formally, we have the following definition.

▷ **DEFINITION** The $n \times n$ **identity matrix** is the matrix $I = (\delta_{ij})$, where

$$\delta_{ij} = \begin{cases} 1 & \text{if } i = j \\ 0 & \text{if } i \neq j \end{cases}$$

◁

As an example, let us verify equation (10) in the case $n = 3$.

$$\begin{bmatrix} 1 & 0 & 0 \\ 0 & 1 & 0 \\ 0 & 0 & 1 \end{bmatrix} \begin{bmatrix} 3 & 4 & 1 \\ 2 & 6 & 3 \\ 0 & 1 & 8 \end{bmatrix} = \begin{bmatrix} 3 & 4 & 1 \\ 2 & 6 & 3 \\ 0 & 1 & 8 \end{bmatrix}$$

and

$$\begin{bmatrix} 3 & 4 & 1 \\ 2 & 6 & 3 \\ 0 & 1 & 8 \end{bmatrix} \begin{bmatrix} 1 & 0 & 0 \\ 0 & 1 & 0 \\ 0 & 0 & 1 \end{bmatrix} = \begin{bmatrix} 3 & 4 & 1 \\ 2 & 6 & 3 \\ 0 & 1 & 8 \end{bmatrix}$$

In general, if B is any $m \times n$ matrix and C is any $n \times r$ matrix, then

$$BI = B \qquad \text{and} \qquad IC = C$$

The column vectors of the $n \times n$ identity matrix I are the standard vectors used to define a coordinate system in Euclidean n-space. The standard notation for the jth column vector of I is $\mathbf{e}_j$, rather than the usual $\mathbf{i}_j$. Thus the $n \times n$ identity matrix can be written

$$I = (\mathbf{e}_1, \mathbf{e}_2, \ldots, \mathbf{e}_n)$$

Matrix Inversion

A real number a is said to have a multiplicative inverse if there exists a number b such that $ab = 1$. Any nonzero number a has a multiplicative inverse $b = \frac{1}{a}$. We generalize the concept of multiplicative inverses to matrices with the following definition.

▷ **DEFINITION** An $n \times n$ matrix A is said to be **nonsingular** or **invertible** if there exists a matrix B such that $AB = BA = I$. The matrix B is said to be a **multiplicative inverse** of A.

◁

If B and C are both multiplicative inverses of A, then

$$B = BI = B(AC) = (BA)C = IC = C$$

Thus a matrix can have at most one multiplicative inverse. We will refer to the multiplicative inverse of a nonsingular matrix A as simply the *inverse* of A and denote it by A^{-1}.

EXAMPLE 12. The matrices

$$\begin{bmatrix} 2 & 4 \\ 3 & 1 \end{bmatrix} \quad \text{and} \quad \begin{bmatrix} -\frac{1}{10} & \frac{2}{5} \\ \frac{3}{10} & -\frac{1}{5} \end{bmatrix}$$

are inverses of each other, since

$$\begin{bmatrix} 2 & 4 \\ 3 & 1 \end{bmatrix} \begin{bmatrix} -\frac{1}{10} & \frac{2}{5} \\ \frac{3}{10} & -\frac{1}{5} \end{bmatrix} = \begin{bmatrix} 1 & 0 \\ 0 & 1 \end{bmatrix}$$

and

$$\begin{bmatrix} -\frac{1}{10} & \frac{2}{5} \\ \frac{3}{10} & -\frac{1}{5} \end{bmatrix} \begin{bmatrix} 2 & 4 \\ 3 & 1 \end{bmatrix} = \begin{bmatrix} 1 & 0 \\ 0 & 1 \end{bmatrix} \qquad \blacktriangleleft$$

EXAMPLE 13. The 3×3 matrices

$$\begin{bmatrix} 1 & 2 & 3 \\ 0 & 1 & 4 \\ 0 & 0 & 1 \end{bmatrix} \quad \text{and} \quad \begin{bmatrix} 1 & -2 & 5 \\ 0 & 1 & -4 \\ 0 & 0 & 1 \end{bmatrix}$$

are inverses, since

$$\begin{bmatrix} 1 & 2 & 3 \\ 0 & 1 & 4 \\ 0 & 0 & 1 \end{bmatrix} \begin{bmatrix} 1 & -2 & 5 \\ 0 & 1 & -4 \\ 0 & 0 & 1 \end{bmatrix} = \begin{bmatrix} 1 & 0 & 0 \\ 0 & 1 & 0 \\ 0 & 0 & 1 \end{bmatrix}$$

and

$$\begin{bmatrix} 1 & -2 & 5 \\ 0 & 1 & -4 \\ 0 & 0 & 1 \end{bmatrix} \begin{bmatrix} 1 & 2 & 3 \\ 0 & 1 & 4 \\ 0 & 0 & 1 \end{bmatrix} = \begin{bmatrix} 1 & 0 & 0 \\ 0 & 1 & 0 \\ 0 & 0 & 1 \end{bmatrix} \qquad \blacktriangleleft$$

EXAMPLE 14. The matrix

$$A = \begin{bmatrix} 1 & 0 \\ 0 & 0 \end{bmatrix}$$

has no inverse. Indeed, if B is any 2×2 matrix, then

$$BA = \begin{bmatrix} b_{11} & b_{12} \\ b_{21} & b_{22} \end{bmatrix} \begin{bmatrix} 1 & 0 \\ 0 & 0 \end{bmatrix} = \begin{bmatrix} b_{11} & 0 \\ b_{21} & 0 \end{bmatrix}$$

Thus BA cannot equal I.

◀

▶ **DEFINITION** An $n \times n$ matrix is said to be **singular** if it does not have a multiplicative inverse. ◀

In the next section we will learn how to determine whether a matrix has a multiplicative inverse. We will also learn a method for computing the inverse of a nonsingular matrix.

The Transpose of a Matrix

Given an $m \times n$ matrix A, it is often useful to form a new $n \times m$ matrix whose columns are the rows of A.

▶ **DEFINITION** The **transpose** of an $m \times n$ matrix A is the $n \times m$ matrix B defined by

(11) $$b_{ji} = a_{ij}$$

for $j = 1, \ldots, n$ and $i = 1, \ldots, m$. The transpose of A is denoted by A^T. ◀

It follows from (11) that the jth row of A^T has the same entries, respectively, as the jth column of A, and the ith column of A^T has the same entries, respectively, as the ith row of A.

EXAMPLE 15.

A. If $A = \begin{bmatrix} 1 & 2 & 3 \\ 4 & 5 & 6 \end{bmatrix}$, then $A^T = \begin{bmatrix} 1 & 4 \\ 2 & 5 \\ 3 & 6 \end{bmatrix}$.

B. If $B = \begin{bmatrix} -3 & 2 & 1 \\ 4 & 3 & 2 \\ 1 & 2 & 5 \end{bmatrix}$, then $B^T = \begin{bmatrix} -3 & 4 & 1 \\ 2 & 3 & 2 \\ 1 & 2 & 5 \end{bmatrix}$.

C. If $C = \begin{bmatrix} 1 & 2 \\ 2 & 3 \end{bmatrix}$, then $C^T = \begin{bmatrix} 1 & 2 \\ 2 & 3 \end{bmatrix}$. ◀

There are four basic algebraic rules involving transposes.

> **Algebraic Rules for Transposes**
> 1. $(A^T)^T = A$
> 2. $(\alpha A)^T = \alpha A^T$
> 3. $(A + B)^T = A^T + B^T$
> 4. $(AB)^T = B^T A^T$

The first three rules are straightforward. We leave it to the reader to verify that they are valid. To prove the fourth rule, we need only show that the (i, j) entries of $(AB)^T$ and $B^T A^T$ are equal. If A is an $m \times n$ matrix, then, in order for the multiplications to be possible, B must have n rows. The (i, j) entry of $(AB)^T$ is the (j, i) entry of AB. It is computed by multiplying the jth row vector of A times the i column vector of B.

$$(12) \quad \mathbf{a}(j, :)\mathbf{b}_i = (a_{j1}, a_{j2}, \ldots, a_{jn}) \begin{bmatrix} b_{1i} \\ b_{2i} \\ \vdots \\ b_{ni} \end{bmatrix} = a_{j1}b_{1i} + a_{j2}b_{2i} + \cdots + a_{jn}b_{ni}$$

The (i, j) entry of $B^T A^T$ is computed by the ith row of B^T times the jth column of A^T. Since the ith row of B^T is the transpose of the ith column of B and the j column of A^T is the transpose as the jth row of A, it follows that the (i, j) entry of $B^T A^T$ is given by

$$(13) \quad \mathbf{b}_i^T \mathbf{a}(j, :)^T = (b_{1i}, b_{2i}, \ldots, b_{ni}) \begin{bmatrix} a_{j1} \\ a_{j2} \\ \vdots \\ a_{jn} \end{bmatrix} = b_{1i}a_{j1} + b_{2i}a_{j2} + \cdots + b_{ni}a_{jn}$$

It follows from (12) and (13) that the (i, j) entries of $(AB)^T$ and $B^T A^T$ are equal. The following example illustrates the idea behind the last proof.

EXAMPLE 16. Let

$$A = \begin{bmatrix} 1 & 2 & 1 \\ 3 & 3 & 5 \\ 2 & 4 & 1 \end{bmatrix}, \quad B = \begin{bmatrix} 1 & 0 & 2 \\ 2 & 1 & 1 \\ 5 & 4 & 1 \end{bmatrix}$$

Note that the $(3, 2)$ entry of AB is computed using the third row of A and the second column of B.

$$AB = \begin{bmatrix} 1 & 2 & 1 \\ 3 & 3 & 5 \\ 2 & 4 & 1 \end{bmatrix} \begin{bmatrix} 1 & 0 & 2 \\ 2 & 1 & 1 \\ 5 & 4 & 1 \end{bmatrix} = \begin{bmatrix} 10 & 6 & 5 \\ 34 & 23 & 14 \\ 15 & 8 & 9 \end{bmatrix}$$

When the product is transposed, the $(3, 2)$ entry of AB becomes the $(2, 3)$ entry of $(AB)^T$.

$$(AB)^T = \begin{bmatrix} 10 & 34 & 15 \\ 6 & 23 & 8 \\ 5 & 14 & 9 \end{bmatrix}$$

On the other hand, the $(2, 3)$ entry of $B^T A^T$ is computed using the second row of B^T and the third column of A^T.

$$B^T A^T = \begin{bmatrix} 1 & 2 & 5 \\ 0 & 1 & 4 \\ 2 & 1 & 1 \end{bmatrix} \begin{bmatrix} 1 & 3 & 2 \\ 2 & 3 & 4 \\ 1 & 5 & 1 \end{bmatrix} = \begin{bmatrix} 10 & 34 & 15 \\ 6 & 23 & 8 \\ 5 & 14 & 9 \end{bmatrix}$$

In both cases the arithmetic for computing the $(3, 2)$ entry is the same.　◀

The matrix C in Example 15 is its own transpose. This often happens with matrices that arise in applications.

▶ **DEFINITION** An $n \times n$ matrix A is said to be **symmetric** if $A^T = A$.　◀

The following are some examples of symmetric matrices:

$$\begin{bmatrix} 1 & 0 \\ 0 & -4 \end{bmatrix} \qquad \begin{bmatrix} 2 & 3 & 4 \\ 3 & 1 & 5 \\ 4 & 5 & 3 \end{bmatrix} \qquad \begin{bmatrix} 0 & 1 & 2 \\ 1 & 1 & -2 \\ 2 & -2 & -3 \end{bmatrix}$$

One type of application that leads to symmetric matrices is problems involving networks. These problems are often solved using the techniques of an area of mathematics called *graph theory*.

APPLICATION 5: NETWORKS AND GRAPHS

Graph theory is one of the important areas of applied mathematics. It is used to model problems in virtually all the applied sciences. Graph theory is particularly useful in applications involving communication networks.

A *graph* is defined to be a set of points called *vertices* together with a set of unordered pairs of vertices, which are referred to as *edges*. Figure 1.3.2 gives a geometrical representation of a graph. We can think of the vertices V_1, V_2, V_3, V_4, V_5 as corresponding to the nodes in a communications network.

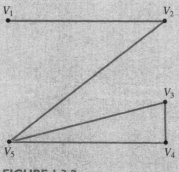

FIGURE 1.3.2

The line segments joining the vertices correspond to the edges:

$$\{V_1, V_2\}, \ \{V_2, V_5\}, \ \{V_3, V_4\}, \ \{V_3, V_5\}, \ \{V_4, V_5\}$$

Each edge represents a direct communication link between two nodes of the network.

An actual communications network could involve a large number of vertices and edges. Indeed, if there are millions of vertices, a graphical picture of the network would be quite confusing. An alternative is to use a matrix representation for the network. If the graph contains a total of n vertices, we can define an $n \times n$ matrix A by

$$a_{ij} = \begin{cases} 1 & \text{if } \{V_i, V_j\} \text{ is an edge of the graph} \\ 0 & \text{if there is no edge joining } V_i \text{ and } V_j \end{cases}$$

The matrix A is called the *adjacency matrix* of the graph. The adjacency matrix for the graph in Figure 1.3.2 is given by

$$A = \begin{bmatrix} 0 & 1 & 0 & 0 & 0 \\ 1 & 0 & 0 & 0 & 1 \\ 0 & 0 & 0 & 1 & 1 \\ 0 & 0 & 1 & 0 & 1 \\ 0 & 1 & 1 & 1 & 0 \end{bmatrix}$$

Note that the matrix A is symmetric. Indeed, any adjacency matrix must be symmetric, for if $\{V_i, V_j\}$ is an edge of the graph, then $a_{ij} = a_{ji} = 1$ and $a_{ij} = a_{ji} = 0$ if there is no edge joining V_i and V_j. In either case, $a_{ij} = a_{ji}$.

We can think of a *walk* in a graph as a sequence of edges linking one vertex to another. For example, in Figure 1.3.2 the edges $\{V_1, V_2\}$, $\{V_2, V_5\}$ represent a walk from vertex V_1 to vertex V_5. The length of the walk is said to be 2 since it consists of two edges. A simple way to describe the walk is to indicate the movement between vertices using arrows. Thus $V_1 \rightarrow V_2 \rightarrow V_5$ denotes a walk of length 2 from V_1 to V_5. Similarly, $V_4 \rightarrow V_5 \rightarrow V_2 \rightarrow V_1$ represents a walk of length 3 from V_4 to V_1. It is possible to traverse the same edges more than once in a walk. For example, $V_5 \rightarrow V_3 \rightarrow V_5 \rightarrow V_3$ is a walk of length 3 from V_5 to V_3. In general, by taking powers of the adjacency matrix we can determine the number of walks of any specified length between two vertices.

▷ **THEOREM 1.3.3** *If A is an n × n adjacency matrix of a graph and $a_{ij}^{(k)}$ represents the ijth entry of A^k, then $a_{ij}^{(k)}$ is equal to the number of walks of length k from V_i to V_j.*

▶ *Proof.* The proof is by mathematical induction. In the case $k = 1$, it follows from the definition of the adjacency matrix that a_{ij} represents the number of walks of length 1 from V_i to V_j. Assume for some m that each entry of A^m is equal to the number of walks of length m between the corresponding vertices. Thus $a_{il}^{(m)}$ is the number of walks of length m from V_i to V_l. If there is an edge $\{V_l, V_j\}$, then $a_{il}^{(m)} a_{lj} = a_{il}^{(m)}$ is the number of walks of length $m + 1$ from V_i to V_j of the form

$$V_i \to \cdots \to V_l \to V_j$$

It follows that the total number of walks of length $m + 1$ from V_i to V_j is given by

$$a_{i1}^{(m)} a_{1j} + a_{i2}^{(m)} a_{2j} + \cdots + a_{in}^{(m)} a_{nj}$$

But this is just the (i, j) entry of A^{m+1}.   ◁

EXAMPLE 17. To determine the number of walks of length 3 between any two vertices of the graph in Figure 1.3.2, we need only compute

$$A^3 = \begin{bmatrix} 0 & 2 & 1 & 1 & 0 \\ 2 & 0 & 1 & 1 & 4 \\ 1 & 1 & 2 & 3 & 4 \\ 1 & 1 & 3 & 2 & 4 \\ 0 & 4 & 4 & 4 & 2 \end{bmatrix}$$

Thus the number of walks of length 3 from V_3 to V_5 is $a_{35}^{(3)} = 4$. Note that the matrix A^3 is symmetric. This reflects the fact that there are the same number of walks of length 3 from V_i to V_j as there are from V_j to V_i.   ◁

APPLICATION 6: INFORMATION RETRIEVAL

The growth of digital libraries on the Internet has led to dramatic improvements in the storage and retrieval of information. Modern retrieval methods are based on matrix theory and linear algebra.

In a typical situation, a database consists of a collection of documents and we wish to search the collection and find the documents that best match some particular search conditions. Depending on the type of database, we could search for such items as research articles in journals, Web pages on the Internet, books in a library, or movies in a film collection.

To see how the searches are done, let us assume that our database consists of n documents and that there are m key words that can be used for searches. Not all words are allowable since it would not be practical to search for common words such as articles or prepositions. If the key words are ordered alphabetically, then we can represent the database by an $m \times n$ matrix A. Each document is represented by a column of the matrix. The first entry in the jth column of A would be a number representing the relative frequency of the first key word in the jth document. The entry a_{2j} represents the relative frequency of the second key word, and so on. The list of key words to be used in the search is represented by a vector $\mathbf{x}$ in R^m. The ith entry of $\mathbf{x}$ is taken to be 1 if the ith word in the list of key words is on our search list; otherwise, we set $x_i = 0$. To carry out the search, we simply multiply A^T times $\mathbf{x}$.

For example, suppose that our database, consists of these book titles:

B1. *Applied Linear Algebra*
B2. *Elementary Linear Algebra*
B3. *Elementary Linear Algebra with Applications*
B4. *Linear Algebra and Its Applications*
B5. *Linear Algebra with Applications*
B6. *Matrix Algebra with Applications*
B7. *Matrix Theory*

The collection of key words is given by the following alphabetical list:

algebra, application, elementary, linear, matrix, theory

None of the titles repeats any key word more than once, so for simplicity we will just use 0's and 1's for the entries of the database matrix, rather than relative frequencies. Thus the (i, j) entry of the matrix will be 1 if the ith word appears in the title of the jth book and 0 if it does not. We will assume that our search engine is sophisticated enough to equate various forms of a word. So, for example, in our list of titles the words *applied* and *applications* are both counted as forms of the word *application*. The database matrix for our list of books is the array defined by Table 8.

TABLE 8

ARRAY REPRESENTATION FOR DATABASE OF LINEAR ALGEBRA BOOKS

	Books						
Key Words	B1	B2	B3	B4	B5	B6	B7
algebra	1	1	1	1	1	1	0
application	1	0	1	1	1	1	0
elementary	0	1	1	0	0	0	0
linear	1	1	1	1	1	0	0
matrix	0	0	0	0	0	1	1
theory	0	0	0	0	0	0	1

If the words we are searching for are *applied, linear*, and *algebra*, then the database matrix and search vector are given by

$$
A = \begin{bmatrix} 1 & 1 & 1 & 1 & 1 & 1 & 0 \\ 1 & 0 & 1 & 1 & 1 & 1 & 0 \\ 0 & 1 & 1 & 0 & 0 & 0 & 0 \\ 1 & 1 & 1 & 1 & 1 & 0 & 0 \\ 0 & 0 & 0 & 0 & 0 & 1 & 1 \\ 0 & 0 & 0 & 0 & 0 & 0 & 1 \end{bmatrix}
\qquad
\mathbf{x} = \begin{bmatrix} 1 \\ 1 \\ 0 \\ 1 \\ 0 \\ 0 \end{bmatrix}
$$

If we set $\mathbf{y} = A^T \mathbf{x}$, then

$$
\mathbf{y} = \begin{bmatrix} 1 & 1 & 0 & 1 & 0 & 0 \\ 1 & 0 & 1 & 1 & 0 & 0 \\ 1 & 1 & 1 & 1 & 0 & 0 \\ 1 & 1 & 0 & 1 & 0 & 0 \\ 1 & 1 & 0 & 1 & 0 & 0 \\ 1 & 1 & 0 & 0 & 1 & 0 \\ 0 & 0 & 0 & 0 & 1 & 1 \end{bmatrix} \begin{bmatrix} 1 \\ 1 \\ 0 \\ 1 \\ 0 \\ 0 \end{bmatrix} = \begin{bmatrix} 3 \\ 2 \\ 3 \\ 3 \\ 3 \\ 2 \\ 0 \end{bmatrix}
$$

The value of y_1 is the number of search word matches in the title of the first book, the value of y_2 is the number of matches in the second book title, and so on. Since $y_1 = y_3 = y_4 = y_5 = 3$, the titles of books B1, B3, B4, and B5 must contain all three search words. If the search is set up to find titles matching all search words, then the search engine will report the titles of the first, third, fourth, and fifth books. If the search is set up to match one or more search words, then the search engine will report first the four titles that match all the words and then the two titles that match two of the words.

Modern searches could easily involve millions of documents with hundreds of thousands of possible key words. Indeed, as of January 2001, there were more than 1.3 billion Web pages on the Internet, and it is not uncommon for search engines to acquire or update as many as 10 million Web pages in a single day. The database matrix in this case would be very large, but searches can be simplified dramatically since the matrices and search vectors are *sparse*, that is, most of the entries in any column are 0's. If we did a search to find all Web pages on the Internet containing the key words *linear* and *algebra*, we could easily turn up thousands of pages, some of which may not even be about linear algebra. If we were to increase the number of search words and require that all search words be matched, then we would run a risk of excluding some crucial linear algebra pages. For Web pages, the entries of the database matrix should represent the relative frequencies of the key words in the documents. Rather than match all words of the expanded search list, our Web search should give priority to those pages that match most of the key words with high relative frequencies. To accomplish this, we need to find the columns of the database matrix A that are "closest" to the search vector $\mathbf{x}$. One way to measure how close two vectors are is to define *the angle between the vectors*. We will do this in Section 1 of Chapter 5.

We will also revisit the information retrieval application again after we have learned about the *singular value decomposition* (Chapter 6, Section 5). This decomposition can be used to find a simpler approximation to the database matrix which will speed up the searches dramatically. Often it has the added advantage of filtering out *noise*; that is, using the approximate version of the database matrix may automatically have the effect of eliminating pages that use key words in unwanted contexts. For example, a dental student and a mathematics student could both use *calculus* as one of their search words. Since the list of mathematics search words does not contain any other dental terms, a mathematics search using an approximation database matrix is likely to eliminate all pages relating to dentistry. Similarly, the mathematics pages would be filtered out in the dental student's search.

REFERENCES

1. Berry, Michael W., and Murray Browne, *Understanding Search Engines – Mathematical Modeling and Text Retrieval*, SIAM, Philadelphia, 1999.

EXERCISES

1. If

$$A = \begin{bmatrix} 3 & 1 & 4 \\ -2 & 0 & 1 \\ 1 & 2 & 2 \end{bmatrix} \quad \text{and} \quad B = \begin{bmatrix} 1 & 0 & 2 \\ -3 & 1 & 1 \\ 2 & -4 & 1 \end{bmatrix}$$

compute:

(a) $2A$ (b) $A + B$ (c) $2A - 3B$ (d) $(2A)^T - (3B)^T$

(e) AB (f) BA (g) $A^T B^T$ (h) $(BA)^T$

2. For each of the following pairs of matrices, determine whether it is possible to multiply the first matrix times the second. If it is possible, perform the multiplication.

(a) $\begin{bmatrix} 3 & 5 & 1 \\ -2 & 0 & 2 \end{bmatrix} \begin{bmatrix} 2 & 1 \\ 1 & 3 \\ 4 & 1 \end{bmatrix}$ (b) $\begin{bmatrix} 4 & -2 \\ 6 & -4 \\ 8 & -6 \end{bmatrix} \begin{bmatrix} 1 & 2 & 3 \end{bmatrix}$

(c) $\begin{bmatrix} 1 & 4 & 3 \\ 0 & 1 & 4 \\ 0 & 0 & 2 \end{bmatrix} \begin{bmatrix} 3 & 2 \\ 1 & 1 \\ 4 & 5 \end{bmatrix}$ (d) $\begin{bmatrix} 4 & 6 \\ 2 & 1 \end{bmatrix} \begin{bmatrix} 3 & 1 & 5 \\ 4 & 1 & 6 \end{bmatrix}$

(e) $\begin{bmatrix} 4 & 6 & 1 \\ 2 & 1 & 1 \end{bmatrix} \begin{bmatrix} 3 & 1 & 5 \\ 4 & 1 & 6 \end{bmatrix}$ (f) $\begin{bmatrix} 2 \\ -1 \\ 3 \end{bmatrix} \begin{bmatrix} 3 & 2 & 4 & 5 \end{bmatrix}$

3. For which of the pairs in Exercise 2 is it possible to multiply the second matrix times the first, and what would the dimension of the product be?

4. Write each of the following systems of equations as a matrix equation.

(a) $3x_1 + 2x_2 = 1$
$2x_1 - 3x_2 = 5$

(b) $x_1 + x_2 = 5$
$2x_1 + x_2 - x_3 = 6$
$3x_1 - 2x_2 + 2x_3 = 7$

(c) $2x_1 + x_2 + x_3 = 4$
$x_1 - x_2 + 2x_3 = 2$
$3x_1 - 2x_2 - x_3 = 0$

5. If

$$A = \begin{bmatrix} 3 & 4 \\ 1 & 1 \\ 2 & 7 \end{bmatrix}$$

verify that:

(a) $5A = 3A + 2A$ (b) $6A = 3(2A)$ (c) $(A^T)^T = A$

6. If

$$A = \begin{bmatrix} 4 & 1 & 6 \\ 2 & 3 & 5 \end{bmatrix} \quad \text{and} \quad B = \begin{bmatrix} 1 & 3 & 0 \\ -2 & 2 & -4 \end{bmatrix}$$

verify that:

(a) $A + B = B + A$ (b) $3(A + B) = 3A + 3B$
(c) $(A + B)^T = A^T + B^T$

7. If

$$A = \begin{bmatrix} 2 & 1 \\ 6 & 3 \\ -2 & 4 \end{bmatrix} \quad \text{and} \quad B = \begin{bmatrix} 2 & 4 \\ 1 & 6 \end{bmatrix}$$

verify that:

(a) $3(AB) = (3A)B = A(3B)$ (b) $(AB)^T = B^T A^T$

8. If

$$A = \begin{bmatrix} 2 & 4 \\ 1 & 3 \end{bmatrix}, \quad B = \begin{bmatrix} -2 & 1 \\ 0 & 4 \end{bmatrix}, \quad C = \begin{bmatrix} 3 & 1 \\ 2 & 1 \end{bmatrix}$$

verify that:

(a) $(A + B) + C = A + (B + C)$ (b) $(AB)C = A(BC)$

(c) $A(B + C) = AB + AC$ (d) $(A + B)C = AC + BC$

9. Prove the associative law of multiplication for 2×2 matrices; that is, let

$$A = \begin{bmatrix} a_{11} & a_{12} \\ a_{21} & a_{22} \end{bmatrix}, \qquad B = \begin{bmatrix} b_{11} & b_{12} \\ b_{21} & b_{22} \end{bmatrix}, \qquad C = \begin{bmatrix} c_{11} & c_{12} \\ c_{21} & c_{22} \end{bmatrix}$$

and show that

$$(AB)C = A(BC)$$

10. Let

$$A = \begin{bmatrix} \frac{1}{2} & -\frac{1}{2} \\ -\frac{1}{2} & \frac{1}{2} \end{bmatrix}$$

Compute A^2 and A^3. What will A^n turn out to be?

11. Let

$$A = \begin{bmatrix} \frac{1}{2} & -\frac{1}{2} & -\frac{1}{2} & -\frac{1}{2} \\ -\frac{1}{2} & \frac{1}{2} & -\frac{1}{2} & -\frac{1}{2} \\ -\frac{1}{2} & -\frac{1}{2} & \frac{1}{2} & -\frac{1}{2} \\ -\frac{1}{2} & -\frac{1}{2} & -\frac{1}{2} & \frac{1}{2} \end{bmatrix}$$

Compute A^2 and A^3. What will A^{2n} and A^{2n+1} turn out to be?

12. Let

$$A = \begin{bmatrix} 0 & 1 & 0 & 0 \\ 0 & 0 & 1 & 0 \\ 0 & 0 & 0 & 1 \\ 0 & 0 & 0 & 0 \end{bmatrix}$$

Show that $A^n = O$ for $n \geq 4$.

13. Given

$$A = \begin{bmatrix} 1 & 2 \\ 1 & -2 \end{bmatrix}, \qquad \mathbf{b} = \begin{bmatrix} 4 \\ 0 \end{bmatrix}, \qquad \mathbf{c} = \begin{bmatrix} -3 \\ -2 \end{bmatrix}$$

(a) Write $\mathbf{b}$ as a linear combination of the column vectors $\mathbf{a}_1$ and $\mathbf{a}_2$.

(b) Use the result from part (a) to determine a solution to the linear system $A\mathbf{x} = \mathbf{b}$. Does the system have any other solutions? Explain.

(c) Write $\mathbf{c}$ as a linear combination of the column vectors $\mathbf{a}_1$ and $\mathbf{a}_2$.

14. For each of the following choices of A and $\mathbf{b}$, determine whether the system $A\mathbf{x} = \mathbf{b}$ is consistent by examining how $\mathbf{b}$ relates to the column vectors of A. Explain your answers in each case.

(a) $A = \begin{bmatrix} 2 & 1 \\ -2 & -1 \end{bmatrix}$, $\mathbf{b} = \begin{bmatrix} 3 \\ 1 \end{bmatrix}$ (b) $A = \begin{bmatrix} 1 & 4 \\ 2 & 3 \end{bmatrix}$, $\mathbf{b} = \begin{bmatrix} 5 \\ 5 \end{bmatrix}$

(c) $A = \begin{bmatrix} 3 & 2 & 1 \\ 3 & 2 & 1 \\ 3 & 2 & 1 \end{bmatrix}$, $\mathbf{b} = \begin{bmatrix} 1 \\ 0 \\ -1 \end{bmatrix}$

15. Let

$$A = \begin{bmatrix} a_{11} & a_{12} \\ a_{21} & a_{22} \end{bmatrix}$$

Show that if $d = a_{11}a_{22} - a_{21}a_{12} \neq 0$ then

$$A^{-1} = \frac{1}{d} \begin{bmatrix} a_{22} & -a_{12} \\ -a_{21} & a_{11} \end{bmatrix}$$

16. Let A be a nonsingular matrix. Show that A^{-1} is also nonsingular and $(A^{-1})^{-1} = A$.

17. Prove that if A is nonsingular then A^T is nonsingular and

$$(A^T)^{-1} = (A^{-1})^T$$

[*Hint:* $(AB)^T = B^T A^T$.]

18. Let A be a nonsingular $n \times n$ matrix. Use mathematical induction to prove that A^m is nonsingular and

$$(A^m)^{-1} = (A^{-1})^m$$

for $m = 1, 2, 3, \ldots$.

19. Explain why each of the following arithmetic rules will not work in general when the real numbers a and b are replaced by $n \times n$ matrices A and B.

(a) $(a + b)^2 = a^2 + 2ab + b^2$
(b) $(a + b)(a - b) = a^2 - b^2$

20. Find 2×2 matrices A and B that both are not the zero matrix for which $AB = O$.

21. Find nonzero matrices A, B, C such that

$$AC = BC \quad \text{and} \quad A \neq B$$

22. The matrix

$$A = \begin{bmatrix} 1 & -1 \\ 1 & -1 \end{bmatrix}$$

has the property that $A^2 = O$. Is it possible for a nonzero symmetric 2×2 matrix to have this property? Prove your answer.

23. Is the product of two symmetric matrices necessarily symmetric? Prove your answer.

24. Let A be an $m \times n$ matrix.

    (a) Explain why the matrix multiplications $A^T A$ and $A A^T$ are possible.

    (b) Show that $A^T A$ and $A A^T$ are both symmetric.

25. Let A and B be symmetric $n \times n$ matrices. Prove that $AB = BA$ if and only if AB is also symmetric.

26. A matrix A is said to be *skew-symmetric* if $A^T = -A$. Show that if a matrix is skew-symmetric then its diagonal entries must all be 0.

27. Let A be an $n \times n$ matrix and let

$$B = A + A^T \qquad \text{and} \qquad C = A - A^T$$

    (a) Show that B is symmetric and C is skew-symmetric.

    (b) Show that every $n \times n$ matrix can be represented as a sum of a symmetric matrix and a skew-symmetric matrix.

28. Suppose that in Application 1 Bob loses 8 pounds. If he continues the same exercise program, how many calories will he burn up each day?

29. In Application 3, how many married women and how many single women will there be after 3 years?

30. In Application 6, suppose that we are searching the database of seven linear algebra books for the search words *elementary, matrix, algebra*. Form a search vector **x** and then compute a vector **y** that represents the results of the search. Explain the significance of the entries of the vector **y**.

31. Given the matrix

$$A = \begin{bmatrix} 0 & 1 & 0 & 1 & 1 \\ 1 & 0 & 1 & 1 & 0 \\ 0 & 1 & 0 & 0 & 1 \\ 1 & 1 & 0 & 0 & 1 \\ 1 & 0 & 1 & 1 & 0 \end{bmatrix}$$

    (a) Draw a graph that has A as its adjacency matrix. Be sure to label the vertices of the graph.

    (b) By inspecting the graph, determine the number of walks of length 2 from V_2 to V_3 and from V_2 to V_5.

    (c) Compute the second row of A^3 and use it to determine the number of walks of length 3 from V_2 to V_3 and from V_2 to V_5.

32. Given the graph

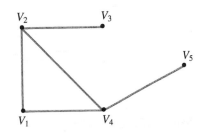

(a) Determine the adjacency matrix A of the graph.

(b) Compute A^2. What do the entries in the first row of A^2 tell you about walks of length 2 that start from V_1?

(c) Compute A^3. How many walks of length 3 are there from V_2 to V_4? How many walks of length less than or equal to 3 are there from V_2 to V_4?

33. Let A be a 2×2 matrix with $a_{11} \neq 0$ and let $\alpha = a_{21}/a_{11}$. Show that A can be factored into a product of the form

$$\begin{bmatrix} 1 & 0 \\ \alpha & 1 \end{bmatrix} \begin{bmatrix} a_{11} & a_{12} \\ 0 & b \end{bmatrix}$$

What is the value of b?

4 ELEMENTARY MATRICES

In this section we view the process of solving a linear system in terms of matrix multiplications, rather than row operations. Given a linear system $A\mathbf{x} = \mathbf{b}$, we can multiply both sides by a sequence of special matrices to obtain an equivalent system in row echelon form. The special matrices we will use are called *elementary matrices*. We will use them to see how to compute the inverse of a nonsingular matrix and also to obtain an important matrix factorization. We begin by considering the effects of multiplying both sides of a linear system by a nonsingular matrix.

Equivalent Systems

Given an $m \times n$ linear system $A\mathbf{x} = \mathbf{b}$, we can obtain an equivalent system by multiplying both sides of the equation by a nonsingular $m \times m$ matrix M.

(1) $$A\mathbf{x} = \mathbf{b}$$

(2) $$MA\mathbf{x} = M\mathbf{b}$$

Clearly, any solution to (1) will also be a solution to (2). On the other hand, if $\hat{\mathbf{x}}$ is a solution to (2), then

$$M^{-1}(MA\hat{\mathbf{x}}) = M^{-1}(M\mathbf{b})$$
$$A\hat{\mathbf{x}} = \mathbf{b}$$

so the two systems are equivalent.

To obtain an equivalent system that is easier to solve, we can apply a sequence of nonsingular matrices $E_1, \dots, E_k$ to both sides of the equation $A\mathbf{x} = \mathbf{b}$ to obtain a simpler system:

$$U\mathbf{x} = \mathbf{c}$$

where $U = E_k \cdots E_1 A$ and $\mathbf{c} = E_k \cdots E_2 E_1 \mathbf{b}$. The new system will be equivalent to the original provided that $M = E_k \cdots E_1$ is nonsingular. However, M is the product of nonsingular matrices. The following theorem shows that any product of nonsingular matrices is nonsingular.

▶ **THEOREM 1.4.1** *If A and B are nonsingular $n \times n$ matrices, then AB is also nonsingular and $(AB)^{-1} = B^{-1}A^{-1}$.*

▶*Proof.*

$$(B^{-1}A^{-1})AB = B^{-1}(A^{-1}A)B = B^{-1}B = I$$
$$(AB)(B^{-1}A^{-1}) = A(BB^{-1})A^{-1} = AA^{-1} = I \qquad ◀$$

It follows by induction that if $E_1, \dots, E_k$ are all nonsingular then the product $E_1 E_2 \cdots E_k$ is nonsingular and

$$(E_1 E_2 \cdots E_k)^{-1} = E_k^{-1} \cdots E_2^{-1} E_1^{-1}$$

We will show next that any of the three elementary row operations can be accomplished by multiplying A on the left by a nonsingular matrix.

Elementary Matrices

If we start with the identity matrix I and then perform exactly one elementary row operation, the resulting matrix is called an *elementary* matrix.

There are three types of elementary matrices corresponding to the three types of elementary row operations.

Type I An elementary matrix of type I is a matrix obtained by interchanging two rows of I.

EXAMPLE 1. Let

$$E_1 = \begin{bmatrix} 0 & 1 & 0 \\ 1 & 0 & 0 \\ 0 & 0 & 1 \end{bmatrix}$$

E_1 is an elementary matrix of type I, since it was obtained by interchanging the first two rows of I. Let A be a 3×3 matrix.

$$E_1 A = \begin{bmatrix} 0 & 1 & 0 \\ 1 & 0 & 0 \\ 0 & 0 & 1 \end{bmatrix} \begin{bmatrix} a_{11} & a_{12} & a_{13} \\ a_{21} & a_{22} & a_{23} \\ a_{31} & a_{32} & a_{33} \end{bmatrix} = \begin{bmatrix} a_{21} & a_{22} & a_{23} \\ a_{11} & a_{12} & a_{13} \\ a_{31} & a_{32} & a_{33} \end{bmatrix}$$

$$A E_1 = \begin{bmatrix} a_{11} & a_{12} & a_{13} \\ a_{21} & a_{22} & a_{23} \\ a_{31} & a_{32} & a_{33} \end{bmatrix} \begin{bmatrix} 0 & 1 & 0 \\ 1 & 0 & 0 \\ 0 & 0 & 1 \end{bmatrix} = \begin{bmatrix} a_{12} & a_{11} & a_{13} \\ a_{22} & a_{21} & a_{23} \\ a_{32} & a_{31} & a_{33} \end{bmatrix}$$

Multiplying A on the left by E_1 interchanges the first and second rows of A. Right multiplication of A by E_1 is equivalent to the elementary column operation of interchanging the first and second columns. ◀

Type II An elementary matrix of type II is a matrix obtained by multiplying a row of I by a nonzero constant.

EXAMPLE 2.

$$E_2 = \begin{bmatrix} 1 & 0 & 0 \\ 0 & 1 & 0 \\ 0 & 0 & 3 \end{bmatrix}$$

is an elementary matrix of type II.

$$\begin{bmatrix} 1 & 0 & 0 \\ 0 & 1 & 0 \\ 0 & 0 & 3 \end{bmatrix} \begin{bmatrix} a_{11} & a_{12} & a_{13} \\ a_{21} & a_{22} & a_{23} \\ a_{31} & a_{32} & a_{33} \end{bmatrix} = \begin{bmatrix} a_{11} & a_{12} & a_{13} \\ a_{21} & a_{22} & a_{23} \\ 3a_{31} & 3a_{32} & 3a_{33} \end{bmatrix}$$

$$\begin{bmatrix} a_{11} & a_{12} & a_{13} \\ a_{21} & a_{22} & a_{23} \\ a_{31} & a_{32} & a_{33} \end{bmatrix} \begin{bmatrix} 1 & 0 & 0 \\ 0 & 1 & 0 \\ 0 & 0 & 3 \end{bmatrix} = \begin{bmatrix} a_{11} & a_{12} & 3a_{13} \\ a_{21} & a_{22} & 3a_{23} \\ a_{31} & a_{32} & 3a_{33} \end{bmatrix}$$

Multiplication on the left by E_2 performs the elementary row operation of multiplying the third row by 3, while multiplication on the right by E_2 performs the elementary column operation of multiplying the third column by 3. ◀

Type III An elementary matrix of type III is a matrix obtained from I by adding a multiple of one row to another row.

EXAMPLE 3.

$$E_3 = \begin{pmatrix} 1 & 0 & 3 \\ 0 & 1 & 0 \\ 0 & 0 & 1 \end{pmatrix}$$

is an elementary matrix of type III. If A is a 3×3 matrix, then

$$E_3 A = \begin{pmatrix} a_{11} + 3a_{31} & a_{12} + 3a_{32} & a_{13} + 3a_{33} \\ a_{21} & a_{22} & a_{23} \\ a_{31} & a_{32} & a_{33} \end{pmatrix}$$

$$A E_3 = \begin{pmatrix} a_{11} & a_{12} & 3a_{11} + a_{13} \\ a_{21} & a_{22} & 3a_{21} + a_{23} \\ a_{31} & a_{32} & 3a_{31} + a_{33} \end{pmatrix}$$

Multiplication on the left by E_3 adds 3 times the third row to the first row. Multiplication on the right adds 3 times the first column to the third column. ◀

In general, suppose that E is an $n \times n$ elementary matrix. We can think of E as being obtained from I by either a row operation or a column operation. If A is an $n \times r$ matrix, *premultiplying A by E has the effect of performing that same row operation on A.* If B is an $m \times n$ matrix, *postmultiplying B by E is equivalent to performing that same column operation on B.*

▶ **THEOREM I.4.2** *If E is an elementary matrix, then E is nonsingular and E^{-1} is an elementary matrix of the same type.*

▶ **Proof.** If E is the elementary matrix of type I formed from I by interchanging the ith and jth rows, then E can be transformed back into I by interchanging these same rows again. Thus $EE = I$ and hence E is its own inverse. If E is the elementary matrix of type II formed by multiplying the ith row of I by a nonzero scalar α, then E can be transformed into the identity by multiplying either its ith row or its ith column by $1/\alpha$. Thus

$$E^{-1} = \begin{pmatrix} 1 & & & & & & \\ & \ddots & & & & O & \\ & & 1 & & & & \\ & & & 1/\alpha & & & \\ & & & & 1 & & \\ & O & & & & \ddots & \\ & & & & & & 1 \end{pmatrix} \quad i\text{th row}$$

Finally, suppose that E is the elementary matrix of type III formed from I by adding m times the ith row to the jth row.

$$E = \begin{pmatrix} 1 & & & & & & & \\ \vdots & \ddots & & & & O & & \\ 0 & \cdots & 1 & & & & & \\ \vdots & & & \ddots & & & & \\ 0 & \cdots & m & \cdots & 1 & & & \\ \vdots & & & & & \ddots & & \\ 0 & \cdots & 0 & \cdots & 0 & \cdots & 1 & \end{pmatrix} \begin{matrix} \\ \\ i\text{th row} \\ \\ j\text{th row} \\ \\ \end{matrix}$$

E can be transformed back into I by either subtracting m times the ith row from the jth row or by subtracting m times the jth column from the ith column. Thus

$$E^{-1} = \begin{pmatrix} 1 & & & & & & & \\ \vdots & \ddots & & & & O & & \\ 0 & \cdots & 1 & & & & & \\ \vdots & & & \ddots & & & & \\ 0 & \cdots & -m & \cdots & 1 & & & \\ \vdots & & & & & \ddots & & \\ 0 & \cdots & 0 & \cdots & 0 & \cdots & 1 & \end{pmatrix} \qquad \blacktriangleleft$$

▶ **DEFINITION** A matrix B is **row equivalent** to A if there exists a finite sequence $E_1, E_2, \ldots, E_k$ of elementary matrices such that

$$B = E_k E_{k-1} \cdots E_1 A \qquad \blacktriangleleft$$

In other words, B is row equivalent to A if B can be obtained from A by a finite number of row operations. In particular, two augmented matrices $(A \,|\, \mathbf{b})$ and $(B \,|\, \mathbf{c})$ are row equivalent if and only if $A\mathbf{x} = \mathbf{b}$ and $B\mathbf{x} = \mathbf{c}$ are equivalent systems. The following properties of row equivalent matrices are easily established.

    I. If A is row equivalent to B, then B is row equivalent to A.

    II. If A is row equivalent to B, and B is row equivalent to C, then A is row equivalent to C.

Property (I) can be proved using Theorem 1.4.2. The details of the proofs of (I) and (II) are left as an exercise for the reader.

▶ **THEOREM 1.4.3 (Equivalent Conditions for Nonsingularity)** *Let A be an $n \times n$ matrix. The following are equivalent:*

    (a) *A is nonsingular.*

    (b) $A\mathbf{x} = \mathbf{0}$ *has only the trivial solution* $\mathbf{0}$.

    (c) A *is row equivalent to* I.

▶ *Proof.* We prove first that statement (a) implies statement (b). If A is nonsingular and $\hat{\mathbf{x}}$ is a solution to $A\mathbf{x} = \mathbf{0}$, then

$$\hat{\mathbf{x}} = I\hat{\mathbf{x}} = (A^{-1}A)\hat{\mathbf{x}} = A^{-1}(A\hat{\mathbf{x}}) = A^{-1}\mathbf{0} = \mathbf{0}$$

Thus $A\mathbf{x} = \mathbf{0}$ has only the trivial solution. Next we show that statement (b) implies statement (c). If we use elementary row operations, the system can be transformed into the form $U\mathbf{x} = \mathbf{0}$, where U is in row echelon form. If one of the diagonal elements of U were 0, the last row of U would consist entirely of 0's. But then $A\mathbf{x} = \mathbf{0}$ would be equivalent to a system with more unknowns than equations and hence by Theorem 1.2.1 would have a nontrivial solution. Thus U must be a triangular matrix with diagonal elements all equal to 1. It follows then that I is the reduced row echelon form of A and hence A is row equivalent to I.

    Finally, we will show that statement (c) implies statement (a). If A is row equivalent to I, there exist elementary matrices $E_1, E_2, \ldots, E_k$ such that

$$A = E_k E_{k-1} \cdots E_1 I = E_k E_{k-1} \cdots E_1$$

But since E_i is invertible, $i = 1, \ldots, k$, the product $E_k E_{k-1} \cdots E_1$ is also invertible. Hence A is nonsingular and

$$A^{-1} = (E_k E_{k-1} \cdots E_1)^{-1} = E_1^{-1} E_2^{-1} \cdots E_k^{-1} \qquad ◀$$

▶ **COROLLARY 1.4.4** *The system of n linear equations in n unknowns* $A\mathbf{x} = \mathbf{b}$ *has a unique solution if and only if* A *is nonsingular.*

▶ *Proof.* If A is nonsingular, then $A^{-1}\mathbf{b}$ is the only solution to $A\mathbf{x} = \mathbf{b}$. Conversely, suppose that $A\mathbf{x} = \mathbf{b}$ has a unique solution $\hat{\mathbf{x}}$. If A is singular, $A\mathbf{x} = \mathbf{0}$ has a solution $\mathbf{z} \neq \mathbf{0}$. Let $\mathbf{y} = \hat{\mathbf{x}} + \mathbf{z}$. Clearly, $\mathbf{y} \neq \hat{\mathbf{x}}$ and

$$A\mathbf{y} = A(\hat{\mathbf{x}} + \mathbf{z}) = A\hat{\mathbf{x}} + A\mathbf{z} = \mathbf{b} + \mathbf{0} = \mathbf{b}$$

Thus $\mathbf{y}$ is also a solution to $A\mathbf{x} = \mathbf{b}$, which is a contradiction. Therefore, if $A\mathbf{x} = \mathbf{b}$ has a unique solution, A must be nonsingular.   ◀

    If A is nonsingular, A is row equivalent to I, so there exist elementary matrices $E_1, \ldots, E_k$ such that

$$E_k E_{k-1} \cdots E_1 A = I$$

Multiplying both sides of this equation on the right by A^{-1}, we obtain

$$E_k E_{k-1} \cdots E_1 I = A^{-1}$$

Thus the same series of elementary row operations that transforms a nonsingular matrix A into I will transform I into A^{-1}. This gives us a method for computing A^{-1}. If we augment A by I and perform the elementary row operations that transform A into I on the augmented matrix, then I will be transformed into A^{-1}. That is, the reduced row echelon form of the augmented matrix $(A|I)$ will be $(I|A^{-1})$.

EXAMPLE 4. Compute A^{-1} if

$$A = \begin{bmatrix} 1 & 4 & 3 \\ -1 & -2 & 0 \\ 2 & 2 & 3 \end{bmatrix}$$

SOLUTION.

$$\begin{bmatrix} 1 & 4 & 3 & | & 1 & 0 & 0 \\ -1 & -2 & 0 & | & 0 & 1 & 0 \\ 2 & 2 & 3 & | & 0 & 0 & 1 \end{bmatrix} \rightarrow \begin{bmatrix} 1 & 4 & 3 & | & 1 & 0 & 0 \\ 0 & 2 & 3 & | & 1 & 1 & 0 \\ 0 & -6 & -3 & | & -2 & 0 & 1 \end{bmatrix}$$

$$\rightarrow \begin{bmatrix} 1 & 4 & 3 & | & 1 & 0 & 0 \\ 0 & 2 & 3 & | & 1 & 1 & 0 \\ 0 & 0 & 6 & | & 1 & 3 & 1 \end{bmatrix} \rightarrow \begin{bmatrix} 1 & 4 & 0 & | & \frac{1}{2} & -\frac{3}{2} & -\frac{1}{2} \\ 0 & 2 & 0 & | & \frac{1}{2} & -\frac{1}{2} & -\frac{1}{2} \\ 0 & 0 & 6 & | & 1 & 3 & 1 \end{bmatrix}$$

$$\rightarrow \begin{bmatrix} 1 & 0 & 0 & | & -\frac{1}{2} & -\frac{1}{2} & \frac{1}{2} \\ 0 & 2 & 0 & | & \frac{1}{2} & -\frac{1}{2} & -\frac{1}{2} \\ 0 & 0 & 6 & | & 1 & 3 & 1 \end{bmatrix} \rightarrow \begin{bmatrix} 1 & 0 & 0 & | & -\frac{1}{2} & -\frac{1}{2} & \frac{1}{2} \\ 0 & 1 & 0 & | & \frac{1}{4} & -\frac{1}{4} & -\frac{1}{4} \\ 0 & 0 & 1 & | & \frac{1}{6} & \frac{1}{2} & \frac{1}{6} \end{bmatrix}$$

Thus

$$A^{-1} = \begin{bmatrix} -\frac{1}{2} & -\frac{1}{2} & \frac{1}{2} \\ \frac{1}{4} & -\frac{1}{4} & -\frac{1}{4} \\ \frac{1}{6} & \frac{1}{2} & \frac{1}{6} \end{bmatrix}$$ ◀

EXAMPLE 5. Solve the system

$$\begin{aligned} x_1 + 4x_2 + 3x_3 &= 12 \\ -x_1 - 2x_2 &= -12 \\ 2x_1 + 2x_2 + 3x_3 &= 8 \end{aligned}$$

The coefficient matrix of this system is the matrix A of the last example. The solution to the system then is

$$\mathbf{x} = A^{-1}\mathbf{b} = \begin{bmatrix} -\frac{1}{2} & -\frac{1}{2} & \frac{1}{2} \\ \frac{1}{4} & -\frac{1}{4} & -\frac{1}{4} \\ \frac{1}{6} & \frac{1}{2} & \frac{1}{6} \end{bmatrix} \begin{bmatrix} 12 \\ -12 \\ 8 \end{bmatrix} = \begin{bmatrix} 4 \\ 4 \\ -\frac{8}{3} \end{bmatrix}$$ ◀

Diagonal and Triangular Matrices

An $n \times n$ matrix A is said to be *upper triangular* if $a_{ij} = 0$ for $i > j$ and *lower triangular* if $a_{ij} = 0$ for $i < j$. Also, A is said to be *triangular* if it is either upper triangular or lower triangular. For example, the 3×3 matrices

$$\begin{pmatrix} 3 & 2 & 1 \\ 0 & 2 & 1 \\ 0 & 0 & 5 \end{pmatrix} \quad \text{and} \quad \begin{pmatrix} 1 & 0 & 0 \\ 6 & 2 & 0 \\ 1 & 4 & 3 \end{pmatrix}$$

are both triangular. The first is upper triangular and the second is lower triangular.

A triangular matrix may have 0's on the diagonal. However, for a linear system $A\mathbf{x} = \mathbf{b}$ to be in triangular form, the coefficient matrix A must be triangular with nonzero diagonal entries.

An $n \times n$ matrix A is *diagonal* if $a_{ij} = 0$ whenever $i \neq j$. The matrices

$$\begin{pmatrix} 1 & 0 \\ 0 & 2 \end{pmatrix} \qquad \begin{pmatrix} 1 & 0 & 0 \\ 0 & 3 & 0 \\ 0 & 0 & 1 \end{pmatrix} \qquad \begin{pmatrix} 0 & 0 & 0 \\ 0 & 2 & 0 \\ 0 & 0 & 0 \end{pmatrix}$$

are all diagonal. A diagonal matrix is both upper triangular and lower triangular.

Triangular Factorization

If an $n \times n$ matrix A can be reduced to upper triangular form using only row operation **III**, then it is possible to represent the reduction process in terms of a matrix factorization. We illustrate how this is done in the following example.

EXAMPLE 6. Let

$$A = \begin{pmatrix} 2 & 4 & 2 \\ 1 & 5 & 2 \\ 4 & -1 & 9 \end{pmatrix}$$

and let us carry out the reduction process using only row operation **III**. At the first step we subtract $\frac{1}{2}$ times the first row from the second and then we subtract twice the first row from the third.

$$\begin{pmatrix} 2 & 4 & 2 \\ 1 & 5 & 2 \\ 4 & -1 & 9 \end{pmatrix} \rightarrow \begin{pmatrix} 2 & 4 & 2 \\ 0 & 3 & 1 \\ 0 & -9 & 5 \end{pmatrix}$$

To keep track of the multiples of the first row that were subtracted, we set $l_{21} = \frac{1}{2}$ and $l_{31} = 2$. We complete the elimination process by eliminating the -9 in the (3,2) position.

$$\begin{pmatrix} 2 & 4 & 2 \\ 0 & 3 & 1 \\ 0 & -9 & 5 \end{pmatrix} \rightarrow \begin{pmatrix} 2 & 4 & 2 \\ 0 & 3 & 1 \\ 0 & 0 & 8 \end{pmatrix}$$

Let $l_{32} = -3$, the multiple of the second row subtracted from row three. If we call the resulting matrix U and set

$$L = \begin{bmatrix} 1 & 0 & 0 \\ l_{21} & 1 & 0 \\ l_{31} & l_{32} & 1 \end{bmatrix} = \begin{bmatrix} 1 & 0 & 0 \\ \frac{1}{2} & 1 & 0 \\ 2 & -3 & 1 \end{bmatrix}$$

then it is easily verified that

$$LU = \begin{bmatrix} 1 & 0 & 0 \\ \frac{1}{2} & 1 & 0 \\ 2 & -3 & 1 \end{bmatrix} \begin{bmatrix} 2 & 4 & 2 \\ 0 & 3 & 1 \\ 0 & 0 & 8 \end{bmatrix} = \begin{bmatrix} 2 & 4 & 2 \\ 1 & 5 & 2 \\ 4 & -1 & 9 \end{bmatrix} = A \qquad \blacktriangleleft$$

The matrix L in the previous example is lower triangular with 1's on the diagonal. We say that L is *unit lower triangular*. The factorization of the matrix A into a product of a unit lower triangular matrix L times an upper triangular matrix U is often referred to as an *LU factorization*.

To see why the factorization in Example 6 works, let us view the reduction process in terms of elementary matrices. The three row operations that were applied to the matrix A can be represented in terms of multiplications by elementary matrices

(3) $$E_3 E_2 E_1 A = U$$

where

$$E_1 = \begin{bmatrix} 1 & 0 & 0 \\ -\frac{1}{2} & 1 & 0 \\ 0 & 0 & 1 \end{bmatrix}, \quad E_2 = \begin{bmatrix} 1 & 0 & 0 \\ 0 & 1 & 0 \\ -2 & 0 & 1 \end{bmatrix}, \quad E_3 = \begin{bmatrix} 1 & 0 & 0 \\ 0 & 1 & 0 \\ 0 & 3 & 1 \end{bmatrix}$$

correspond to the row operations in the reduction process. Since each of the elementary matrices is nonsingular, we can multiply equation (3) by their inverses.

$$A = E_1^{-1} E_2^{-1} E_3^{-1} U$$

[We multiply in reverse order since $(E_3 E_2 E_1)^{-1} = E_1^{-1} E_2^{-1} E_3^{-1}$.] However, when the inverses are multiplied in this order, the multipliers l_{21}, l_{31}, l_{32} fill in below the diagonal in the product.

$$E_1^{-1} E_2^{-1} E_3^{-1} = \begin{bmatrix} 1 & 0 & 0 \\ \frac{1}{2} & 1 & 0 \\ 0 & 0 & 1 \end{bmatrix} \begin{bmatrix} 1 & 0 & 0 \\ 0 & 1 & 0 \\ 2 & 0 & 1 \end{bmatrix} \begin{bmatrix} 1 & 0 & 0 \\ 0 & 1 & 0 \\ 0 & -3 & 1 \end{bmatrix} = L$$

In general, if an $n \times n$ matrix A can be reduced to upper triangular form using only row operation **III**, then A has an LU factorization. The matrix L is unit lower triangular, and if $i > j$, then l_{ij} is the multiple of the jth row subtracted from the ith row during the reduction process.

The LU factorization is a very useful way of viewing the elimination process. We will find it particularly useful in Chapter 7 when we study computer methods for solving linear systems. Many of the major topics in linear algebra can be viewed in

terms of matrix factorizations. We will study other interesting and important factorizations in Chapters 5 through 7.

1. Which of the following are elementary matrices? Classify each elementary matrix
   by type.

   (a) $\begin{bmatrix} 0 & 1 \\ 1 & 0 \end{bmatrix}$
   (b) $\begin{bmatrix} 2 & 0 \\ 0 & 3 \end{bmatrix}$
   (c) $\begin{bmatrix} 1 & 0 & 0 \\ 0 & 1 & 0 \\ 5 & 0 & 1 \end{bmatrix}$
   (d) $\begin{bmatrix} 1 & 0 & 0 \\ 0 & 5 & 0 \\ 0 & 0 & 1 \end{bmatrix}$

2. Find the inverse of each matrix in Exercise 1. For each elementary matrix, verify
   that its inverse is an elementary matrix of the same type.

3. For each of the following pairs of matrices, find an elementary matrix E such
   that $EA = B$.

   (a) $A = \begin{bmatrix} 2 & -1 \\ 5 & 3 \end{bmatrix}$ $B = \begin{bmatrix} -4 & 2 \\ 5 & 3 \end{bmatrix}$

   (b) $A = \begin{bmatrix} 2 & 1 & 3 \\ -2 & 4 & 5 \\ 3 & 1 & 4 \end{bmatrix}$ $B = \begin{bmatrix} 2 & 1 & 3 \\ 3 & 1 & 4 \\ -2 & 4 & 5 \end{bmatrix}$

   (c) $A = \begin{bmatrix} 4 & -2 & 3 \\ 1 & 0 & 2 \\ -2 & 3 & 1 \end{bmatrix}$ $B = \begin{bmatrix} 4 & -2 & 3 \\ 1 & 0 & 2 \\ 0 & 3 & 5 \end{bmatrix}$

4. For each of the following pairs of matrices, find an elementary matrix E such
   that $AE = B$.

   (a) $A = \begin{bmatrix} 4 & 1 & 3 \\ 2 & 1 & 4 \\ 1 & 3 & 2 \end{bmatrix}$, $B = \begin{bmatrix} 3 & 1 & 4 \\ 4 & 1 & 2 \\ 2 & 3 & 1 \end{bmatrix}$

   (b) $A = \begin{bmatrix} 2 & 4 \\ 1 & 6 \end{bmatrix}$, $B = \begin{bmatrix} 2 & -2 \\ 1 & 3 \end{bmatrix}$

   (c) $A = \begin{bmatrix} 4 & -2 & 3 \\ -2 & 4 & 2 \\ 6 & 1 & -2 \end{bmatrix}$, $B = \begin{bmatrix} 2 & -2 & 3 \\ -1 & 4 & 2 \\ 3 & 1 & -2 \end{bmatrix}$

5. Given

   $$A = \begin{bmatrix} 1 & 2 & 4 \\ 2 & 1 & 3 \\ 1 & 0 & 2 \end{bmatrix}, \quad B = \begin{bmatrix} 1 & 2 & 4 \\ 2 & 1 & 3 \\ 2 & 2 & 6 \end{bmatrix}, \quad C = \begin{bmatrix} 1 & 2 & 4 \\ 0 & -1 & -3 \\ 2 & 2 & 6 \end{bmatrix}$$

   (a) Find an elementary matrix E such that $EA = B$.

(b) Find an elementary matrix F such that $FB = C$.

(c) Is C row equivalent to A? Explain.

6. Given

$$A = \begin{bmatrix} 2 & 1 & 1 \\ 6 & 4 & 5 \\ 4 & 1 & 3 \end{bmatrix}$$

(a) Find elementary matrices E_1, E_2, E_3 such that

$$E_3 E_2 E_1 A = U$$

where U is an upper triangular matrix.

(b) Determine the inverses of E_1, E_2, E_3 and set $L = E_1^{-1} E_2^{-1} E_3^{-1}$. What type of matrix is L? Verify that $A = LU$.

7. Compute the LU factorization of each of the following matrices.

(a) $\begin{bmatrix} 3 & 1 \\ 9 & 5 \end{bmatrix}$

(b) $\begin{bmatrix} 2 & 4 \\ -2 & 1 \end{bmatrix}$

(c) $\begin{bmatrix} 1 & 1 & 1 \\ 3 & 5 & 6 \\ -2 & 2 & 7 \end{bmatrix}$

(d) $\begin{bmatrix} -2 & 1 & 2 \\ 4 & 1 & -2 \\ -6 & -3 & 4 \end{bmatrix}$

8. Let

$$A = \begin{bmatrix} 1 & 0 & 1 \\ 3 & 3 & 4 \\ 2 & 2 & 3 \end{bmatrix}$$

(a) Verify that

$$A^{-1} = \begin{bmatrix} 1 & 2 & -3 \\ -1 & 1 & -1 \\ 0 & -2 & 3 \end{bmatrix}$$

(b) Use A^{-1} to solve $A\mathbf{x} = \mathbf{b}$ for the following choices of $\mathbf{b}$.

(i) $\mathbf{b} = (1, 1, 1)^T$ (ii) $\mathbf{b} = (1, 2, 3)^T$ (iii) $\mathbf{b} = (-2, 1, 0)^T$

9. Find the inverse of each of the following matrices.

(a) $\begin{bmatrix} -1 & 1 \\ 1 & 0 \end{bmatrix}$

(b) $\begin{bmatrix} 2 & 5 \\ 1 & 3 \end{bmatrix}$

(c) $\begin{bmatrix} 2 & 6 \\ 3 & 8 \end{bmatrix}$

(d) $\begin{bmatrix} 3 & 0 \\ 9 & 3 \end{bmatrix}$

(e) $\begin{bmatrix} 1 & 1 & 1 \\ 0 & 1 & 1 \\ 0 & 0 & 1 \end{bmatrix}$

(f) $\begin{bmatrix} 2 & 0 & 5 \\ 0 & 3 & 0 \\ 1 & 0 & 3 \end{bmatrix}$

$$(g) \begin{bmatrix} -1 & -3 & -3 \\ 2 & 6 & 1 \\ 3 & 8 & 3 \end{bmatrix} \qquad (h) \begin{bmatrix} 1 & 0 & 1 \\ -1 & 1 & 1 \\ -1 & -2 & -3 \end{bmatrix}$$

10. Given

$$A = \begin{bmatrix} 3 & 1 \\ 5 & 2 \end{bmatrix} \qquad \text{and} \qquad B = \begin{bmatrix} 1 & 2 \\ 3 & 4 \end{bmatrix}$$

compute A^{-1} and use it to:

(a) Find a 2×2 matrix X such that $AX = B$.
(b) Find a 2×2 matrix Y such that $YA = B$.

11. Given

$$A = \begin{bmatrix} 5 & 3 \\ 3 & 2 \end{bmatrix}, \qquad B = \begin{bmatrix} 6 & 2 \\ 2 & 4 \end{bmatrix}, \qquad C = \begin{bmatrix} 4 & -2 \\ -6 & 3 \end{bmatrix}$$

Solve each of the following matrix equations.

(a) $AX + B = C$ (b) $XA + B = C$ (c) $AX + B = X$ (d) $XA + C = X$

12. Is the transpose of an elementary matrix an elementary matrix of the same type? Is the product of two elementary matrices an elementary matrix?

13. Let U and R be $n \times n$ upper triangular matrices and set $T = UR$. Show that T is also upper triangular and that $t_{jj} = u_{jj}r_{jj}$ for $j = 1, \ldots, n$.

14. Let A be a 3×3 matrix and suppose that

$$2\mathbf{a}_1 + \mathbf{a}_2 - 4\mathbf{a}_3 = \mathbf{0}$$

How many solutions will the system $A\mathbf{x} = \mathbf{0}$ have? Explain. Is A nonsingular? Explain.

15. Let A and B be $n \times n$ matrices and let $C = AB$. Prove that if B is singular then C must be singular. [*Hint:* Use Theorem 1.4.3.]

16. Let U be an $n \times n$ upper triangular matrix with nonzero diagonal entries.

(a) Explain why U must be nonsingular.
(b) Explain why U^{-1} must be upper triangular.

17. Let A be a nonsingular $n \times n$ matrix and let B be an $n \times r$ matrix. Show that the reduced row echelon form of $(A|B)$ is $(I|C)$, where $C = A^{-1}B$.

18. In general, matrix multiplication is not commutative (i.e., $AB \neq BA$). However, in certain special cases the commutative property does hold. Show that:

(a) If D_1 and D_2 are $n \times n$ diagonal matrices, then $D_1 D_2 = D_2 D_1$.
(b) If A is an $n \times n$ matrix and

$$B = a_0 I + a_1 A + a_2 A^2 + \cdots + a_k A^k$$

where $a_0, a_1, \ldots, a_k$ are scalars, then $AB = BA$.

19. Show that if A is a symmetric nonsingular matrix then A^{-1} is also symmetric.

20. Prove that if A is row equivalent to B then B is row equivalent to A.

21. (a) Prove that, if A is row equivalent to B and B is row equivalent to C, then A is row equivalent to C.

(b) Prove that any two nonsingular $n \times n$ matrices are row equivalent.

22. Prove that B is row equivalent to A if and only if there exists a nonsingular matrix M such that $B = MA$.

23. Given a vector $\mathbf{x} \in R^{n+1}$, the $(n+1) \times (n+1)$ matrix V defined by

$$v_{ij} = \begin{cases} 1 & \text{if } j = 1 \\ x_i^{j-1} & \text{for } j = 2, \ldots, n+1 \end{cases}$$

is called the Vandermonde matrix.

(a) Show that if

$$V\mathbf{c} = \mathbf{y}$$

and

$$p(x) = c_1 + c_2 x + \cdots + c_{n+1} x^n$$

then

$$p(x_i) = y_i, \qquad i = 1, 2, \ldots, n+1$$

(b) Suppose that $x_1, x_2, \ldots, x_{n+1}$ are all distinct. Show that if $\mathbf{c}$ is a solution to $V\mathbf{x} = \mathbf{0}$ then the coefficients $c_1, c_2, \ldots, c_n$ must all be zero, and hence V must be nonsingular.

5 PARTITIONED MATRICES

Often it is useful to think of a matrix as being composed of a number of submatrices. A matrix C can be partitioned into smaller matrices by drawing horizontal lines between the rows and vertical lines between the columns. The smaller matrices are often referred to as *blocks*. For example, let

$$C = \begin{pmatrix} 1 & -2 & 4 & 1 & 3 \\ 2 & 1 & 1 & 1 & 1 \\ 3 & 3 & 2 & -1 & 2 \\ 4 & 6 & 2 & 2 & 4 \end{pmatrix}$$

If lines are drawn between the second and third rows and between the third and fourth columns, then C will be divided into four submatrices, C_{11}, C_{12}, C_{21}, and C_{22}.

$$\begin{bmatrix} C_{11} & C_{12} \\ C_{21} & C_{22} \end{bmatrix} = \left(\begin{array}{ccc|cc} 1 & -2 & 4 & 1 & 3 \\ 2 & 1 & 1 & 1 & 1 \\ \hline 3 & 3 & 2 & -1 & 2 \\ 4 & 6 & 2 & 2 & 4 \end{array} \right)$$

One useful way of partitioning a matrix is into columns. For example, if

$$B = \begin{bmatrix} -1 & 2 & 1 \\ 2 & 3 & 1 \\ 1 & 4 & 1 \end{bmatrix}$$

we can partition B into three column submatrices:

$$B = (\mathbf{b}_1, \mathbf{b}_2, \mathbf{b}_3) = \left[\begin{array}{c|c|c} -1 & 2 & 1 \\ 2 & 3 & 1 \\ 1 & 4 & 1 \end{array} \right]$$

Suppose that we are given a matrix A with three columns, then the product AB can be viewed as a block multiplication. Each of the blocks of B is multiplied by A and the result is a matrix with three blocks, $A\mathbf{b}_1$, $A\mathbf{b}_2$, $A\mathbf{b}_3$, that is,

$$AB = A(\mathbf{b}_1, \mathbf{b}_2, \mathbf{b}_3) = (A\mathbf{b}_1, A\mathbf{b}_2, A\mathbf{b}_3)$$

For example, if

$$A = \begin{bmatrix} 1 & 3 & 1 \\ 2 & 1 & -2 \end{bmatrix}$$

$$A\mathbf{b}_1 = \begin{bmatrix} 6 \\ -2 \end{bmatrix}, \quad A\mathbf{b}_2 = \begin{bmatrix} 15 \\ -1 \end{bmatrix}, \quad A\mathbf{b}_3 = \begin{bmatrix} 5 \\ 1 \end{bmatrix}$$

and hence

$$A(\mathbf{b}_1, \mathbf{b}_2, \mathbf{b}_3) = \left[\begin{array}{c|c|c} 6 & 15 & 5 \\ -2 & -1 & 1 \end{array} \right]$$

In general, if A is an $m \times n$ matrix and B is an $n \times r$ that has been partitioned into columns $(\mathbf{b}_1, \ldots, \mathbf{b}_r)$, then the block multiplication of A times B is given by

$$AB = (A\mathbf{b}_1, A\mathbf{b}_2, \ldots, A\mathbf{b}_r)$$

In particular,

$$(\mathbf{a}_1, \ldots, \mathbf{a}_n) = A = AI = (A\mathbf{e}_1, \ldots, A\mathbf{e}_n)$$

Let A be an $m \times n$ matrix. If we partition A into rows, then

$$A = \begin{bmatrix} \mathbf{a}(1, :) \\ \mathbf{a}(2, :) \\ \vdots \\ \mathbf{a}(m, :) \end{bmatrix}$$

If B is an $n \times r$ matrix, the ith row of the product AB is determined by multiplying the ith row of A times B. Thus the ith row of AB is $\mathbf{a}(i, :)B$. In general, the product AB can be partitioned into rows as follows:

$$AB = \begin{bmatrix} \mathbf{a}(1, :)B \\ \mathbf{a}(2, :)B \\ \vdots \\ \mathbf{a}(m, :)B \end{bmatrix}$$

To illustrate this result, let us look at an example. If

$$A = \begin{bmatrix} 2 & 5 \\ 3 & 4 \\ 1 & 7 \end{bmatrix} \qquad \text{and} \qquad B = \begin{bmatrix} 3 & 2 & -3 \\ -1 & 1 & 1 \end{bmatrix}$$

then

$$\mathbf{a}(1, :)B = \begin{bmatrix} 1 & 9 & -1 \end{bmatrix}$$

$$\mathbf{a}(2, :)B = \begin{bmatrix} 5 & 10 & -5 \end{bmatrix}$$

$$\mathbf{a}(3, :)B = \begin{bmatrix} -4 & 9 & 4 \end{bmatrix}$$

These are the row vectors of the product AB.

$$AB = \begin{bmatrix} \mathbf{a}(1, :)B \\ \mathbf{a}(2, :)B \\ \mathbf{a}(3, :)B \end{bmatrix} = \begin{bmatrix} 1 & 9 & -1 \\ \hline 5 & 10 & -5 \\ \hline -4 & 9 & 4 \end{bmatrix}$$

Next we consider how to compute the product AB in terms of more general partitions of A and B.

Block Multiplication

Let A be an $m \times n$ matrix and B an $n \times r$ matrix. It is often useful to partition A and B and express the product in terms of the submatrices of A and B. Consider the following four cases.

CASE I

$B = \begin{bmatrix} B_1 & B_2 \end{bmatrix}$, where B_1 is an $n \times t$ matrix and B_2 is an $n \times (r - t)$ matrix.

$$\begin{aligned} AB &= A(\mathbf{b}_1, \ldots, \mathbf{b}_t, \mathbf{b}_{t+1}, \ldots, \mathbf{b}_r) \\ &= (A\mathbf{b}_1, \ldots, A\mathbf{b}_t, A\mathbf{b}_{t+1}, \ldots, A\mathbf{b}_r) \\ &= (A(\mathbf{b}_1, \ldots, \mathbf{b}_t), A(\mathbf{b}_{t+1}, \ldots, \mathbf{b}_r)) \\ &= \begin{bmatrix} AB_1 & AB_2 \end{bmatrix} \end{aligned}$$

Thus,

$$A \begin{bmatrix} B_1 & B_2 \end{bmatrix} = \begin{bmatrix} AB_1 & AB_2 \end{bmatrix}$$

CASE 2

$A = \begin{bmatrix} A_1 \\ A_2 \end{bmatrix}$, where A_1 is a $k \times n$ matrix and A_2 is an $(m - k) \times n$ matrix.

$$\begin{bmatrix} A_1 \\ A_2 \end{bmatrix} B = \begin{bmatrix} \mathbf{a}(1,:) \\ \vdots \\ \mathbf{a}(k,:) \\ \hline \mathbf{a}(k+1,:) \\ \vdots \\ \mathbf{a}(m,:) \end{bmatrix} B = \begin{bmatrix} \mathbf{a}(1,:)B \\ \vdots \\ \mathbf{a}(k,:)B \\ \hline \mathbf{a}(k+1,:)B \\ \vdots \\ \mathbf{a}(m,:)B \end{bmatrix}$$

$$= \begin{bmatrix} \begin{bmatrix} \mathbf{a}(1,:) \\ \vdots \\ \mathbf{a}(k,:) \end{bmatrix} B \\ \begin{bmatrix} \mathbf{a}(k+1,:) \\ \vdots \\ \mathbf{a}(m,:) \end{bmatrix} B \end{bmatrix} = \begin{bmatrix} A_1 B \\ A_2 B \end{bmatrix}$$

Thus,

$$\begin{bmatrix} A_1 \\ A_2 \end{bmatrix} B = \begin{bmatrix} A_1 B \\ A_2 B \end{bmatrix}$$

CASE 3

$A = \begin{bmatrix} A_1 & A_2 \end{bmatrix}$ and $B = \begin{bmatrix} B_1 \\ B_2 \end{bmatrix}$, where A_1 is an $m \times s$ matrix, A_2 is an $m \times (n-s)$ matrix, B_1 is an $s \times r$ matrix, and B_2 is an $(n - s) \times r$ matrix. If $C = AB$, then

$$c_{ij} = \sum_{l=1}^{n} a_{il}b_{lj} = \sum_{l=1}^{s} a_{il}b_{lj} + \sum_{l=s+1}^{n} a_{il}b_{lj}$$

Thus c_{ij} is the sum of the (i, j) entry of $A_1 B_1$ and the (i, j) entry of $A_2 B_2$. Therefore,

$$AB = C = A_1 B_1 + A_2 B_2$$

and it follows that

$$\begin{bmatrix} A_1 & A_2 \end{bmatrix} \begin{bmatrix} B_1 \\ B_2 \end{bmatrix} = A_1 B_1 + A_2 B_2$$

CASE 4

Let A and B both be partitioned as follows:

$$A = \begin{bmatrix} A_{11} & A_{12} \\ \hline A_{21} & A_{22} \end{bmatrix} \begin{matrix} k \\ m-k \end{matrix}, \qquad B = \begin{bmatrix} B_{11} & B_{12} \\ \hline B_{21} & B_{22} \end{bmatrix} \begin{matrix} s \\ n-s \end{matrix}$$

$$\qquad\quad s \qquad n-s \qquad\qquad\qquad t \qquad r-t$$

Let

$$A_1 = \begin{bmatrix} A_{11} \\ A_{21} \end{bmatrix} \qquad A_2 = \begin{bmatrix} A_{12} \\ A_{22} \end{bmatrix}$$

$$B_1 = \begin{bmatrix} B_{11} & B_{12} \end{bmatrix} \qquad B_2 = \begin{bmatrix} B_{21} & B_{22} \end{bmatrix}$$

It follows from case 3 that

$$AB = \begin{bmatrix} A_1 & A_2 \end{bmatrix} \begin{bmatrix} B_1 \\ B_2 \end{bmatrix} = A_1 B_1 + A_2 B_2$$

It follows from cases 1 and 2 that

$$A_1 B_1 = \begin{bmatrix} A_{11} \\ A_{21} \end{bmatrix} B_1 = \begin{bmatrix} A_{11} B_1 \\ A_{21} B_1 \end{bmatrix} = \begin{bmatrix} A_{11} B_{11} & A_{11} B_{12} \\ A_{21} B_{11} & A_{21} B_{12} \end{bmatrix}$$

$$A_2 B_2 = \begin{bmatrix} A_{12} \\ A_{22} \end{bmatrix} B_2 = \begin{bmatrix} A_{12} B_2 \\ A_{22} B_2 \end{bmatrix} = \begin{bmatrix} A_{12} B_{21} & A_{12} B_{22} \\ A_{22} B_{21} & A_{22} B_{22} \end{bmatrix}$$

Therefore,

$$\begin{pmatrix} A_{11} & A_{12} \\ A_{21} & A_{22} \end{pmatrix} \begin{pmatrix} B_{11} & B_{12} \\ B_{21} & B_{22} \end{pmatrix} = \begin{pmatrix} A_{11}B_{11} + A_{12}B_{21} & A_{11}B_{12} + A_{12}B_{22} \\ A_{21}B_{11} + A_{22}B_{21} & A_{21}B_{12} + A_{22}B_{22} \end{pmatrix}$$

In general, if the blocks have the proper dimensions, the block multiplication can be carried out in the same manner as ordinary matrix multiplication. If

$$A = \begin{bmatrix} A_{11} & \cdots & A_{1t} \\ \vdots & & \\ A_{s1} & \cdots & A_{st} \end{bmatrix} \qquad \text{and} \qquad B = \begin{bmatrix} B_{11} & \cdots & B_{1r} \\ \vdots & & \\ B_{t1} & \cdots & B_{tr} \end{bmatrix}$$

then

$$AB = \begin{pmatrix} C_{11} & \cdots & C_{1r} \\ \vdots & & \\ C_{s1} & \cdots & C_{sr} \end{pmatrix}$$

where

$$C_{ij} = \sum_{k=1}^{t} A_{ik} B_{kj}$$

The multiplication can be carried out in this manner only if the number of columns of A_{ik} equals the number of rows of B_{kj} for each k.

EXAMPLE I. Let

$$A = \begin{pmatrix} 1 & 1 & 1 & 1 \\ 2 & 2 & 1 & 1 \\ 3 & 3 & 2 & 2 \end{pmatrix}$$

and

$$B = \begin{pmatrix} B_{11} & B_{12} \\ B_{21} & B_{22} \end{pmatrix} = \left(\begin{array}{cc|cc} 1 & 1 & 1 & 1 \\ 1 & 2 & 1 & 1 \\ \hline 3 & 1 & 1 & 1 \\ 3 & 2 & 1 & 2 \end{array} \right)$$

Partition A into four blocks and perform the block multiplication.

SOLUTION. Since each B_{kj} has two rows, the A_{ik}'s must each have two columns. Thus there are two possibilities:

$$\text{(i)} \qquad \begin{pmatrix} A_{11} & A_{12} \\ A_{21} & A_{22} \end{pmatrix} = \left(\begin{array}{cc|cc} 1 & 1 & 1 & 1 \\ 2 & 2 & 1 & 1 \\ 3 & 3 & 2 & 2 \end{array} \right)$$

in which case

$$\left(\begin{array}{cc|cc} 1 & 1 & 1 & 1 \\ 2 & 2 & 1 & 1 \\ 3 & 3 & 2 & 2 \end{array} \right) \left(\begin{array}{cc|cc} 1 & 1 & 1 & 1 \\ 1 & 2 & 1 & 1 \\ \hline 3 & 1 & 1 & 1 \\ 3 & 2 & 1 & 2 \end{array} \right) = \left(\begin{array}{cc|cc} 8 & 6 & 4 & 5 \\ \hline 10 & 9 & 6 & 7 \\ \hline 18 & 15 & 10 & 12 \end{array} \right)$$

or

$$\text{(ii)} \qquad \begin{pmatrix} A_{11} & A_{12} \\ A_{21} & A_{22} \end{pmatrix} = \left(\begin{array}{cc|cc} 1 & 1 & 1 & 1 \\ 2 & 2 & 1 & 1 \\ \hline 3 & 3 & 2 & 2 \end{array} \right)$$

in which case

$$
\begin{pmatrix} 1 & 1 & 1 & 1 \\ 2 & 2 & 1 & 1 \\ 3 & 3 & 2 & 2 \end{pmatrix} \begin{pmatrix} 1 & 1 & 1 & 1 \\ 1 & 2 & 1 & 1 \\ 3 & 1 & 1 & 1 \\ 3 & 2 & 1 & 2 \end{pmatrix} = \begin{pmatrix} 8 & 6 & 4 & 5 \\ 10 & 9 & 6 & 7 \\ 18 & 15 & 10 & 12 \end{pmatrix}
$$

◀

EXAMPLE 2. Let A be an $n \times n$ matrix of the form

$$
\begin{bmatrix} A_{11} & O \\ O & A_{22} \end{bmatrix}
$$

where A_{11} is a $k \times k$ matrix $(k < n)$. Show that A is nonsingular if and only if A_{11} and A_{22} are nonsingular.

SOLUTION. If A_{11} and A_{22} are nonsingular, then

$$
\begin{bmatrix} A_{11}^{-1} & O \\ O & A_{22}^{-1} \end{bmatrix} \begin{bmatrix} A_{11} & O \\ O & A_{22} \end{bmatrix} = \begin{bmatrix} I_k & O \\ O & I_{n-k} \end{bmatrix} = I
$$

and

$$
\begin{bmatrix} A_{11} & O \\ O & A_{22} \end{bmatrix} \begin{bmatrix} A_{11}^{-1} & O \\ O & A_{22}^{-1} \end{bmatrix} = \begin{bmatrix} I_k & O \\ O & I_{n-k} \end{bmatrix} = I
$$

so A is nonsingular and

$$
A^{-1} = \begin{bmatrix} A_{11}^{-1} & O \\ O & A_{22}^{-1} \end{bmatrix}
$$

Conversely, if A is nonsingular, then let $B = A^{-1}$ and partition B in the same manner as A. Since

$$
BA = I = AB
$$

it follows that

$$
\begin{bmatrix} B_{11} & B_{12} \\ B_{21} & B_{22} \end{bmatrix} \begin{bmatrix} A_{11} & O \\ O & A_{22} \end{bmatrix} = \begin{bmatrix} I_k & O \\ O & I_{n-k} \end{bmatrix} = \begin{bmatrix} A_{11} & O \\ O & A_{22} \end{bmatrix} \begin{bmatrix} B_{11} & B_{12} \\ B_{21} & B_{22} \end{bmatrix}
$$

$$
\begin{bmatrix} B_{11}A_{11} & B_{12}A_{22} \\ B_{21}A_{11} & B_{22}A_{22} \end{bmatrix} = \begin{bmatrix} I_k & O \\ O & I_{n-k} \end{bmatrix} = \begin{bmatrix} A_{11}B_{11} & A_{11}B_{12} \\ A_{22}B_{21} & A_{22}B_{22} \end{bmatrix}
$$

Thus

$$
B_{11}A_{11} = I_k = A_{11}B_{11}
$$

$$
B_{22}A_{22} = I_{n-k} = A_{22}B_{22}
$$

and hence A_{11} and A_{22} are both nonsingular with inverses B_{11} and B_{22}, respectively. ◀

Outer Product Expansions

Given two vectors $\mathbf{x}$ and $\mathbf{y}$ in R^n, we can multiply them together if we transpose one of the vectors first. The matrix product $\mathbf{x}^T\mathbf{y}$ is the product of a row vector (a $1 \times n$ matrix) times a column vector (an $n \times 1$ matrix). The result will be a 1×1 matrix or simply a scalar.

$$\mathbf{x}^T\mathbf{y} = (x_1, x_2, \ldots, x_n) \begin{pmatrix} y_1 \\ y_2 \\ \vdots \\ y_n \end{pmatrix} = x_1 y_1 + x_2 y_2 + \cdots + x_n y_n$$

This type of product is referred to as a *scalar product* or an *inner product*. The scalar product is one of the most commonly performed operations. For example, when we multiply two matrices, each entry of the product is computed as a scalar product (a row vector times a column vector).

It is also useful to multiply a column vector times a row vector. The matrix product $\mathbf{x}\mathbf{y}^T$ is the product of an $n \times 1$ matrix times an $1 \times n$ matrix. The result is a full $n \times n$ matrix.

$$\mathbf{x}\mathbf{y}^T = \begin{pmatrix} x_1 \\ x_2 \\ \vdots \\ x_n \end{pmatrix} (y_1, y_2, \ldots, y_n) = \begin{pmatrix} x_1 y_1 & x_1 y_2 & \cdots & x_1 y_n \\ x_2 y_1 & x_2 y_2 & \cdots & x_2 y_n \\ \vdots & & & \\ x_n y_1 & x_n y_2 & \cdots & x_n y_n \end{pmatrix}$$

The product $\mathbf{x}\mathbf{y}^T$ is referred to as the *outer product* of $\mathbf{x}$ and $\mathbf{y}$. The outer product matrix has special structure in that each of its rows is a multiple of $\mathbf{y}^T$ and each of its column vectors is a multiple of $\mathbf{x}$. For example, if

$$\mathbf{x} = \begin{pmatrix} 4 \\ 1 \\ 3 \end{pmatrix} \quad \text{and} \quad \mathbf{y} = \begin{pmatrix} 3 \\ 5 \\ 2 \end{pmatrix}$$

then

$$\mathbf{x}\mathbf{y}^T = \begin{pmatrix} 4 \\ 1 \\ 3 \end{pmatrix} (3, 5, 2) = \begin{pmatrix} 12 & 20 & 8 \\ 3 & 5 & 2 \\ 9 & 15 & 6 \end{pmatrix}$$

Note that each row is a multiple of $(3, 5, 2)$ and each column is a multiple of $\mathbf{x}$.

We are now ready to generalize the idea of an outer product from vectors to matrices. Suppose that we start with an $m \times n$ matrix X and a $k \times n$ matrix Y. We can then form a matrix product XY^T. If we partition X into columns and Y^T into rows and perform the block multiplication, we see that XY^T can be represented as a sum of outer products of vectors.

$$XY^T = (\mathbf{x}_1, \mathbf{x}_2, \ldots, \mathbf{x}_n) \begin{pmatrix} \mathbf{y}_1^T \\ \mathbf{y}_2^T \\ \vdots \\ \mathbf{y}_n^T \end{pmatrix} = \mathbf{x}_1\mathbf{y}_1^T + \mathbf{x}_2\mathbf{y}_2^T + \cdots + \mathbf{x}_n\mathbf{y}_n^T$$

This representation is referred to as an *outer product expansion*. These types of expansions play an important part in many applications. In Section 5 of Chapter 6 we will see how outer product expansions are used in digital imaging and in information retrieval applications.

EXAMPLE 3. Given

$$X = \begin{bmatrix} 3 & 1 \\ 2 & 4 \\ 1 & 2 \end{bmatrix} \qquad \text{and} \qquad Y = \begin{bmatrix} 1 & 2 \\ 2 & 4 \\ 3 & 1 \end{bmatrix}$$

compute the outer product expansion of XY^T.

SOLUTION.

$$\begin{aligned} XY^T &= \begin{bmatrix} 3 & 1 \\ 2 & 4 \\ 1 & 2 \end{bmatrix} \begin{bmatrix} 1 & 2 & 3 \\ 2 & 4 & 1 \end{bmatrix} \\ &= \begin{bmatrix} 3 \\ 2 \\ 1 \end{bmatrix} (1, 2, 3) + \begin{bmatrix} 1 \\ 4 \\ 2 \end{bmatrix} (2, 4, 1) \\ &= \begin{bmatrix} 3 & 6 & 9 \\ 2 & 4 & 6 \\ 1 & 2 & 3 \end{bmatrix} + \begin{bmatrix} 2 & 4 & 1 \\ 8 & 16 & 4 \\ 4 & 8 & 2 \end{bmatrix} \end{aligned}$$

◀

EXERCISES

1. Let A be a nonsingular $n \times n$ matrix. Perform the following multiplications.

(a) $A^{-1}(A \quad I)$

(b) $\begin{bmatrix} A \\ I \end{bmatrix} A^{-1}$

(c) $(A \quad I)^T (A \quad I)$

(d) $(A \quad I)(A \quad I)^T$

(e) $\begin{bmatrix} A^{-1} \\ I \end{bmatrix} (A \quad I)$

2. Let $B = A^TA$. Show that $b_{ij} = \mathbf{a}_i^T \mathbf{a}_j$.

3. Let

$$A = \begin{bmatrix} 1 & 1 \\ 2 & -1 \end{bmatrix} \qquad \text{and} \qquad B = \begin{bmatrix} 2 & 1 \\ 1 & 3 \end{bmatrix}$$

(a) Calculate $A\mathbf{b}_1$ and $A\mathbf{b}_2$.

(b) Calculate $\mathbf{a}(1, :)B$ and $\mathbf{a}(2, :)B$.

(c) Multiply AB and verify that its column vectors are the vectors in part (a) and its row vectors are the vectors in part (b).

4. Let

$$I = \begin{bmatrix} 1 & 0 \\ 0 & 1 \end{bmatrix}, \qquad E = \begin{bmatrix} 0 & 1 \\ 1 & 0 \end{bmatrix}, \qquad O = \begin{bmatrix} 0 & 0 \\ 0 & 0 \end{bmatrix}$$

$$C = \begin{bmatrix} 1 & 0 \\ -1 & 1 \end{bmatrix}, \qquad D = \begin{bmatrix} 2 & 0 \\ 0 & 2 \end{bmatrix}.$$

and

$$B = \begin{bmatrix} B_{11} & B_{12} \\ B_{21} & B_{22} \end{bmatrix} = \left[\begin{array}{cc|cc} 1 & 1 & 1 & 1 \\ 1 & 2 & 1 & 1 \\ \hline 3 & 1 & 1 & 1 \\ 3 & 2 & 1 & 2 \end{array} \right]$$

Perform each of the following block multiplications.

(a) $\begin{bmatrix} O & I \\ I & O \end{bmatrix} \begin{bmatrix} B_{11} & B_{12} \\ B_{21} & B_{22} \end{bmatrix}$ (b) $\begin{bmatrix} C & O \\ O & C \end{bmatrix} \begin{bmatrix} B_{11} & B_{12} \\ B_{21} & B_{22} \end{bmatrix}$

(c) $\begin{bmatrix} D & O \\ O & I \end{bmatrix} \begin{bmatrix} B_{11} & B_{12} \\ B_{21} & B_{22} \end{bmatrix}$ (d) $\begin{bmatrix} E & O \\ O & E \end{bmatrix} \begin{bmatrix} B_{11} & B_{12} \\ B_{21} & B_{22} \end{bmatrix}$

5. Perform each of the following block multiplications.

(a) $\left[\begin{array}{ccc|c} 1 & 1 & 1 & -1 \\ 2 & 1 & 2 & -1 \end{array} \right] \left[\begin{array}{ccc} 4 & -2 & 1 \\ 2 & 3 & 1 \\ \hline 1 & 1 & 2 \\ 1 & 2 & 3 \end{array} \right]$ (b) $\left[\begin{array}{cc} 4 & -2 \\ 2 & 3 \\ \hline 1 & 1 \\ 1 & 2 \end{array} \right] \left[\begin{array}{ccc|c} 1 & 1 & 1 & -1 \\ 2 & 1 & 2 & -1 \end{array} \right]$

(c) $\left[\begin{array}{cc|cc} \frac{3}{5} & -\frac{4}{5} & 0 & 0 \\ \frac{4}{5} & \frac{3}{5} & 0 & 0 \\ \hline 0 & 0 & 1 & 0 \end{array} \right] \left[\begin{array}{cc|c} \frac{3}{5} & \frac{4}{5} & 0 \\ -\frac{4}{5} & \frac{3}{5} & 0 \\ \hline 0 & 0 & 1 \\ 0 & 0 & 0 \end{array} \right]$ (d) $\left[\begin{array}{ccc|cc} 0 & 0 & 1 & 0 & 0 \\ 0 & 1 & 0 & 0 & 0 \\ 1 & 0 & 0 & 0 & 0 \\ \hline 0 & 0 & 0 & 0 & 1 \\ 0 & 0 & 0 & 1 & 0 \end{array} \right] \left[\begin{array}{cc} 1 & -1 \\ 2 & -2 \\ 3 & -3 \\ \hline 4 & -4 \\ 5 & -5 \end{array} \right]$

6. Given

$$X = \begin{bmatrix} 2 & 1 & 5 \\ 4 & 2 & 3 \end{bmatrix} \qquad Y = \begin{bmatrix} 1 & 2 & 4 \\ 2 & 3 & 1 \end{bmatrix}$$

(a) Compute the outer product expansion of XY^T.

(b) Compute the outer product expansion of YX^T. How is the outer product expansion of YX^T related to the outer product expansion of XY^T?

7. Let

$$A = \begin{bmatrix} A_{11} & A_{12} \\ A_{21} & A_{22} \end{bmatrix} \quad \text{and} \quad A^T = \begin{bmatrix} A_{11}^T & A_{21}^T \\ A_{12}^T & A_{22}^T \end{bmatrix}$$

Is it possible to perform the block multiplications of AA^T and A^TA? Explain.

8. Let A be an $m \times n$ matrix, X an $n \times r$ matrix, and B an $m \times r$ matrix. Show that

$$AX = B$$

if and only if

$$A\mathbf{x}_j = \mathbf{b}_j, \quad j = 1, \dots, r$$

9. Let A be an $n \times n$ matrix and let D be a $n \times n$ diagonal matrix.

(a) Show that $D = (d_{11}\mathbf{e}_1, d_{22}\mathbf{e}_2, \dots, d_{nn}\mathbf{e}_n)$.

(b) Show that $AD = (d_{11}\mathbf{a}_1, d_{22}\mathbf{a}_2, \dots, d_{nn}\mathbf{a}_n)$.

10. Let U be an $m \times m$ matrix, V be an $n \times n$ matrix, and let

$$\Sigma = \begin{bmatrix} \Sigma_1 \\ O \end{bmatrix}$$

where Σ_1 is an $n \times n$ diagonal matrix with diagonal entries $\sigma_1, \sigma_2, \dots, \sigma_n$ and O is the $(m - n) \times n$ zero matrix.

(a) If $U = (U_1, U_2)$, where U_1 has n columns, show that

$$U\Sigma = U_1\Sigma_1$$

(b) Show that if $A = U\Sigma V^T$ then A can be expressed as an outer product expansion of the form

$$A = \sigma_1\mathbf{u}_1\mathbf{v}_1^T + \sigma_2\mathbf{u}_2\mathbf{v}_2^T + \cdots + \sigma_n\mathbf{u}_n\mathbf{v}_n^T$$

11. Let

$$A = \begin{bmatrix} A_{11} & A_{12} \\ O & A_{22} \end{bmatrix}$$

where all four blocks are $n \times n$ matrices.

(a) If A_{11} and A_{22} are nonsingular, show that A must also be nonsingular and that A^{-1} must be of the form

$$\left[\begin{array}{c|c} A_{11}^{-1} & C \\ \hline O & A_{22}^{-1} \end{array} \right]$$

(b) Determine C.

12. Let

$$A = \begin{bmatrix} O & I \\ B & O \end{bmatrix}$$

where all four submatrices are $k \times k$. Determine A^2 and A^4.

13. Let I denote the $n \times n$ identity matrix. Find a block form for the inverse of each of the following $2n \times 2n$ matrices.

(a) $\begin{bmatrix} O & I \\ I & O \end{bmatrix}$

(b) $\begin{bmatrix} I & O \\ B & I \end{bmatrix}$

14. Let A and B be $m \times n$ and $n \times r$ matrices, respectively, and define $(m+n) \times (m+n)$ matrices S and M by

$$S = \begin{bmatrix} I & A \\ O & I \end{bmatrix}, \qquad M = \begin{bmatrix} AB & O \\ B & O \end{bmatrix}$$

Determine the block form of S^{-1} and use it to compute the block form of the product $S^{-1}MS$.

15. Let

$$A = \begin{bmatrix} A_{11} & A_{12} \\ A_{21} & A_{22} \end{bmatrix}$$

where A_{11} is a $k \times k$ nonsingular matrix. Show that A can be factored into a product

$$\begin{bmatrix} I & O \\ B & I \end{bmatrix} \begin{bmatrix} A_{11} & A_{12} \\ O & C \end{bmatrix}$$

where

$$B = A_{21}A_{11}^{-1} \qquad \text{and} \qquad C = A_{22} - A_{21}A_{11}^{-1}A_{12}$$

16. Given A, B, L, M, S, T are $n \times n$ matrices with A, B, M nonsingular and L, S, T singular. Is it possible to find matrices X and Y such that

$$\begin{bmatrix} O & I & O & O & O & O \\ O & O & I & O & O & O \\ O & O & O & I & O & O \\ O & O & O & O & I & O \\ O & O & O & O & O & X \\ Y & O & O & O & O & O \end{bmatrix} \begin{bmatrix} M \\ A \\ T \\ L \\ A \\ B \end{bmatrix} = \begin{bmatrix} A \\ T \\ L \\ A \\ S \\ T \end{bmatrix}$$

If so, show how; if not, explain why.

17. Let A be an $n \times n$ matrix and $\mathbf{x} \in R^n$.

(a) A scalar c can also be considered as a 1×1 matrix $C = (c)$ and a vector $\mathbf{b} \in R^n$ can be considered as an $n \times 1$ matrix B. Show that, although the matrix multiplication CB is not defined, the matrix product BC is equal to $c\mathbf{b}$, the scalar multiplication of c times $\mathbf{b}$.

(b) Partition A into columns and $\mathbf{x}$ into rows and perform the block multiplication of A times $\mathbf{x}$.

(c) Show that

$$A\mathbf{x} = x_1\mathbf{a}_1 + x_2\mathbf{a}_2 + \cdots + x_n\mathbf{a}_n$$

18. Show that, if A is an $n \times n$ matrix with the property $A\mathbf{x} = \mathbf{0}$ for all $\mathbf{x} \in R^n$, then $A = O$. [*Hint:* Let $\mathbf{x} = \mathbf{e}_j$ for $j = 1, \ldots, n$.]

19. Let B and C be $n \times n$ matrices with the property $B\mathbf{x} = C\mathbf{x}$ for all $\mathbf{x} \in R^n$. Show that $B = C$.

20. Consider a system of the form

$$\begin{bmatrix} A & \mathbf{a} \\ \mathbf{c}^T & \beta \end{bmatrix} \begin{bmatrix} \mathbf{x} \\ x_{n+1} \end{bmatrix} = \begin{bmatrix} \mathbf{b} \\ b_{n+1} \end{bmatrix}$$

where A is a nonsingular $n \times n$ matrix and $\mathbf{a}$, $\mathbf{b}$, and $\mathbf{c}$ are vectors in R^n.

(a) Multiply both sides of the system by

$$\begin{bmatrix} A^{-1} & \mathbf{0} \\ -\mathbf{c}^T A^{-1} & 1 \end{bmatrix}$$

to obtain an equivalent triangular system.

(b) Set $\mathbf{y} = A^{-1}\mathbf{a}$ and $\mathbf{z} = A^{-1}\mathbf{b}$. Show that if $\beta - \mathbf{c}^T \mathbf{y} \neq 0$ then the solution of the system can be determined by letting

$$x_{n+1} = \frac{b_{n+1} - \mathbf{c}^T \mathbf{z}}{\beta - \mathbf{c}^T \mathbf{y}}$$

and then setting

$$\mathbf{x} = \mathbf{z} - x_{n+1}\mathbf{y}$$

MATLAB EXERCISES

The following exercises are to be solved computationally using the software package MATLAB, which is described in the Appendix of this book. The exercises also contain questions that should be answered relating to the underlying mathematical principles illustrated in the computations. Save a record of your session in a file. After editing and printing out the file, the answers to the questions can then be filled in directly on the printout.

MATLAB has a help facility that explains all its operations and commands. For example, to obtain information on the MATLAB command **rand** you need only type: **help rand**. The commands used in the MATLAB exercises for this chapter are **inv**, **round**, **rand**, **flops**, **rref**, **format**, **sum**, **eye**, **triu**, **ones**, **zeros**, **magic**. The operations introduced are $+, -, *, ', \backslash$. The $+$ and $-$ represent the usual addition and subtraction operations for both scalars and matrices. The $*$ corresponds to multiplication of either scalars or matrices, and the $'$ operation corresponds to the transpose operation. If A is a nonsingular $n \times n$ matrix and B is any $n \times r$ matrix, the operation $A\backslash B$ is equivalent to computing $A^{-1}B$.

1. Use MATLAB to generate random 4×4 matrices A and B. For each of the following compute $A1$, $A2$, $A3$, $A4$ as indicated and determine which of the matrices are equal. You can use MATLAB to test whether two matrices are equal by computing their difference.

(a) $A1 = A * B$, $A2 = B * A$, $A3 = (A' * B')'$, $A4 = (B' * A')'$

(b) $A1 = A' * B'$, $A2 = (A * B)'$, $A3 = B' * A'$, $A4 = (B * A)'$

(c) $A1 = \mathbf{inv}(A * B)$, $A2 = \mathbf{inv}(A) * \mathbf{inv}(B)$, $A3 = \mathbf{inv}(B * A)$, $A4 = \mathbf{inv}(B) * \mathbf{inv}(A)$

(d) $A1 = \mathbf{inv}((A * B)')$, $A2 = \mathbf{inv}(A' * B')$, $A3 = \mathbf{inv}(A') * \mathbf{inv}(B')$, $A4 = (\mathbf{inv}(A) * \mathbf{inv}(B))'$

2. Generate an 8×8 matrix and a vector in R^8, both having integer entries, by setting

$$A = \mathbf{round}(10 * \mathbf{rand}(8)) \quad \text{and} \quad b = \mathbf{round}(10 * \mathbf{rand}(8, 1))$$

(a) We can estimate the amount of arithmetic operations involved in solving the system $Ax = b$ by using the MATLAB function **flops**. The value of the variable **flops** is MATLAB's estimate of the total number of floating-point arithmetic operations that have been carried out so far in the current MATLAB session. The value of **flops** can be reset to 0 by typing **flops**(0). Reset **flops** to 0 and then find the solution **x** to the system $Ax = b$ using the "\" operation. Now type **flops** to determine approximately how many arithmetic operations were carried out in solving the system.

(b) Next let us solve the system using Gauss–Jordan reduction. First reset **flops** to 0. Compute the reduced row echelon form of the augmented matrix $(A \quad \mathbf{b})$. This can be done with the MATLAB command

$$U = \mathbf{rref}([A \quad \mathbf{b}])$$

In exact arithmetic the last column of the reduced row echelon form of the augmented matrix should be the solution to the system. Why? Explain. Set **y** equal to the last column of U and type **flops** to estimate the number of floating operations that were used in computing **y**. Which method of solving the system was more efficient? Using the "\" operation or the Gauss–Jordan reduction? (*Note:* The "\" operation is essentially reduction to triangular form followed by back substitution.)

(c) The solutions **x** and **y** obtained from the two methods look to be the same, but, if you examine more digits of the vectors using MATLAB's **format long**, you will see that they are not identical. To how many digits do the two vectors agree? An easier way to compare the two vectors is to use **format short** and to look at the difference $\mathbf{x} - \mathbf{y}$.

(d) Which of the two computed solutions **x** and **y** is more accurate? To answer this, compare each of the products $A\mathbf{x}$ and $A\mathbf{y}$ to the right-hand side **b**. The simplest way to do this is to look at the differences $\mathbf{r} = \mathbf{b} - A\mathbf{x}$ and $\mathbf{s} = \mathbf{b} - A\mathbf{y}$. The vectors **r** and **s** are called the residual vectors for the computed solutions **x** and **y**, respectively. Which of the computed solutions has the smallest residual vector?

3. Set $A = \mathbf{round}(10 * \mathbf{rand}(6))$. By construction, the matrix A will have integer entries. Let us change the sixth column of A so as to make the matrix singular. Set

$$B = A', \qquad A(:, 6) = -\mathbf{sum}(B(1:5, :))'$$

(a) Set $\mathbf{x} = \mathbf{ones}(6, 1)$ and use MATLAB to compute $A * \mathbf{x}$. Why do we know that A must be singular? Explain. Check that A is singular by computing its reduced row echelon form.

(b) Set

$$B = \mathbf{x} * [1 : 6]$$

The product AB should equal the zero matrix. Why? Explain. Verify that this is so by computing AB using the MATLAB operation $*$.

(c) Set

$$C = \mathbf{round}(10 * \mathbf{rand}(6)) \qquad \text{and} \qquad D = B + C$$

Although $C \neq D$, the products AC and AD should be equal. Why? Explain. Compute $A * C$ and $A * D$ and verify that they are indeed equal.

4. Construct a matrix as follows. Set

$$B = \mathbf{eye}(10) - \mathbf{triu}(\mathbf{ones}(10), 1)$$

Why do we know that B must be nonsingular? Set

$$C = \mathbf{inv}(B) \qquad \text{and} \qquad \mathbf{x} = C(:, 10)$$

Now change B slightly by setting $B(10, 1) = -1/256$. Use MATLAB to compute the product $B\mathbf{x}$. From the result of this computation, what can you conclude about the new matrix B? Is it still nonsingular? Explain. Use MATLAB to compute its reduced row echelon form.

5. Generate a matrix A by setting

$$A = \mathbf{round}(10 * \mathbf{rand}(6))$$

and generate a vector $\mathbf{b}$ by setting

$$\mathbf{b} = \mathbf{round}(20 * \mathbf{rand}(6, 1)) - 10$$

(a) Since A was generated randomly, we would expect it to be nonsingular. The system $A\mathbf{x} = \mathbf{b}$ should have a unique solution. Find the solution using the "\" operation. Use MATLAB to compute the reduced row echelon form U of $[A \ \mathbf{b}]$. How does the last column of U compare with the solution $\mathbf{x}$? In exact arithmetic they should be the same. Why? Explain. To compare the two, compute the difference $U(:, 7) - \mathbf{x}$ or examine both using **format long.**

(b) Let us now change A so as to make it singular. Set

$$A(:, 3) = A(:, 1 : 2) * [4 \ 3]'$$

Use MATLAB to compute $\mathbf{rref}([A \ \mathbf{b}])$. How many solutions will the system $A\mathbf{x} = \mathbf{b}$ have? Explain.

(c) Set

$$\mathbf{y} = \mathbf{round}(20 * \mathbf{rand}(6, 1)) - 10 \quad \text{and} \quad \mathbf{c} = A * \mathbf{y}$$

Why do we know that the system $A\mathbf{x} = \mathbf{c}$ must be consistent? Explain. Compute the reduced row echelon form U of $[A \ \mathbf{c}]$. How many solutions does the system $A\mathbf{x} = \mathbf{c}$ have? Explain.

(d) The free variable determined by the echelon form should be x_3. By examining the system corresponding to the matrix U, you should be able to determine the solution corresponding to $x_3 = 0$. Enter this solution in MATLAB as a column vector $\mathbf{w}$. To check that $A\mathbf{w} = \mathbf{c}$, compute the residual vector $\mathbf{c} - A\mathbf{w}$.

(e) Set $U(:, 7) = \mathtt{zeros}(6, 1)$. The matrix U should now correspond to the reduced row echelon form of $(A \mid \mathbf{0})$. Use U to determine the solution to the homogeneous system when the free variable $x_3 = 1$ (do this by hand) and enter your result as a vector $\mathbf{z}$. Check your answer by computing $A * \mathbf{z}$.

(f) Set $\mathbf{v} = \mathbf{w} + 3 * \mathbf{z}$. The vector $\mathbf{v}$ should be a solution to the system $A\mathbf{x} = \mathbf{c}$. Why? Explain. Verify that $\mathbf{v}$ is a solution by using MATLAB to compute the residual vector $\mathbf{c} - A\mathbf{v}$. What is the value of the free variable x_3 for this solution? How could we determine all possible solutions to the system in terms of the vectors $\mathbf{w}$ and $\mathbf{z}$? Explain.

6. Consider the graph

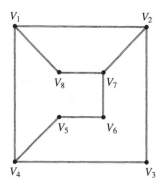

(a) Determine the adjacency matrix A for the graph and enter it in MATLAB.

(b) Compute A^2 and determine the number of walks of length 2 from (i) V_1 to V_7, (ii) V_4 to V_8, (iii) V_5 to V_6, (iv) V_8 to V_3.

(c) Compute A^4, A^6, A^8 and answer the questions in part (b) for walks of lengths 4, 6, and 8. Make a conjecture as to when there will be no walks of even length from vertex V_i to vertex V_j.

(d) Compute A^3, A^5, A^7 and answer the questions from part (b) for walks of lengths 3, 5, and 7. Does your conjecture from part (c) hold for walks of odd length? Explain. Make a conjecture as to whether there are any walks of length k from V_i to V_j based on whether $i + j + k$ is odd or even.

(e) If we add the edges $\{V_3, V_6\}$, $\{V_5, V_8\}$ to the graph, the adjacency matrix B for the new graph can be generated by setting $B = A$ and then setting

$$B(3, 6) = 1, \qquad B(6, 3) = 1, \qquad B(5, 8) = 1, \qquad B(8, 5) = 1$$

Compute B^k, for $k = 2, 3, 4, 5$. Is your conjecture from part (d) still valid for the new graph?

(f) Add the edge $\{V_6, V_8\}$ to the figure and construct the adjacency matrix C for the resulting graph. Compute powers of C to determine whether your conjecture from part (d) will still hold for this new graph.

7. In Application 3 of Section 3, the numbers of married and single women after 1 and 2 years were determined by computing the products AX and A^2X for the given matrices A and X. Use **format long** and enter these matrices in MATLAB. Compute A^k and A^kX for $k = 5, 10, 15, 20$. What is happening to A^k as k gets large? What is the long-run distribution of married and single women in the town?

8. The following table describes a seven-stage model for the life cycle of the loggerhead turtle.

SEVEN-STAGE MODEL FOR LOGGERHEAD TURTLE
DEMOGRAPHICS

Stage Number	Description (age in years)	Annual Survivorship	Eggs Laid per Year
1	Eggs, hatchlings (<1)	0.6747	0
2	Small juveniles (1–7)	0.7857	0
3	Large juveniles (8–15)	0.6758	0
4	Subadults (16–21)	0.7425	0
5	Novice breeders (22)	0.8091	127
6	First-year remigrants (23)	0.8091	4
7	Mature breeders (24–54)	0.8091	80

The corresponding Leslie matrix is given by

$$
L = \begin{bmatrix}
0 & 0 & 0 & 0 & 127 & 4 & 80 \\
0.6747 & 0.7370 & 0 & 0 & 0 & 0 & 0 \\
0 & 0.0486 & 0.6610 & 0 & 0 & 0 & 0 \\
0 & 0 & 0.0147 & 0.6907 & 0 & 0 & 0 \\
0 & 0 & 0 & 0.0518 & 0 & 0 & 0 \\
0 & 0 & 0 & 0 & 0.8091 & 0 & 0 \\
0 & 0 & 0 & 0 & 0 & 0.8091 & 0.8089
\end{bmatrix}
$$

Suppose that the number of turtles in each stage of the initial turtle population is described by the vector

$$\mathbf{x}_0 = (200,000 \quad 130,000 \quad 100,000 \quad 70,000 \quad 500 \quad 400 \quad 1100)^T$$

(a) Enter L in MATLAB and then set

$$x0 = (200000, 130000, 100000, 70000, 500, 400, 1100)'$$

Use the command

$$x50 = \text{round}(L\char94 50*x0)$$

to compute $\mathbf{x}_{50}$. Compute also the values of $\mathbf{x}_{100}, \mathbf{x}_{150}, \mathbf{x}_{200}, \mathbf{x}_{250}$, and $\mathbf{x}_{300}$.

(b) Loggerhead turtles lay their eggs on land. Suppose that conservationists take special measures to protect these eggs and as a result the survival rate for eggs and hatchlings increases to 77 percent. To incorporate this change into our model, we need only change the (2,1) entry of L to 0.77. Make this modification to the matrix L and repeat part (a). Has the survival potential of the loggerhead turtle improved significantly?

(c) Suppose that instead of improving the survival rate for eggs and hatchlings we could devise a means of protecting the small juveniles so that their survival rate increases to 88 percent. Use equations (7) and (8) from Application 4 of Section 3 to determine the proportion of small juveniles that survive and remain in the same stage and the proportion that survive and grow to the next stage. Modify your original matrix L accordingly and repeat part (a) using the new matrix. Has the survival potential of the loggerhead turtle improved significantly?

9. Set $A = \mathbf{magic}(8)$ and then compute its reduced row echelon form. The lead 1's should correspond to the first three variables x_1, x_2, x_3 and the remaining five variables are all free.

(a) Set $\mathbf{c} = [1 : 8]'$ and determine whether the system $A\mathbf{x} = \mathbf{c}$ is consistent by computing the reduced row echelon form of $[A \quad \mathbf{c}]$. Does the system turn out to be consistent? Explain.

(b) Set

$$\mathbf{b} = [8 \quad -8 \quad -8 \quad 8 \quad 8 \quad -8 \quad -8 \quad 8]';$$

and consider the system $A\mathbf{x} = \mathbf{b}$. This system should be consistent. Verify that it is by computing $U = \mathbf{rref}([A \quad \mathbf{b}])$. We should be able to find a solution for any choice of the five free variables. Indeed, set $\mathbf{x2} = \mathbf{round}(10 * \mathbf{rand}(5, 1))$. If $\mathbf{x2}$ represents the last five coordinates of a solution to the system, then we should be able to determine $\mathbf{x1} = (x_1, x_2, x_3)^T$ in terms of $\mathbf{x2}$. To do this, set $U = \mathbf{rref}([A \quad \mathbf{b}])$. The nonzero rows of U correspond to a linear system with block form

(1)
$$\begin{bmatrix} I & V \end{bmatrix} \begin{bmatrix} \mathbf{x1} \\ \mathbf{x2} \end{bmatrix} = \mathbf{c}$$

To solve equation (1), set

$$V = U(1 : 3, \; 4 : 8), \quad \mathbf{c} = U(1 : 3, \; 9)$$

and use MATLAB to compute $\mathbf{x1}$ in terms of $\mathbf{x2}$, $\mathbf{c}$, and V. Set $\mathbf{x} = [\mathbf{x1}; \; \mathbf{x2}]$ and verify that $\mathbf{x}$ is a solution to the system.

10. Set

$$B = [-1, -1; \; 1, 1] \quad \text{and} \quad A = [\mathbf{zeros}(2), \mathbf{eye}(2); \; \mathbf{eye}(2), B]$$

and verify that $B^2 = O$.

(a) Use MATLAB to compute A^2, A^4, A^6, and A^8. Make a conjecture as to what the block form of A^{2k} will be in terms of the submatrices I, O, and B. Use mathematical induction to prove that your conjecture is true for any positive integer k.

(b) Use MATLAB to compute A^3, A^5, A^7, and A^9. Make a conjecture as to what the block form of A^{2k-1} will be in terms of the submatrices I, O, and B. Prove your conjecture.

11. (a) The MATLAB commands

$$A = \textbf{round}(10 * \textbf{rand}(6)), \quad B = A' * A$$

will result in a symmetric matrix with integer entries. Why? Explain. Compute B in this way and verify these claims. Next, partition B into four 3×3 submatrices. To determine the submatrices in MATLAB, set

$$B11 = B(1:3, \ 1:3), \quad B12 = B(1:3, \ 4:6)$$

and define $B21$ and $B22$ in a similar manner using rows 4 through 6 of B.

(b) Set $C = \textbf{inv}(B11)$. It should be the case that $C^T = C$ and $B21^T = B12$. Why? Explain. Use the MATLAB operation $'$ to compute the transposes and verify these claims. Next, set

$$E = B21 * C \quad \text{and} \quad F = B22 - B21 * C * B21'$$

and use the MATLAB functions **eye** and **zeros** to construct

$$L = \begin{bmatrix} I & O \\ E & I \end{bmatrix}, \quad D = \begin{bmatrix} B11 & O \\ O & F \end{bmatrix}$$

Compute $H = L * D * L'$ and compare it to B by computing $H - B$. Prove that if all computations had been done in exact arithmetic LDL^T would equal B exactly.

CHAPTER TEST

This chapter test consists of 10 true–false questions. In each case answer *true* if the statement is always true and *false* otherwise. In the case of a true statement, explain or prove your answer. In the case of a false statement, give an example to show that the statement is not always true. For example, consider the following statements about $n \times n$ matrices A and B.

(i) $A + B = B + A$

(ii) $AB = BA$

Statement **(i)** is always *true*. Explanation: The (i, j) entry of $A + B$ is $a_{ij} + b_{ij}$ and the (i, j) entry of $B + A$ is $b_{ij} + a_{ij}$. Since $a_{ij} + b_{ij} = b_{ij} + a_{ij}$ for each i and j, it follows that $A + B = B + A$.

The answer for statement **(ii)** is *false*. Although the statement may be true in some cases, it is not always true. To show this, we need only exhibit one instance where equality fails to hold. Thus, for example, if

$$A = \begin{bmatrix} 1 & 2 \\ 3 & 1 \end{bmatrix} \quad \text{and} \quad B = \begin{bmatrix} 2 & 3 \\ 1 & 1 \end{bmatrix}$$

then

$$AB = \begin{bmatrix} 4 & 5 \\ 7 & 10 \end{bmatrix} \quad \text{and} \quad BA = \begin{bmatrix} 11 & 7 \\ 4 & 3 \end{bmatrix}$$

This proves that statement **(ii)** is false.

1. If the row echelon form of A involves free variables, then the system $A\mathbf{x} = \mathbf{b}$ will have infinitely many solutions.

2. A homogeneous linear system is always consistent.

3. An $n \times n$ matrix A is nonsingular if and only if the reduced row echelon form of A is I (the identity matrix).

4. If A and B are nonsingular $n \times n$ matrices, then $A + B$ is also nonsingular and $(A + B)^{-1} = A^{-1} + B^{-1}$.

5. If A and B are nonsingular $n \times n$ matrices, then AB is also nonsingular and $(AB)^{-1} = A^{-1}B^{-1}$.

6. If A and B are $n \times n$ matrices, then $(A - B)^2 = A^2 - 2AB + B^2$.

7. If $AB = AC$ and $A \neq O$ (the zero matrix), then $B = C$.

8. The product of two elementary matrices is an elementary matrix.

9. If $\mathbf{x}$ and $\mathbf{y}$ are nonzero vectors in R^n and $A = \mathbf{x}\mathbf{y}^T$, then the row echelon form of A will have exactly one nonzero row.

10. Let A be an 4×3 matrix with $\mathbf{a}_2 = \mathbf{a}_3$. If $\mathbf{b} = \mathbf{a}_1 + \mathbf{a}_2 + \mathbf{a}_3$, then the system $A\mathbf{x} = \mathbf{b}$ will have infinitely many solutions.

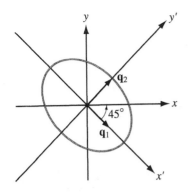

CHAPTER

2

DETERMINANTS

With each square matrix it is possible to associate a real number called the determinant of the matrix. The value of this number will tell us whether the matrix is singular.

In Section 1 the definition of the determinant of a matrix is given. In Section 2 we study properties of determinants and derive an elimination method for evaluating determinants. The elimination method is generally the simplest method to use for evaluating the determinant of an $n \times n$ matrix when $n > 3$. In Section 3 we see how determinants can be applied to solving $n \times n$ linear systems and how they can be used to calculate the inverse of a matrix. An application involving cryptography is also presented in Section 3. Further applications of determinants are presented in Chapters 3 and 6.

 ## THE DETERMINANT OF A MATRIX

With each $n \times n$ matrix A it is possible to associate a scalar, $\det(A)$, whose value will tell us whether the matrix is nonsingular. Before proceeding to the general definition, let us consider the following cases.

CASE 1 1 × 1 Matrices

If $A = (a)$ is a 1×1 matrix, then A will have a multiplicative inverse if and only if $a \neq 0$. Thus, if we define

$$\det(A) = a$$

then A will be nonsingular if and only if $\det(A) \neq 0$.

CASE 2 2×2 Matrices

Let

$$A = \begin{bmatrix} a_{11} & a_{12} \\ a_{21} & a_{22} \end{bmatrix}$$

By Theorem 1.4.3, A will be nonsingular if and only if it is row equivalent to I. Then, if $a_{11} \neq 0$, we can test whether A is row equivalent to I by performing the following operations:

1. Multiply the second row of A by a_{11}

$$\begin{bmatrix} a_{11} & a_{12} \\ a_{11}a_{21} & a_{11}a_{22} \end{bmatrix}$$

2. Subtract a_{21} times the first row from the new second row

$$\begin{bmatrix} a_{11} & a_{12} \\ 0 & a_{11}a_{22} - a_{21}a_{12} \end{bmatrix}$$

Since $a_{11} \neq 0$, the resulting matrix will be row equivalent to I if and only if

(1) $a_{11}a_{22} - a_{21}a_{12} \neq 0$

If $a_{11} = 0$, we can switch the two rows of A. The resulting matrix

$$\begin{bmatrix} a_{21} & a_{22} \\ 0 & a_{12} \end{bmatrix}$$

will be row equivalent to I if and only if $a_{21}a_{12} \neq 0$. This requirement is equivalent to condition (1) when $a_{11} = 0$. Thus, if A is any 2×2 matrix and we define

$$\det(A) = a_{11}a_{22} - a_{12}a_{21}$$

then A is nonsingular if and only if $\det(A) \neq 0$.

Notation   We can refer to the determinant of a specific matrix by enclosing the array between vertical lines. For example, if

$$A = \begin{bmatrix} 3 & 4 \\ 2 & 1 \end{bmatrix}$$

then

$$\begin{vmatrix} 3 & 4 \\ 2 & 1 \end{vmatrix}$$

represents the determinant of A.

CASE 3 3 × 3 Matrices

We can test whether a 3×3 matrix is nonsingular by performing row operations to see if the matrix is row equivalent to the identity matrix I. To carry out the elimination in the first column of an arbitrary 3×3 matrix A, let us first assume that $a_{11} \neq 0$. The elimination can then be performed by subtracting a_{21}/a_{11} times the first row from the second and a_{31}/a_{11} times the first row from the third.

$$\begin{pmatrix} a_{11} & a_{12} & a_{13} \\ a_{21} & a_{22} & a_{23} \\ a_{31} & a_{32} & a_{33} \end{pmatrix} \rightarrow \begin{pmatrix} a_{11} & a_{12} & a_{13} \\ 0 & \dfrac{a_{11}a_{22} - a_{21}a_{12}}{a_{11}} & \dfrac{a_{11}a_{23} - a_{21}a_{13}}{a_{11}} \\ 0 & \dfrac{a_{11}a_{32} - a_{31}a_{12}}{a_{11}} & \dfrac{a_{11}a_{33} - a_{31}a_{13}}{a_{11}} \end{pmatrix}$$

The matrix on the right will be row equivalent to I if and only if

$$a_{11} \begin{vmatrix} \dfrac{a_{11}a_{22} - a_{21}a_{12}}{a_{11}} & \dfrac{a_{11}a_{23} - a_{21}a_{13}}{a_{11}} \\ \dfrac{a_{11}a_{32} - a_{31}a_{12}}{a_{11}} & \dfrac{a_{11}a_{33} - a_{31}a_{13}}{a_{11}} \end{vmatrix} \neq 0$$

Although the algebra is somewhat messy, this condition can be simplified to

(2) $$a_{11}a_{22}a_{33} - a_{11}a_{32}a_{23} - a_{12}a_{21}a_{33} + a_{12}a_{31}a_{23}$$
$$+ a_{13}a_{21}a_{32} - a_{13}a_{31}a_{22} \neq 0$$

Thus, if we define

(3) $$\det(A) = a_{11}a_{22}a_{33} - a_{11}a_{32}a_{23} - a_{12}a_{21}a_{33}$$
$$+ a_{12}a_{31}a_{23} + a_{13}a_{21}a_{32} - a_{13}a_{31}a_{22}$$

then for the case $a_{11} \neq 0$ the matrix will be nonsingular if and only if $\det(A) \neq 0$.

What if $a_{11} = 0$? Consider the following possibilities:

(i) $a_{11} = 0,\ a_{21} \neq 0$
(ii) $a_{11} = a_{21} = 0,\ a_{31} \neq 0$
(iii) $a_{11} = a_{21} = a_{31} = 0$

In case (i), it is not difficult to show that A is row equivalent to I if and only if

$$-a_{12}a_{21}a_{33} + a_{12}a_{31}a_{23} + a_{13}a_{21}a_{32} - a_{13}a_{31}a_{22} \neq 0$$

But this condition is the same as condition (2) with $a_{11} = 0$. The details of case (i) are left as an exercise for the reader (see Exercise 7).

In case (ii) it follows that

$$A = \begin{pmatrix} 0 & a_{12} & a_{13} \\ 0 & a_{22} & a_{23} \\ a_{31} & a_{32} & a_{33} \end{pmatrix}$$

is row equivalent to I if and only if

$$a_{31}(a_{12}a_{23} - a_{22}a_{13}) \neq 0$$

Again this is a special case of condition (2) with $a_{11} = a_{21} = 0$.

Clearly, in case (iii) the matrix A cannot be row equivalent to I and hence must be singular. In this case, if we set a_{11}, a_{21}, and a_{31} equal to 0 in formula (3), the result will be $\det(A) = 0$.

In general, then, formula (2) gives a necessary and sufficient condition for a 3×3 matrix A to be nonsingular (regardless of the value of a_{11}).

We would now like to define the determinant of an $n \times n$ matrix. To see how to do this, note that the determinant of a 2×2 matrix

$$A = \begin{bmatrix} a_{11} & a_{12} \\ a_{21} & a_{22} \end{bmatrix}$$

can be defined in terms of the two 1×1 matrices

$$M_{11} = (a_{22}) \qquad \text{and} \qquad M_{12} = (a_{21})$$

The matrix M_{11} is formed from A by deleting its first row and first column, and M_{12} is formed from A by deleting its first row and second column.

The determinant of A can be expressed in the form

(4) $$\det(A) = a_{11}a_{22} - a_{12}a_{21} = a_{11}\det(M_{11}) - a_{12}\det(M_{12})$$

For a 3×3 matrix A, we can rewrite equation (3) in the form

$$\det(A) = a_{11}(a_{22}a_{33} - a_{32}a_{23}) - a_{12}(a_{21}a_{33} - a_{31}a_{23}) + a_{13}(a_{21}a_{32} - a_{31}a_{22})$$

For $j = 1, 2, 3$, let M_{1j} denote the 2×2 matrix formed from A by deleting its first row and jth column. The determinant of A can then be represented in the form

(5) $$\det(A) = a_{11}\det(M_{11}) - a_{12}\det(M_{12}) + a_{13}\det(M_{13})$$

where

$$M_{11} = \begin{bmatrix} a_{22} & a_{23} \\ a_{32} & a_{33} \end{bmatrix}, \qquad M_{12} = \begin{bmatrix} a_{21} & a_{23} \\ a_{31} & a_{33} \end{bmatrix}, \qquad M_{13} = \begin{bmatrix} a_{21} & a_{22} \\ a_{31} & a_{32} \end{bmatrix}$$

To see how to generalize (4) and (5) to the case $n > 3$, we introduce the following definition.

▶ **DEFINITION** Let $A = (a_{ij})$ be an $n \times n$ matrix and let M_{ij} denote the $(n-1) \times (n-1)$ matrix obtained from A by deleting the row and column containing a_{ij}. The determinant of M_{ij} is called the **minor** of a_{ij}. We define the **cofactor** A_{ij} of a_{ij} by

$$A_{ij} = (-1)^{i+j}\det(M_{ij}) \qquad \qquad \blacktriangleleft$$

In view of this definition, for a 2×2 matrix A, we may rewrite equation (4) in the form

(6)
$$\det(A) = a_{11}A_{11} + a_{12}A_{12} \qquad (n = 2)$$

Equation (6) is called the *cofactor expansion* of $\det(A)$ along the first row of A. Note that we could also write

(7)
$$\det(A) = a_{21}(-a_{12}) + a_{22}a_{11} = a_{21}A_{21} + a_{22}A_{22}$$

Equation (7) expresses $\det(A)$ in terms of the entries of the second row of A and their cofactors. Actually, there is no reason why we must expand along a row of the matrix; the determinant could just as well be represented by the cofactor expansion along one of the columns.

$$\det(A) = a_{11}a_{22} + a_{21}(-a_{12})$$
$$= a_{11}A_{11} + a_{21}A_{21} \qquad \text{(first column)}$$
$$\det(A) = a_{12}(-a_{21}) + a_{22}a_{11}$$
$$= a_{12}A_{12} + a_{22}A_{22} \qquad \text{(second column)}$$

For a 3×3 matrix A, we have

(8)
$$\det(A) = a_{11}A_{11} + a_{12}A_{12} + a_{13}A_{13}$$

Thus the determinant of a 3×3 matrix can be defined in terms of the elements in the first row of the matrix and their corresponding cofactors.

EXAMPLE I. If

$$A = \begin{bmatrix} 2 & 5 & 4 \\ 3 & 1 & 2 \\ 5 & 4 & 6 \end{bmatrix}$$

then

$$\det(A) = a_{11}A_{11} + a_{12}A_{12} + a_{13}A_{13}$$
$$= (-1)^2 a_{11} \det(M_{11}) + (-1)^3 a_{12} \det(M_{12}) + (-1)^4 a_{13} \det(M_{13})$$
$$= 2 \begin{vmatrix} 1 & 2 \\ 4 & 6 \end{vmatrix} - 5 \begin{vmatrix} 3 & 2 \\ 5 & 6 \end{vmatrix} + 4 \begin{vmatrix} 3 & 1 \\ 5 & 4 \end{vmatrix}$$
$$= 2(6 - 8) - 5(18 - 10) + 4(12 - 5)$$
$$= -16 \qquad \blacktriangleleft$$

As in the case of 2×2 matrices, the determinant of a 3×3 matrix can be represented as a cofactor expansion using any row or column. For example, equation (3) can be rewritten in the form

$$\det(A) = a_{12}a_{31}a_{23} - a_{13}a_{31}a_{22} - a_{11}a_{32}a_{23} + a_{13}a_{21}a_{32} + a_{11}a_{22}a_{33} - a_{12}a_{21}a_{33}$$

$$= a_{31}(a_{12}a_{23} - a_{31}a_{22}) - a_{32}(a_{11}a_{23} - a_{13}a_{21}) + a_{33}(a_{11}a_{22} - a_{12}a_{21})$$

$$= a_{31}A_{31} + a_{32}A_{32} + a_{33}A_{33}$$

This is the cofactor expansion along the third row of A.

EXAMPLE 2. Let A be the matrix in Example 1. The cofactor expansion of $\det(A)$ along the second column is given by

$$\det(A) = -5\begin{vmatrix} 3 & 2 \\ 5 & 6 \end{vmatrix} + 1\begin{vmatrix} 2 & 4 \\ 5 & 6 \end{vmatrix} - 4\begin{vmatrix} 2 & 4 \\ 3 & 2 \end{vmatrix}$$

$$= -5(18 - 10) + 1(12 - 20) - 4(4 - 12) = -16 \qquad \triangleleft$$

The determinant of a 4×4 matrix can be defined in terms of a cofactor expansion along any row or column. To compute the value of the 4×4 determinant, we would have to evaluate four 3×3 determinants.

▶ **DEFINITION** The **determinant** of an $n \times n$ matrix A, denoted $\det(A)$, is a scalar associated with the matrix A that is defined inductively as follows:

$$\det(A) = \begin{cases} a_{11} & \text{if } n = 1 \\ a_{11}A_{11} + a_{12}A_{12} + \cdots + a_{1n}A_{1n} & \text{if } n > 1 \end{cases}$$

where

$$A_{1j} = (-1)^{1+j} \det(M_{1j}) \qquad j = 1, \ldots, n$$

are the cofactors associated with the entries in the first row of A. ◀

As we have seen, it is not necessary to limit ourselves to using the first row for the cofactor expansion. We state the following theorem without proof.

▶ **THEOREM 2.1.1** *If A is an $n \times n$ matrix with $n \geq 2$, then $\det(A)$ can be expressed as a cofactor expansion using any row or column of A.*

$$\det(A) = a_{i1}A_{i1} + a_{i2}A_{i2} + \cdots + a_{in}A_{in}$$

$$= a_{1j}A_{1j} + a_{2j}A_{2j} + \cdots + a_{nj}A_{nj}$$

for $i = 1, \ldots, n$ and $j = 1, \ldots, n$. ◀

The cofactor expansion of a 4×4 determinant will involve four 3×3 determinants. We can often save work by expanding along the row or column that contains the most zeros. For example, to evaluate

$$\begin{vmatrix} 0 & 2 & 3 & 0 \\ 0 & 4 & 5 & 0 \\ 0 & 1 & 0 & 3 \\ 2 & 0 & 1 & 3 \end{vmatrix}$$

we would expand down the first column. The first three terms will drop out, leaving

$$-2 \begin{vmatrix} 2 & 3 & 0 \\ 4 & 5 & 0 \\ 1 & 0 & 3 \end{vmatrix} = -2 \cdot 3 \cdot \begin{vmatrix} 2 & 3 \\ 4 & 5 \end{vmatrix} = 12$$

The cofactor expansion can be used to establish some important results about determinants. These results are given in the following theorems.

▶ THEOREM 2.1.2 *If A is an $n \times n$ matrix, then $\det(A^T) = \det(A)$.*

▶ *Proof.* The proof is by induction on n. Clearly, the result holds if $n = 1$, since a 1×1 matrix is necessarily symmetric. Assume that the result holds for all $k \times k$ matrices and that A is a $(k+1) \times (k+1)$ matrix. Expanding $\det(A)$ along the first row of A, we get

$$\det(A) = a_{11} \det(M_{11}) - a_{12} \det(M_{12}) + - \cdots \pm a_{1,k+1} \det(M_{1,k+1})$$

Since the M_{ij}'s are all $k \times k$ matrices, it follows from the induction hypothesis that

(9) $$\det(A) = a_{11} \det(M_{11}^T) - a_{12} \det(M_{12}^T) + - \cdots \pm a_{1,k+1} \det(M_{1,k+1}^T)$$

The right-hand side of (9) is just the expansion by minors of $\det(A^T)$ using the first column of A^T. Therefore,

$$\det(A^T) = \det(A)$$ ◀

▶ THEOREM 2.1.3 *If A is an $n \times n$ triangular matrix, the determinant of A equals the product of the diagonal elements of A.*

▶ *Proof.* In view of Theorem 2.1.2, it suffices to prove the theorem for lower triangular matrices. The result follows easily using the cofactor expansion and induction on n. The details of this are left for the reader (see Exercise 8).   ◀

▶ THEOREM 2.1.4 *Let A be an $n \times n$ matrix.*

(i) *If A has a row or column consisting entirely of zeros, then $\det(A) = 0$.*

(ii) *If A has two identical rows or two identical columns, then $\det(A) = 0$.*   ◀

Both of these results can be easily proved using the cofactor expansion. The proofs are left for the reader (see Exercises 9 and 10).

In the next section we look at the effect of row operations on the value of the determinant. This will allow us to make use of Theorem 2.1.3 to derive a more efficient method for computing the value of a determinant.

EXERCISES

1. Given

$$A = \begin{bmatrix} 3 & 2 & 4 \\ 1 & -2 & 3 \\ 2 & 3 & 2 \end{bmatrix}$$

(a) Find the values of det(M_{21}), det(M_{22}), and det(M_{23}).

(b) Find the values of A_{21}, A_{22}, and A_{23}.

(c) Use your answers from part (b) to compute det(A).

2. Use determinants to determine whether the following 2×2 matrices are nonsingular.

(a) $\begin{bmatrix} 3 & 5 \\ 2 & 4 \end{bmatrix}$
   (b) $\begin{bmatrix} 3 & 6 \\ 2 & 4 \end{bmatrix}$
   (c) $\begin{bmatrix} 3 & -6 \\ 2 & 4 \end{bmatrix}$

3. Evaluate the following determinants.

(a) $\begin{vmatrix} 3 & 5 \\ -2 & -3 \end{vmatrix}$
   (b) $\begin{vmatrix} 5 & -2 \\ -8 & 4 \end{vmatrix}$
   (c) $\begin{vmatrix} 3 & 1 & 2 \\ 2 & 4 & 5 \\ 2 & 4 & 5 \end{vmatrix}$

(d) $\begin{vmatrix} 4 & 3 & 0 \\ 3 & 1 & 2 \\ 5 & -1 & -4 \end{vmatrix}$
   (e) $\begin{vmatrix} 1 & 3 & 2 \\ 4 & 1 & -2 \\ 2 & 1 & 3 \end{vmatrix}$
   (f) $\begin{vmatrix} 2 & -1 & 2 \\ 1 & 3 & 2 \\ 5 & 1 & 6 \end{vmatrix}$

(g) $\begin{vmatrix} 2 & 0 & 0 & 1 \\ 0 & 1 & 0 & 0 \\ 1 & 6 & 2 & 0 \\ 1 & 1 & -2 & 3 \end{vmatrix}$
   (h) $\begin{vmatrix} 2 & 1 & 2 & 1 \\ 3 & 0 & 1 & 1 \\ -1 & 2 & -2 & 1 \\ -3 & 2 & 3 & 1 \end{vmatrix}$

4. Evaluate the following determinants by inspection.

(a) $\begin{vmatrix} 3 & 5 \\ 2 & 4 \end{vmatrix}$
   (b) $\begin{vmatrix} 2 & 0 & 0 \\ 4 & 1 & 0 \\ 7 & 3 & -2 \end{vmatrix}$
   (c) $\begin{vmatrix} 3 & 0 & 0 \\ 2 & 1 & 1 \\ 1 & 2 & 2 \end{vmatrix}$
   (d) $\begin{vmatrix} 4 & 0 & 2 & 1 \\ 5 & 0 & 4 & 2 \\ 2 & 0 & 3 & 4 \\ 1 & 0 & 2 & 3 \end{vmatrix}$

5. Evaluate the following determinant. Write your answer as a polynomial in x.

$$\begin{vmatrix} a - x & b & c \\ 1 & -x & 0 \\ 0 & 1 & -x \end{vmatrix}$$

6. Find all values of λ for which the following determinant will equal 0.

$$\begin{vmatrix} 2 - \lambda & 4 \\ 3 & 3 - \lambda \end{vmatrix}$$

7. Let A be a 3×3 matrix with $a_{11} = 0$ and $a_{21} \neq 0$. Show that A is row equivalent to I if and only if

$$-a_{12}a_{21}a_{33} + a_{12}a_{31}a_{23} + a_{13}a_{21}a_{32} - a_{13}a_{31}a_{22} \neq 0$$

8. Write out the details of the proof of Theorem 2.1.3.

9. Prove that if a row or a column of an $n \times n$ matrix A consists entirely of zeros then $\det(A) = 0$.

10. Use mathematical induction to prove that if A is an $(n + 1) \times (n + 1)$ matrix with two identical rows then $\det(A) = 0$.

11. Let A and B be 2×2 matrices.

(a) Does $\det(A + B) = \det(A) + \det(B)$?
(b) Does $\det(AB) = \det(A)\det(B)$?
(c) Does $\det(AB) = \det(BA)$?

Justify your answers.

12. Let A and B be 2×2 matrices and let

$$C = \begin{bmatrix} a_{11} & a_{12} \\ b_{21} & b_{22} \end{bmatrix}, \quad D = \begin{bmatrix} b_{11} & b_{12} \\ a_{21} & a_{22} \end{bmatrix}, \quad E = \begin{bmatrix} 0 & \alpha \\ \beta & 0 \end{bmatrix}$$

(a) Show that $\det(A + B) = \det(A) + \det(B) + \det(C) + \det(D)$.
(b) Show that if $B = EA$ then $\det(A + B) = \det(A) + \det(B)$.

13. Let A be a symmetric tridiagonal matrix (i.e., A is symmetric and $a_{ij} = 0$ whenever $|i - j| > 1$). Let B be the matrix formed from A by deleting the first two rows and columns. Show that

$$\det(A) = a_{11} \det(M_{11}) - a_{12}^2 \det(B)$$

2 PROPERTIES OF DETERMINANTS

In this section we consider the effects of row operations on the determinant of a matrix. Once these effects have been established, we will prove that a matrix A is singular if and only if its determinant is zero, and we will develop a method for evaluating determinants using row operations. Also, we will establish an important theorem about the determinant of the product of two matrices. We begin with the following lemma.

▷ **LEMMA 2.2.1** *Let A be an $n \times n$ matrix. If A_{jk} denotes the cofactor of a_{jk} for $k = 1, \ldots, n$, then*

(1) $$a_{i1}A_{j1} + a_{i2}A_{j2} + \cdots + a_{in}A_{jn} = \begin{cases} \det(A) & \text{if } i = j \\ 0 & \text{if } i \neq j \end{cases}$$

▶ **Proof.** If $i = j$, (1) is just the cofactor expansion of $\det(A)$ along the ith row of A. To prove (1) in the case $i \neq j$, let A^* be the matrix obtained by replacing the jth row of A by the ith row of A.

$$A^* = \begin{pmatrix} a_{11} & a_{12} & \cdots & a_{1n} \\ \vdots & & & \\ a_{i1} & a_{i2} & \cdots & a_{in} \\ \vdots & & & \\ a_{i1} & a_{i2} & \cdots & a_{in} \\ \vdots & & & \\ a_{n1} & a_{n2} & \cdots & a_{nn} \end{pmatrix} \quad j\text{th row}$$

Since two rows of A^* are the same, its determinant must be zero. It follows from the cofactor expansion of $\det(A^*)$ along the jth row that

$$0 = \det(A^*) = a_{i1}A_{j1}^* + a_{i2}A_{j2}^* + \cdots + a_{in}A_{jn}^*$$
$$= a_{i1}A_{j1} + a_{i2}A_{j2} + \cdots + a_{in}A_{jn} \qquad \blacktriangleleft$$

Let us now consider the effects of each of the three row operations on the value of the determinant.

Row Operation I

Two rows of A are interchanged.
If A is a 2×2 matrix and

$$E = \begin{bmatrix} 0 & 1 \\ 1 & 0 \end{bmatrix}$$

then

$$\det(EA) = \begin{vmatrix} a_{21} & a_{22} \\ a_{11} & a_{12} \end{vmatrix} = a_{21}a_{12} - a_{22}a_{11} = -\det(A)$$

For $n > 2$, let E_{ij} be the elementary matrix that switches rows i and j of A. It is a simple induction proof to show that $\det(E_{ij}A) = -\det(A)$. We illustrate the idea behind the proof for the case $n = 3$. Suppose that the first and third rows of a 3×3 matrix A have been interchanged. Expanding $\det(E_{13}A)$ along the second row and making use of the result for 2×2 matrices, we see that

$$\det(E_{13}A) = \begin{vmatrix} a_{31} & a_{32} & a_{33} \\ a_{21} & a_{22} & a_{23} \\ a_{11} & a_{12} & a_{13} \end{vmatrix}$$

$$= -a_{21}\begin{vmatrix} a_{32} & a_{33} \\ a_{12} & a_{13} \end{vmatrix} + a_{22}\begin{vmatrix} a_{31} & a_{33} \\ a_{11} & a_{13} \end{vmatrix} - a_{23}\begin{vmatrix} a_{31} & a_{31} \\ a_{11} & a_{12} \end{vmatrix}$$

$$= a_{21}\begin{vmatrix} a_{12} & a_{13} \\ a_{32} & a_{33} \end{vmatrix} - a_{22}\begin{vmatrix} a_{11} & a_{13} \\ a_{31} & a_{33} \end{vmatrix} + a_{23}\begin{vmatrix} a_{11} & a_{12} \\ a_{31} & a_{32} \end{vmatrix}$$

$$= -\det(A)$$

In general, if A is an $n \times n$ matrix and E_{ij} is the $n \times n$ elementary matrix formed by interchanging the ith and jth rows of I, then

$$\det(E_{ij}A) = -\det(A)$$

In particular,

$$\det(E_{ij}) = \det(E_{ij}I) = -\det(I) = -1$$

Thus, for any elementary matrix E of type I,

$$\det(EA) = -\det(A) = \det(E)\det(A)$$

Row Operation II

A row of A is multiplied by a nonzero constant.

Let E denote the elementary matrix of type II formed from I by multiplying the ith row by the nonzero constant α. If $\det(EA)$ is expanded by cofactors along the ith row, then

$$\det(EA) = \alpha a_{i1}A_{i1} + \alpha a_{i2}A_{i2} + \cdots + \alpha a_{in}A_{in}$$
$$= \alpha(a_{i1}A_{i1} + a_{i2}A_{i2} + \cdots + a_{in}A_{in})$$
$$= \alpha \det(A)$$

In particular,

$$\det(E) = \det(EI) = \alpha \det(I) = \alpha$$

and hence

$$\det(EA) = \alpha \det(A) = \det(E)\det(A)$$

Row Operation III

A multiple of one row is added to another row.

Let E be the elementary matrix of type III formed from I by adding c times the ith row to the jth row. Since E is triangular and its diagonal elements are all 1, it follows that $\det(E) = 1$. We will show that

$$\det(EA) = \det(A) = \det(E)\det(A)$$

If $\det(EA)$ is expanded by cofactors along the jth row, it follows from Lemma 2.2.1 that

$$\det(EA) = (a_{j1}+ca_{i1})A_{j1} + (a_{j2}+ca_{i2})A_{j2} + \cdots + (a_{jn}+ca_{in})A_{jn}$$
$$= (a_{j1}A_{j1} + \cdots + a_{jn}A_{jn}) + c(a_{i1}A_{j1} + \cdots + a_{in}A_{jn})$$
$$= \det(A)$$

Thus,

$$\det(EA) = \det(A) = \det(E)\det(A)$$

Summary

In summation, if E is an elementary matrix, then

$$\det(EA) = \det(E)\det(A)$$

where

$$(2) \qquad \det(E) = \begin{cases} -1 & \text{if } E \text{ is of type I} \\ \alpha \neq 0 & \text{if } E \text{ is of type II} \\ 1 & \text{if } E \text{ is of type III} \end{cases}$$

Similar results hold for column operations. Indeed, if E is an elementary matrix, then

$$\det(AE) = \det\big((AE)^T\big) = \det\big(E^T A^T\big)$$
$$= \det\big(E^T\big)\det\big(A^T\big) = \det(E)\det(A)$$

Thus, the effects that row or column operations have on the value of the determinant can be summarized as follows:

    I. Interchanging two rows (or columns) of a matrix changes the sign of the determinant.

    II. Multiplying a single row or column of a matrix by a scalar has the effect of multiplying the value of the determinant by that scalar.

    III. Adding a multiple of one row (or column) to another does not change the value of the determinant.

NOTE As a consequence of III, if one row (or column) of a matrix is a multiple of another, the determinant of the matrix must equal zero.

Main Results

We can now make use of the effects of row operations on determinants to prove two major theorems and to establish a simpler method of computing determinants. It follows from (2) that all elementary matrices have nonzero determinants. This observation can be used to prove the following theorem.

▶ **THEOREM 2.2.2** *An $n \times n$ matrix A is singular if and only if*

$$\det(A) = 0$$

▶*Proof.* The matrix A can be reduced to row echelon form with a finite number of row operations. Thus

$$U = E_k E_{k-1} \cdots E_1 A$$

where U is in row echelon form and the E_i's are all elementary matrices.

$$\det(U) = \det(E_k E_{k-1} \cdots E_1 A)$$
$$= \det(E_k)\det(E_{k-1}) \cdots \det(E_1)\det(A)$$

Since the determinants of the E_i's are all nonzero, it follows that $\det(A) = 0$ if and only if $\det(U) = 0$. If A is singular, then U has a row consisting entirely of zeros and hence $\det(U) = 0$. If A is nonsingular, U is triangular with 1's along the diagonal and hence $\det(U) = 1$.   ◀

From the proof of Theorem 2.2.2 we can obtain a method for computing $\det(A)$. Reduce A to row echelon form.

$$U = E_k E_{k-1} \cdots E_1 A$$

If the last row of U consists entirely of zeros, A is singular and $\det(A) = 0$. Otherwise, A is nonsingular and

$$\det(A) = \left[\det(E_k)\det(E_{k-1}) \cdots \det(E_1)\right]^{-1}$$

Actually, if A is nonsingular, it is simpler to reduce A to triangular form. This can be done using only row operations I and III. Thus

$$T = E_m E_{m-1} \cdots E_1 A$$

and hence

$$\det(A) = \pm \det(T) = \pm t_{11} t_{22} \cdots t_{nn}$$

where the t_{ii}'s are the diagonal entries of T. The sign will be positive if row operation I has been used an even number of times and negative otherwise.

EXAMPLE I.   Evaluate

$$\begin{vmatrix} 2 & 1 & 3 \\ 4 & 2 & 1 \\ 6 & -3 & 4 \end{vmatrix}$$

SOLUTION.

$$\begin{vmatrix} 2 & 1 & 3 \\ 4 & 2 & 1 \\ 6 & -3 & 4 \end{vmatrix} = \begin{vmatrix} 2 & 1 & 3 \\ 0 & 0 & -5 \\ 0 & -6 & -5 \end{vmatrix} = (-1)\begin{vmatrix} 2 & 1 & 3 \\ 0 & -6 & -5 \\ 0 & 0 & -5 \end{vmatrix}$$

$$= (-1)(2)(-6)(-5)$$

$$= -60 \qquad ◀$$

We now have two methods for evaluating the determinant of an $n \times n$ matrix A. If $n > 3$ and A has nonzero entries, elimination is the most efficient method in the sense that it involves fewer arithmetic operations. In Table 1 the number of arithmetic operations involved in each method is given for $n = 2, 3, 4, 5, 10$. It is not difficult to derive general formulas for the number of operations in each of the methods (see Exercises 17 and 18).

We have seen that, for any elementary matrix E,

$$\det(EA) = \det(E)\det(A) = \det(AE)$$

This is a special case of the following theorem.

TABLE 1

	Cofactors		Elimination	
n	Additions	Multiplications	Additions	Multiplications and Divisions
2	1	2	1	3
3	5	9	5	10
4	23	40	14	23
5	119	205	30	45
10	3,628,799	6,235,300	285	339

▶ THEOREM 2.2.3 *If A and B are $n \times n$ matrices, then*

$$\det(AB) = \det(A)\det(B)$$

▶*Proof.* If B is singular, it follows from Theorem 1.4.3 that AB is also singular (see Exercise 14 of Chapter 1, Section 4), and therefore

$$\det(AB) = 0 = \det(A)\det(B)$$

If B is nonsingular, B can be written as a product of elementary matrices. We have already seen that the result holds for elementary matrices. Thus

$$\det(AB) = \det(A E_k E_{k-1} \cdots E_1)$$
$$= \det(A)\det(E_k)\det(E_{k-1}) \cdots \det(E_1)$$
$$= \det(A)\det(E_k E_{k-1} \cdots E_1)$$
$$= \det(A)\det(B) \qquad \blacktriangleleft$$

If A is singular, the computed value of $\det(A)$ using exact arithmetic must be 0. However, this result is unlikely if the computations are done by computer. Since computers use a finite number system, roundoff errors are usually unavoidable. Consequently, it is more likely that the computed value of $\det(A)$ will only be near 0. Because of roundoff errors, it is virtually impossible to determine computationally whether a matrix is exactly singular. In computer applications it is often more meaningful to ask whether a matrix is "close" to being singular. In general, the value of $\det(A)$ is not a good indicator of nearness to singularity. In Section 5 of Chapter 6 we will discuss how to determine whether a matrix is close to being singular.

EXERCISES

1. Evaluate each of the following determinants by inspection.

(a) $\begin{vmatrix} 0 & 0 & 3 \\ 0 & 4 & 1 \\ 2 & 3 & 1 \end{vmatrix}$ (b) $\begin{vmatrix} 1 & 1 & 1 & 3 \\ 0 & 3 & 1 & 1 \\ 0 & 0 & 2 & 2 \\ -1 & -1 & -1 & 2 \end{vmatrix}$ (c) $\begin{vmatrix} 0 & 0 & 0 & 1 \\ 1 & 0 & 0 & 0 \\ 0 & 1 & 0 & 0 \\ 0 & 0 & 1 & 0 \end{vmatrix}$

2. Let

$$A = \begin{bmatrix} 0 & 1 & 2 & 3 \\ 1 & 1 & 1 & 1 \\ -2 & -2 & 3 & 3 \\ 1 & 2 & -2 & -3 \end{bmatrix}$$

(a) Use the elimination method to evaluate $\det(A)$.

(b) Use the value of $\det(A)$ to evaluate

$$\begin{vmatrix} 0 & 1 & 2 & 3 \\ -2 & -2 & 3 & 3 \\ 1 & 2 & -2 & -3 \\ 1 & 1 & 1 & 1 \end{vmatrix} + \begin{vmatrix} 0 & 1 & 2 & 3 \\ 1 & 1 & 1 & 1 \\ -1 & -1 & 4 & 4 \\ 2 & 3 & -1 & -2 \end{vmatrix}$$

3. For each of the following, compute the determinant and state whether the matrix is singular or nonsingular.

(a) $\begin{bmatrix} 3 & 1 \\ 6 & 2 \end{bmatrix}$

(b) $\begin{bmatrix} 3 & 1 \\ 4 & 2 \end{bmatrix}$

(c) $\begin{bmatrix} 3 & 3 & 1 \\ 0 & 1 & 2 \\ 0 & 2 & 3 \end{bmatrix}$

(d) $\begin{bmatrix} 2 & 1 & 1 \\ 4 & 3 & 5 \\ 2 & 1 & 2 \end{bmatrix}$

(e) $\begin{bmatrix} 2 & -1 & 3 \\ -1 & 2 & -2 \\ 1 & 4 & 0 \end{bmatrix}$

(f) $\begin{bmatrix} 1 & 1 & 1 & 1 \\ 2 & -1 & 3 & 2 \\ 0 & 1 & 2 & 1 \\ 0 & 0 & 7 & 3 \end{bmatrix}$

4. Find all possible choices of c that would make the following matrix singular.

$$\begin{bmatrix} 1 & 1 & 1 \\ 1 & 9 & c \\ 1 & c & 3 \end{bmatrix}$$

5. Let A be an $n \times n$ matrix and α a scalar. Show that

$$\det(\alpha A) = \alpha^n \det(A)$$

6. Let A be a nonsingular matrix. Show that

$$\det(A^{-1}) = \frac{1}{\det(A)}$$

7. Let A and B be 3×3 matrices with $\det(A) = 4$ and $\det(B) = 5$. Find the value of:

(a) $\det(AB)$

(b) $\det(3A)$

(c) $\det(2AB)$

(d) $\det(A^{-1}B)$

8. Let E_1, E_2, E_3 be 3×3 elementary matrices of types I, II, and III, respectively, and let A be a 3×3 matrix with $\det(A) = 6$. Assume, additionally, that E_2 was formed from I by multiplying its second row by 3. Find the values of each of the following.

   (a) $\det(E_1 A)$ (b) $\det(E_2 A)$ (c) $\det(E_3 A)$
   (d) $\det(A E_1)$ (e) $\det(E_1^2)$ (f) $\det(E_1 E_2 E_3)$

9. Let A and B be row equivalent matrices and suppose that B can be obtained from A using only row operations I and III. How do the values of $\det(A)$ and $\det(B)$ compare? How will the values compare if B can be obtained from A using only row operation III? Explain your answers.

10. Consider the 3×3 Vandermonde matrix

$$V = \begin{bmatrix} 1 & x_1 & x_1^2 \\ 1 & x_2 & x_2^2 \\ 1 & x_3 & x_3^2 \end{bmatrix}$$

   (a) Show that $\det(V) = (x_2 - x_1)(x_3 - x_1)(x_3 - x_2)$. [*Hint:* Make use of row operation III.]
   (b) What conditions must the scalars x_1, x_2, x_3 satisfy in order for V to be nonsingular?

11. Suppose that a 3×3 matrix A factors into a product

$$\begin{bmatrix} 1 & 0 & 0 \\ l_{21} & 1 & 0 \\ l_{31} & l_{32} & 1 \end{bmatrix} \begin{bmatrix} u_{11} & u_{12} & u_{13} \\ 0 & u_{22} & u_{23} \\ 0 & 0 & u_{33} \end{bmatrix}$$

Determine the value of $\det(A)$.

12. Let A and B be $n \times n$ matrices. Prove that the product AB is nonsingular if and only if A and B are both nonsingular.

13. Let A and B be $n \times n$ matrices. Prove that if $AB = I$ then $BA = I$. What is the significance of this result in terms of the definition of a nonsingular matrix?

14. A matrix A is said to be *skew symmetric* if $A^T = -A$. For example,

$$A = \begin{bmatrix} 0 & 1 \\ -1 & 0 \end{bmatrix}$$

   is skew symmetric since

$$A^T = \begin{bmatrix} 0 & -1 \\ 1 & 0 \end{bmatrix} = -A$$

Show that, if A is an $n \times n$ skew symmetric matrix and n is odd, then A must be singular.

15. Let A be a nonsingular $n \times n$ matrix with a nonzero cofactor A_{nn} and set

$$c = \frac{\det(A)}{A_{nn}}$$

Show that if we subtract c from A_{nn} then the resulting matrix will be singular.

16. Let $\mathbf{x}$ and $\mathbf{y}$ be elements of R^3, and let $\mathbf{z}$ be the vector in R^3 whose coordinates are defined by

$$z_1 = \begin{vmatrix} x_2 & x_3 \\ y_2 & y_3 \end{vmatrix}, \qquad z_2 = -\begin{vmatrix} x_1 & x_3 \\ y_1 & y_3 \end{vmatrix}, \qquad z_3 = \begin{vmatrix} x_1 & x_2 \\ y_1 & y_2 \end{vmatrix}$$

Let

$$X = (\mathbf{x}, \mathbf{x}, \mathbf{y})^T \qquad \text{and} \qquad Y = (\mathbf{x}, \mathbf{y}, \mathbf{y})^T$$

Show that

$$\mathbf{x}^T \mathbf{z} = \det(X) = 0 \qquad \text{and} \qquad \mathbf{y}^T \mathbf{z} = \det(Y) = 0$$

17. Show that evaluating the determinant of an $n \times n$ matrix by cofactors involves $(n! - 1)$ additions and $\sum_{k=1}^{n-1} n!/k!$ multiplications.

18. Show that the elimination method of computing the value of the determinant of an $n \times n$ matrix involves $[n(n-1)(2n-1)]/6$ additions and $[(n-1)(n^2+n+3)]/3$ multiplications and divisions. [*Hint:* At the ith step of the reduction process it takes $n - i$ divisions to calculate the multiples of the ith row that are to be subtracted from the remaining rows below the pivot. We must then calculate new values for the $(n-i)^2$ entries in rows $i+1$ through n and columns $i+1$ through n.]

3 ▪ CRAMER'S RULE

In this section we learn a method for computing the inverse of a nonsingular matrix A using determinants. We also learn a method for solving $A\mathbf{x} = \mathbf{b}$ using determinants. Both methods depend on Lemma 2.2.1.

The Adjoint of a Matrix

Let A be an $n \times n$ matrix. We define a new matrix called the *adjoint* of A by

$$\text{adj } A = \begin{pmatrix} A_{11} & A_{21} & \cdots & A_{n1} \\ A_{12} & A_{22} & \cdots & A_{n2} \\ \vdots & & & \\ A_{1n} & A_{2n} & \cdots & A_{nn} \end{pmatrix}$$

Thus, to form the adjoint, we must replace each term by its cofactor and then transpose the resulting matrix. By Lemma 2.2.1

$$a_{i1}A_{j1} + a_{i2}A_{j2} + \cdots + a_{in}A_{jn} = \begin{cases} \det(A) & \text{if } i = j \\ 0 & \text{if } i \neq j \end{cases}$$

and hence it follows that

$$A(\operatorname{adj} A) = \det(A)I$$

If A is nonsingular, $\det(A)$ is a nonzero scalar, and we may write

$$A\left(\frac{1}{\det(A)} \operatorname{adj} A\right) = I$$

Thus

$$A^{-1} = \frac{1}{\det(A)} \operatorname{adj} A$$

EXAMPLE 1.   For a 2×2 matrix

$$\operatorname{adj} A = \begin{bmatrix} a_{22} & -a_{12} \\ -a_{21} & a_{11} \end{bmatrix}$$

If A is nonsingular, then

$$A^{-1} = \frac{1}{a_{11}a_{22} - a_{12}a_{21}} \begin{bmatrix} a_{22} & -a_{12} \\ -a_{21} & a_{11} \end{bmatrix}$$

EXAMPLE 2.   Let

$$A = \begin{bmatrix} 2 & 1 & 2 \\ 3 & 2 & 2 \\ 1 & 2 & 3 \end{bmatrix}$$

Compute $\operatorname{adj} A$ and A^{-1}.

SOLUTION.

$$\operatorname{adj} A = \begin{bmatrix} \begin{vmatrix} 2 & 2 \\ 2 & 3 \end{vmatrix} & -\begin{vmatrix} 3 & 2 \\ 1 & 3 \end{vmatrix} & \begin{vmatrix} 3 & 2 \\ 1 & 2 \end{vmatrix} \\[2mm] -\begin{vmatrix} 1 & 2 \\ 2 & 3 \end{vmatrix} & \begin{vmatrix} 2 & 2 \\ 1 & 3 \end{vmatrix} & -\begin{vmatrix} 2 & 1 \\ 1 & 2 \end{vmatrix} \\[2mm] \begin{vmatrix} 1 & 2 \\ 2 & 2 \end{vmatrix} & -\begin{vmatrix} 2 & 2 \\ 3 & 2 \end{vmatrix} & \begin{vmatrix} 2 & 1 \\ 3 & 2 \end{vmatrix} \end{bmatrix}^{T} = \begin{bmatrix} 2 & 1 & -2 \\ -7 & 4 & 2 \\ 4 & -3 & 1 \end{bmatrix}$$

$$A^{-1} = \frac{1}{\det(A)} \, \text{adj} \, A = \frac{1}{5} \begin{bmatrix} 2 & 1 & -2 \\ -7 & 4 & 2 \\ 4 & -3 & 1 \end{bmatrix}$$

◀

Using the formula

$$A^{-1} = \frac{1}{\det(A)} \, \text{adj} \, A$$

we can derive a rule for representing the solution to the system $A\mathbf{x} = \mathbf{b}$ in terms of determinants.

▶ **THEOREM 2.3.1 (Cramer's Rule)** *Let A be an n × n nonsingular matrix, and let* $\mathbf{b} \in R^n$. *Let* A_i *be the matrix obtained by replacing the ith column of A by* $\mathbf{b}$. *If* $\mathbf{x}$ *is the unique solution to* $A\mathbf{x} = \mathbf{b}$, *then*

$$x_i = \frac{\det(A_i)}{\det(A)} \quad \text{for} \quad i = 1, 2, \ldots, n$$

▶*Proof.* Since

$$\mathbf{x} = A^{-1}\mathbf{b} = \frac{1}{\det(A)}(\text{adj} \, A)\mathbf{b}$$

it follows that

$$x_i = \frac{b_1 A_{1i} + b_2 A_{2i} + \cdots + b_n A_{ni}}{\det(A)}$$

$$= \frac{\det(A_i)}{\det(A)}$$

◀

EXAMPLE 3.   Use Cramer's rule to solve

$$x_1 + 2x_2 + x_3 = 5$$
$$2x_1 + 2x_2 + x_3 = 6$$
$$x_1 + 2x_2 + 3x_3 = 9$$

SOLUTION.

$$\det(A) = \begin{vmatrix} 1 & 2 & 1 \\ 2 & 2 & 1 \\ 1 & 2 & 3 \end{vmatrix} = -4 \qquad \det(A_1) = \begin{vmatrix} 5 & 2 & 1 \\ 6 & 2 & 1 \\ 9 & 2 & 3 \end{vmatrix} = -4$$

$$\det(A_2) = \begin{vmatrix} 1 & 5 & 1 \\ 2 & 6 & 1 \\ 1 & 9 & 3 \end{vmatrix} = -4 \qquad \det(A_3) = \begin{vmatrix} 1 & 2 & 5 \\ 2 & 2 & 6 \\ 1 & 2 & 9 \end{vmatrix} = -8$$

Therefore,

$$x_1 = \frac{-4}{-4} = 1, \qquad x_2 = \frac{-4}{-4} = 1, \qquad x_3 = \frac{-8}{-4} = 2$$

◀

Cramer's rule gives us a convenient method for writing the solution to an $n \times n$ system of linear equations in terms of determinants. To compute the solution, however, we must evaluate $n + 1$ determinants of order n. Evaluating even two of these determinants generally involves more computation than solving the system using Gaussian elimination.

APPLICATION I: CODED MESSAGES

A common way of sending a coded message is to assign an integer value to each letter of the alphabet and to send the message as a string of integers. For example, the message

SEND MONEY

might be coded as

$$5, 8, 10, 21, 7, 2, 10, 8, 3$$

Here the S is represented by a 5, the E by an 8, and so on. Unfortunately, this type of code is generally quite easy to break. In a longer message we might be able to guess which letter is represented by a number based on the relative frequency of occurrence for that number. Thus, for example, if 8 is the most frequently occurring number in the coded message, then it is likely that it represents the letter E, the letter that occurs most frequently in the English language.

We can disguise the message further using matrix multiplications. If A is a matrix whose entries are all integers and whose determinant is ± 1, then, since $A^{-1} = \pm \operatorname{adj} A$, the entries of A^{-1} will be integers. We can use such a matrix to transform the message. The transformed message will be more difficult to decipher. To illustrate the technique, let

$$A = \begin{pmatrix} 1 & 2 & 1 \\ 2 & 5 & 3 \\ 2 & 3 & 2 \end{pmatrix}$$

The coded message is put into the columns of a matrix B having three rows.

$$B = \begin{pmatrix} 5 & 21 & 10 \\ 8 & 7 & 8 \\ 10 & 2 & 3 \end{pmatrix}$$

The product

$$AB = \begin{pmatrix} 1 & 2 & 1 \\ 2 & 5 & 3 \\ 2 & 3 & 2 \end{pmatrix} \begin{pmatrix} 5 & 21 & 10 \\ 8 & 7 & 8 \\ 10 & 2 & 3 \end{pmatrix} = \begin{pmatrix} 31 & 37 & 29 \\ 80 & 83 & 69 \\ 54 & 67 & 50 \end{pmatrix}$$

gives the coded message to be sent:

$$31, 80, 54, 37, 83, 67, 29, 69, 50$$

The person receiving the message can decode it by multiplying by A^{-1}

$$\begin{Bmatrix} 1 & -1 & 1 \\ 2 & 0 & -1 \\ -4 & 1 & 1 \end{Bmatrix} \begin{bmatrix} 31 & 37 & 29 \\ 80 & 83 & 69 \\ 54 & 67 & 50 \end{bmatrix} = \begin{Bmatrix} 5 & 21 & 10 \\ 8 & 7 & 8 \\ 10 & 2 & 3 \end{Bmatrix}$$

   To construct a coding matrix A, we can begin with the identity I and successively apply row operation III, being careful to add integer multiples of one row to another. Row operation I can also be used. The resulting matrix A will have integer entries, and since

$$\det(A) = \pm \det(I) = \pm 1$$

A^{-1} will also have integer entries.

REFERENCES

1. Hansen, Robert, *Two-Year College Mathematics Journal*, 13(1), 1982.

EXERCISES

1. For each of the following, compute (i) $\det(A)$, (ii) adj A, and (iii) A^{-1}.

(a) $A = \begin{bmatrix} 1 & 2 \\ 3 & -1 \end{bmatrix}$
     (b) $A = \begin{bmatrix} 3 & 1 \\ 2 & 4 \end{bmatrix}$

(c) $A = \begin{bmatrix} 1 & 3 & 1 \\ 2 & 1 & 1 \\ -2 & 2 & -1 \end{bmatrix}$
     (d) $A = \begin{bmatrix} 1 & 1 & 1 \\ 0 & 1 & 1 \\ 0 & 0 & 1 \end{bmatrix}$

2. Use Cramer's rule to solve each of the following systems.

(a) $\begin{aligned} x_1 + 2x_2 &= 3 \\ 3x_1 - x_2 &= 1 \end{aligned}$
  (b) $\begin{aligned} 2x_1 + 3x_2 &= 2 \\ 3x_1 + 2x_2 &= 5 \end{aligned}$
  (c) $\begin{aligned} 2x_1 + x_2 - 3x_3 &= 0 \\ 4x_1 + 5x_2 + x_3 &= 8 \\ -2x_1 - x_2 + 4x_3 &= 2 \end{aligned}$

(d) $\begin{aligned} x_1 + 3x_2 + x_3 &= 1 \\ 2x_1 + x_2 + x_3 &= 5 \\ -2x_1 + 2x_2 - x_3 &= -8 \end{aligned}$
  (e) $\begin{aligned} x_1 + x_2 &= 0 \\ x_2 + x_3 - 2x_4 &= 1 \\ x_1 + 2x_3 + x_4 &= 0 \\ x_1 + x_2 + x_4 &= 0 \end{aligned}$

3. Given

$$A = \begin{bmatrix} 1 & 2 & 1 \\ 0 & 4 & 3 \\ 1 & 2 & 2 \end{bmatrix}$$

Determine the $(2, 3)$ entry of A^{-1} by computing a quotient of two determinants.

4. Let A be the matrix in Exercise 3. Compute the third column of A^{-1} by using Cramer's rule to solve $Ax = e_3$.

5. Given

$$A = \begin{bmatrix} 1 & 2 & 3 \\ 2 & 3 & 4 \\ 3 & 4 & 5 \end{bmatrix}$$

(a) Compute the determinant of A. Is A nonsingular?
(b) Compute adj A and the product A adj A.

6. If A is singular, what can you say about the product A adj A?

7. Let B_j denote the matrix obtained by replacing the jth column of the identity matrix with a vector $\mathbf{b} = (b_1, \dots, b_n)^T$. Use Cramer's rule to show that

$$b_j = \det(B_j) \qquad \text{for} \quad j = 1, \dots, n$$

8. Let A be a nonsingular $n \times n$ matrix with $n > 1$. Show that

$$\det(\text{adj } A) = (\det(A))^{n-1}$$

9. Let A be a 4×4 matrix. If

$$\text{adj } A = \begin{bmatrix} 2 & 0 & 0 & 0 \\ 0 & 2 & 1 & 0 \\ 0 & 4 & 3 & 2 \\ 0 & -2 & -1 & 2 \end{bmatrix}$$

(a) Calculate the value of $\det(\text{adj } A)$. What should the value of $\det(A)$ be? [*Hint:* Use the result from Exercise 8.]
(b) Find A.

10. Show that if A is nonsingular then adj A is nonsingular and

$$(\text{adj } A)^{-1} = \det(A^{-1})A = \text{adj } A^{-1}$$

11. Show that if A is singular then adj A is also singular.

12. Show that if $\det(A) = 1$ then

$$\text{adj}(\text{adj } A) = A$$

13. Suppose that Q is a matrix with the property $Q^{-1} = Q^T$. Show that

$$q_{ij} = \frac{Q_{ij}}{\det(Q)}$$

14. In coding a message, a blank space was represented by 0, an A by 1, a B by 2, a C by 3, and so on. The message was transformed using the matrix

$$A = \begin{bmatrix} -1 & -1 & 2 & 0 \\ 1 & 1 & -1 & 0 \\ 0 & 0 & -1 & 1 \\ 1 & 0 & 0 & -1 \end{bmatrix}$$

and sent as

$$-19, 19, 25, -21, 0, 18, -18, 15, 3, 10, -8, 3, -2, 20, -7, 12$$

What was the message?

MATLAB EXERCISES

The first four exercises involve integer matrices and illustrate some of the properties of determinants that were covered in this chapter. The last two exercises illustrate some of the differences that may arise when we work with determinants in floating-point arithmetic.

In theory, the value of the determinant should tell us whether the matrix is nonsingular. However, if the matrix is singular and its determinant is computed using finite precision arithmetic, then, because of roundoff errors, the computed value of the determinant may not equal zero. A computed value near zero does not necessarily mean that the matrix is singular or even close to being singular. Furthermore, a matrix may be singular or nearly singular and have a determinant that is not even close to zero (see Exercise 6).

1. Generate random 5×5 matrices with integer entries by setting

$$A = \mathbf{round}(10 * \mathbf{rand}(5)) \qquad \text{and} \qquad B = \mathbf{round}(20 * \mathbf{rand}(5)) - 10$$

Use MATLAB to compute each of the following pairs of numbers. In each case check whether the first is equal to the second.

(a) $\det(A)$ $\quad \det(A^T)$
(b) $\det(A + B)$ $\quad \det(A) + \det(B)$
(c) $\det(AB)$ $\quad \det(A)\det(B)$
(d) $\det(A^T B^T)$ $\quad \det(A^T)\det(B^T)$
(e) $\det(A^{-1})$ $\quad 1/\det(A)$
(f) $\det(AB^{-1})$ $\quad \det(A)/\det(B)$

2. Are $n \times n$ magic squares nonsingular? Use MATLAB to compute $\mathbf{det(magic}(n))$ in the cases $n = 3, 4, \ldots, 10$. What seems to be happening? Check the cases $n = 24$ and 25 to see if the pattern still holds.

3. Set $A = \mathbf{round}(10 * \mathbf{rand}(6))$. In each of the following, use MATLAB to compute a second matrix as indicated. State how the second matrix is related to A and compute the determinants of both matrices. How are the determinants related?

(a) $B = A$; $B(2, :) = A(1, :)$; $B(1, :) = A(2, :)$
(b) $C = A$; $C(3, :) = 4 * A(3, :)$
(c) $D = A$; $D(5, :) = A(5, :) + 2 * A(4, :)$

4. We can generate a random 6×6 matrix A whose entries consist entirely of zeros and ones by setting

$$A = \text{round}(\text{rand}(6))$$

(a) What percentage of these random 0–1 matrices are singular? You can estimate the percentage using MATLAB by setting

$$y = \text{zeros}(1, 100);$$

and then generating 100 test matrices and setting $y(j) = 1$ if the jth matrix is singular and 0 otherwise. The easy way to do this in MATLAB is to use a *for loop*. Generate the loop as follows:

$$\textbf{for} \quad j = 1 : 100$$

$$A = \text{round}(\text{rand}(6));$$

$$y(j) = (\text{det}(A) == 0);$$

end

(*Note*: A semicolon at the end of a line suppresses printout. It is recommended that you include one at the end of each line of calculation that occurs inside a for loop.) To determine how many singular matrices were generated, use the MATLAB command **sum**(y). What percentage of the matrices generated were singular?

(b) For any positive integer n, we can generate a random 6×6 matrix A whose entries are integers from 0 to n by setting

$$A = \text{round}(n * \text{rand}(6))$$

What percentage of random integer matrices generated in this manner will be singular if $n = 3$? If $n = 6$? If $n = 10$? We can estimate the answers to these questions using MATLAB. In each case, generate 100 test matrices and determine how many of the matrices are singular.

5. If a matrix is sensitive to roundoff errors, the computed value of its determinant may differ drastically from the exact value. For an example of this, set

$$U = \text{round}(100 * \text{rand}(10)); \quad U = \text{triu}(U, 1) + 0.1 * \text{eye}(10)$$

In theory,

$$\det(U) = \det(U^T) = 10^{-10}$$

and

$$\det(UU^T) = \det(U)\det(U^T) = 10^{-20}$$

Compute $\det(U)$, $\det(U')$, and $\det(U * U')$ using MATLAB. Do the computed values match the theoretical values?

6. Use MATLAB to construct a matrix A by setting

$$A = \mathbf{vander}(1:6); \quad A = A - \mathbf{diag}(\mathbf{sum}(A'))$$

(a) By construction, the entries in each row of A should all add up to zero. To check this, set $\mathbf{x} = \mathbf{ones}(6, 1)$ and use MATLAB to compute the product $A\mathbf{x}$. The matrix A should be singular. Why? Explain. Use the MATLAB functions $\mathbf{det}$ and $\mathbf{inv}$ to compute the values of $\det(A)$ and A^{-1}. Which MATLAB function is a more reliable indicator of singularity?

(b) Use MATLAB to compute $\det(A^T)$. Are the computed values of $\det(A)$ and $\det(A^T)$ equal? Another way to check if a matrix is singular is to compute its reduced row echelon form. Use MATLAB to compute the reduced row echelon forms of A and A^T.

(c) To see what is going wrong, it helps to know how MATLAB computes determinants. The MATLAB routine for determinants first computes a form of the LU factorization of the matrix. The determinant of the L is ± 1 depending on the whether an even or odd number of row interchanges were used in the computation. The computed value of the determinant of A is the product of the diagonal entries of U multiplied by $\det(L) = \pm 1$. In the special case that the original matrix has integer entries, the exact determinant should take on an integer value. So in this case MATLAB will round its decimal answer to the nearest integer. To see what is happening for our original matrix, use the following commands to compute and display the factor U.

```
format short e
[ L, U ] = lu(A); U
```

In exact arithmetic U should be singular. Is the computed matrix U singular? If not, what goes wrong? Use the following commands to see the rest of the computation of $d = \det(A)$.

```
format short
d = prod(diag(U))
d = round(d)
```

CHAPTER TEST

In each of the following answer *true* if the statement is always true and *false* otherwise. In the case of a true statement, explain or prove your answer. In the case of a false statement, give an example to show that the statement is not always true. In each of the following, assume that all the matrices are $n \times n$.

1. $\det(AB) = \det(BA)$

2. $\det(A + B) = \det(A) + \det(B)$

3. $\det(cA) = c \det(A)$

4. $\det((AB)^T) = \det(A) \det(B)$

5. $\det(A) = \det(B)$ implies $A = B$.

6. $\det(A^k) = \det(A)^k$

7. A triangular matrix is nonsingular if and only if its diagonal entries are all nonzero.

8. If $\mathbf{x}$ is a nonzero vector in R^n and $A\mathbf{x} = \mathbf{0}$, then $\det(A) = 0$.

9. If A and B are row equivalent matrices, then their determinants are equal.

10. If $A \neq O$, but $A^k = O$ (where O denotes the zero matrix) for some positive integer k, then A must be singular.

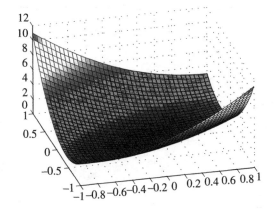

CHAPTER

6

EIGENVALUES

In Section 1 we will be concerned with the equation $A\mathbf{x} = \lambda\mathbf{x}$. This equation occurs in many applications of linear algebra. If the equation has a nonzero solution $\mathbf{x}$, then λ is said to be an *eigenvalue* of A and $\mathbf{x}$ is said to be an *eigenvector* belonging to λ.

Eigenvalues are a common part of our life whether we realize it or not. Wherever there are vibrations there are eigenvalues, the natural frequencies of the vibrations. If you have ever tuned a guitar, you have solved an eigenvalue problem. When engineers design structures, they are concerned with the frequencies of vibration of the structure. This is particularly important in earthquake prone regions such as California. The eigenvalues of a boundary value problem can be used to determine the energy states of an atom or critical loads that cause buckling in a beam. This latter application is presented in Section 1.

In Section 2 we will learn more about how to use eigenvalues and eigenvectors to solve systems of linear differential equations. We will consider a number of applications, including mixture problems, the harmonic motion of a system of springs, and the vibrations of a building. The motion of a building can be modeled by a second-order system of differential equations of the form

$$M\mathbf{Y}''(t) = K\mathbf{Y}(t)$$

where $\mathbf{Y}(t)$ is a vector whose entries are all functions of t and $\mathbf{Y}''(t)$ is the vector of functions formed by taking the second derivatives of each of the entries of $\mathbf{Y}(t)$. The solution of the equation is determined by the eigenvalues and eigenvectors of the matrix $A = M^{-1}K$.

In general, we can view eigenvalues as natural frequencies associated with linear transformations. If A is an $n \times n$ matrix, we can think of A as representing a linear transformation from R^n into itself. Eigenvalues and eigenvectors provide the key to understanding how the operator works. For example, if $\lambda > 0$, the effect of the operator on any eigenvector belonging to λ is simply a stretching or a shrinking by a constant factor. Indeed, the effect of the operator is easily determined on any linear combination of eigenvectors. In particular, if it is possible to find a basis of eigenvectors for R^n, the operator can be represented by a diagonal matrix D with respect to that basis, and the matrix A can be factored into a product XDX^{-1}. In Section 3 we see how this is done and look at a number of applications.

In Section 4 we consider matrices with complex entries. In this setting we will be concerned with matrices whose eigenvectors can be used to form an orthonormal basis for C^n (the vector space of all n-tuples of complex numbers). In Section 5 we introduce the singular value decomposition of a matrix and show four applications. Another important application of this factorization will be presented in Chapter 7.

Section 6 deals with the application of eigenvalues to quadratic equations in several variables and also with applications involving maximums and minimums of functions of several variables. In Section 7 we consider symmetric positive definite matrices. The eigenvalues of such matrices are real and positive. These matrices occur in a wide variety of applications. In particular, we will show the applications to conic sections and to optimization of functions. Finally, in Section 8 we study matrices with nonnegative entries and some applications to economics.

1   EIGENVALUES AND EIGENVECTORS

Many application problems involve applying a linear transformation repeatedly to a given vector. The key to solving these problems is to choose a coordinate system or basis that is in some sense natural for the operator and for which it will be simpler to do calculations involving the operator. With respect to these new basis vectors (*eigenvectors*) we associate scaling factors (*eigenvalues*) which represent the natural frequencies of the operator. We illustrate with a simple example.

EXAMPLE 1.   Let us recall Application 3 from Section 3 of Chapter 1. In a certain town, 30 percent of the married women get divorced each year and 20 percent of the single women get married each year. There are 8000 married women and 2000 single women, and the total population remains constant. Let us investigate the long-range prospects if these percentages of marriages and divorces continue indefinitely into the future.

To find the number of married and single women after 1 year, we multiply the vector $\mathbf{w}_0 = (8000, 2000)^T$ by

$$A = \begin{bmatrix} 0.7 & 0.2 \\ 0.3 & 0.8 \end{bmatrix}$$

The number of married and single women after 1 year is given by

$$\mathbf{w}_1 = A\mathbf{w}_0 = \begin{bmatrix} 0.7 & 0.2 \\ 0.3 & 0.8 \end{bmatrix} \begin{bmatrix} 8000 \\ 2000 \end{bmatrix} = \begin{bmatrix} 6000 \\ 4000 \end{bmatrix}$$

To determine the number of married and single women after 2 years, we compute

$$\mathbf{w}_2 = A\mathbf{w}_1 = A^2\mathbf{w}_0$$

and in general for n years we must compute $\mathbf{w}_n = A^n\mathbf{w}_0$.

Let us compute $\mathbf{w}_{10}, \mathbf{w}_{20}, \mathbf{w}_{30}$ in this way and round the entries of each to the nearest integer.

$$\mathbf{w}_{10} = \begin{bmatrix} 4004 \\ 5996 \end{bmatrix}, \qquad \mathbf{w}_{20} = \begin{bmatrix} 4000 \\ 6000 \end{bmatrix}, \qquad \mathbf{w}_{30} = \begin{bmatrix} 4000 \\ 6000 \end{bmatrix}$$

After a certain point we seem to always get the same answer. In fact, $\mathbf{w}_{12} = (4000, 6000)^T$ and since

$$A\mathbf{w}_{12} = \begin{bmatrix} 0.7 & 0.2 \\ 0.3 & 0.8 \end{bmatrix} \begin{bmatrix} 4000 \\ 6000 \end{bmatrix} = \begin{bmatrix} 4000 \\ 6000 \end{bmatrix}$$

it follows that all the succeeding vectors in the sequence remain unchanged. The vector $(4000, 6000)^T$ is said to be a *steady-state vector* for the process.

Suppose that initially we had different proportions of married and single women. If, for example, we had started with 10,000 married women and 0 single women, then $\mathbf{w}_0 = (10,000, 0)^T$, and we can compute $\mathbf{w}_n$ as before by multiplying $\mathbf{w}_0$ by A^n. In this case it turns out that $\mathbf{w}_{14} = (4000, 6000)^T$, and hence we still end up with the same steady-state vector.

Why does this process converge and why do we seem to get the same steady-state vector even when we change the initial vector? These questions are not difficult to answer if we choose a basis for R^2 consisting of vectors for which the effect of the linear transformation A is easily determined. In particular, if we choose a multiple of the steady-state vector, say $\mathbf{x}_1 = (2, 3)^T$, as our first basis vector, then

$$A\mathbf{x}_1 = \begin{bmatrix} 0.7 & 0.2 \\ 0.3 & 0.8 \end{bmatrix} \begin{bmatrix} 2 \\ 3 \end{bmatrix} = \begin{bmatrix} 2 \\ 3 \end{bmatrix} = \mathbf{x}_1$$

Thus $\mathbf{x}_1$ is also a steady-state vector. It is a natural basis vector to use since the effect of A on $\mathbf{x}_1$ could not be simpler. Although it would be nice to use another steady-state vector as the second basis vector, this is not possible since all the steady-state vectors turn out to be multiples of $\mathbf{x}_1$. However, if we choose $\mathbf{x}_2 = (-1, 1)^T$, then the effect of A on $\mathbf{x}_2$ is also quite simple.

$$A\mathbf{x}_2 = \begin{bmatrix} 0.7 & 0.2 \\ 0.3 & 0.8 \end{bmatrix} \begin{bmatrix} -1 \\ 1 \end{bmatrix} = \begin{bmatrix} -\frac{1}{2} \\ \frac{1}{2} \end{bmatrix} = \frac{1}{2}\mathbf{x}_2$$

Let us now analyze the process using $\mathbf{x}_1$ and $\mathbf{x}_2$ as our basis vectors. If we express the initial vector $\mathbf{w}_0 = (8000, 2000)^T$ as a linear combination

$$\mathbf{w}_0 = 2000 \begin{bmatrix} 2 \\ 3 \end{bmatrix} - 4000 \begin{bmatrix} -1 \\ 1 \end{bmatrix} = 2000\mathbf{x}_1 - 4000\mathbf{x}_2$$

then

$$\mathbf{w}_1 = A\mathbf{w}_0 = 2000A\mathbf{x}_1 - 4000A\mathbf{x}_2 = 2000\mathbf{x}_1 - 4000\left(\frac{1}{2}\right)\mathbf{x}_2$$

$$\mathbf{w}_2 = A\mathbf{w}_1 = 2000\mathbf{x}_1 - 4000\left(\frac{1}{2}\right)^2\mathbf{x}_2$$

and, in general,

$$\mathbf{w}_n = A^n\mathbf{w}_0 = 2000\mathbf{x}_1 - 4000\left(\frac{1}{2}\right)^n\mathbf{x}_2$$

The first component of this sum is the steady-state vector and the second component converges to the zero vector.

Will we always end up with the same steady-state vector for any choice of $\mathbf{w}_0$? Suppose that initially there are p married women. Since there are 10,000 women altogether, the number of single women must be $10,000 - p$. Our initial vector is then

$$\mathbf{w}_0 = \begin{bmatrix} p \\ 10,000 - p \end{bmatrix}$$

If we express $\mathbf{w}_0$ as a linear combination $c_1\mathbf{x}_1 + c_2\mathbf{x}_2$, then, as before,

$$\mathbf{w}_n = A^n\mathbf{w}_0 = c_1\mathbf{x}_1 + \left(\frac{1}{2}\right)^n c_2\mathbf{x}_2$$

The steady-state vector will be $c_1\mathbf{x}_1$. To determine c_1, we write the equation

$$c_1\mathbf{x}_1 + c_2\mathbf{x}_2 = \mathbf{w}_0$$

as a linear system

$$2c_1 - c_2 = p$$
$$3c_1 + c_2 = 10,000 - p$$

Adding the two equations, we see that $c_1 = 2000$. Thus, for any integer p in the range $0 \le p \le 10,000$, the steady-state vector turns out to be

$$2000\mathbf{x}_1 = \begin{bmatrix} 4000 \\ 6000 \end{bmatrix} \qquad \blacktriangleleft$$

The vectors $\mathbf{x}_1$ and $\mathbf{x}_2$ were natural vectors to use in analyzing the process in Example 1 since the effect of the matrix A on each of these vectors was so simple.

$$A\mathbf{x}_1 = \mathbf{x}_1 = 1\mathbf{x}_1 \qquad \text{and} \qquad A\mathbf{x}_2 = \tfrac{1}{2}\mathbf{x}_2$$

For each of these vectors the effect of A was just to multiply the vector by a scalar. The two scalars 1 and $\frac{1}{2}$ can be thought of as the natural frequencies of the linear transformation.

In general, if a linear transformation is represented by an $n \times n$ matrix A and we can find a nonzero vector $\mathbf{x}$ so that $A\mathbf{x} = \lambda\mathbf{x}$, for some scalar λ, then, for this transformation, $\mathbf{x}$ is a natural choice to use as a basis vector for R^n, and the scalar λ defines a natural frequency corresponding to that basis vector. More precisely, we use the following terminology to refer to $\mathbf{x}$ and λ.

▶ **DEFINITION** Let A be an $n \times n$ matrix. A scalar λ is said to be an **eigenvalue** or a **characteristic value** of A if there exists a nonzero vector $\mathbf{x}$ such that $A\mathbf{x} = \lambda\mathbf{x}$. The vector $\mathbf{x}$ is said to be an **eigenvector** or a **characteristic vector** belonging to λ. ◀

EXAMPLE 2. Let

$$A = \begin{bmatrix} 4 & -2 \\ 1 & 1 \end{bmatrix} \quad \text{and} \quad \mathbf{x} = \begin{bmatrix} 2 \\ 1 \end{bmatrix}$$

Since

$$A\mathbf{x} = \begin{bmatrix} 4 & -2 \\ 1 & 1 \end{bmatrix} \begin{bmatrix} 2 \\ 1 \end{bmatrix} = \begin{bmatrix} 6 \\ 3 \end{bmatrix} = 3 \begin{bmatrix} 2 \\ 1 \end{bmatrix} = 3\mathbf{x}$$

it follows that $\lambda = 3$ is an eigenvalue of A and $\mathbf{x} = (2, 1)^T$ is an eigenvector belonging to λ. Actually, any nonzero multiple of $\mathbf{x}$ will be an eigenvector, since

$$A(\alpha\mathbf{x}) = \alpha A\mathbf{x} = \alpha\lambda\mathbf{x} = \lambda(\alpha\mathbf{x})$$

Thus, for example, $(4, 2)^T$ is also an eigenvector belonging to $\lambda = 3$.

$$\begin{bmatrix} 4 & -2 \\ 1 & 1 \end{bmatrix} \begin{bmatrix} 4 \\ 2 \end{bmatrix} = \begin{bmatrix} 12 \\ 6 \end{bmatrix} = 3 \begin{bmatrix} 4 \\ 2 \end{bmatrix} \quad ◀$$

The equation $A\mathbf{x} = \lambda\mathbf{x}$ can be written in the form

$$(1) \qquad\qquad (A - \lambda I)\mathbf{x} = \mathbf{0}$$

Thus λ is an eigenvalue of A if and only if (1) has a nontrivial solution. The set of solutions to (1) is $N(A - \lambda I)$, which is a subspace of R^n. Thus, if λ is an eigenvalue of A, then $N(A - \lambda I) \neq \{\mathbf{0}\}$, and any nonzero vector in $N(A - \lambda I)$ is an eigenvector belonging to λ. The subspace $N(A - \lambda I)$ is called the *eigenspace* corresponding to the eigenvalue λ.

Equation (1) will have a nontrivial solution if and only if $A - \lambda I$ is singular, or, equivalently,

$$(2) \qquad\qquad \det(A - \lambda I) = 0$$

If the determinant in (2) is expanded, we obtain an nth-degree polynomial in the variable λ,

$$p(\lambda) = \det(A - \lambda I)$$

This polynomial is called the *characteristic polynomial*, and equation (2) is called the *characteristic equation* for the matrix A. The roots of the characteristic polynomial are the eigenvalues of A. If we count roots according to multiplicity, the characteristic polynomial will have exactly n roots. Thus A will have n eigenvalues, some of which may be repeated and some of which may be complex numbers. To take care of the latter case, it will be necessary to expand our field of scalars to the complex numbers and to allow complex entries for our vectors and matrices.

We have now established a number of equivalent conditions for λ to be an eigenvalue of A.

Let A be an $n \times n$ matrix and λ be a scalar. The following statements are equivalent:

(a) λ is an eigenvalue of A.

(b) $(A - \lambda I)\mathbf{x} = \mathbf{0}$ has a nontrivial solution.

(c) $N(A - \lambda I) \neq \{\mathbf{0}\}$

(d) $A - \lambda I$ is singular.

(e) $\det(A - \lambda I) = 0$

We will now use statement **(e)** to determine the eigenvalues in a number of examples.

EXAMPLE 3. Find the eigenvalues and the corresponding eigenvectors of the matrix

$$A = \begin{bmatrix} 3 & 2 \\ 3 & -2 \end{bmatrix}$$

SOLUTION. The characteristic equation is

$$\begin{vmatrix} 3 - \lambda & 2 \\ 3 & -2 - \lambda \end{vmatrix} = 0 \quad \text{or} \quad \lambda^2 - \lambda - 12 = 0$$

Thus, the eigenvalues of A are $\lambda_1 = 4$ and $\lambda_2 = -3$. To find the eigenvectors belonging to $\lambda_1 = 4$, we must determine the nullspace of $A - 4I$.

$$A - 4I = \begin{bmatrix} -1 & 2 \\ 3 & -6 \end{bmatrix}$$

Solving $(A - 4I)\mathbf{x} = \mathbf{0}$, we get

$$\mathbf{x} = (2x_2, x_2)^T$$

Thus, any nonzero multiple of $(2, 1)^T$ is an eigenvector belonging to λ_1, and $\{(2, 1)^T\}$ is a basis for the eigenspace corresponding to λ_1. Similarly, to find the eigenvectors for λ_2, we must solve

$$(A + 3I)\mathbf{x} = \mathbf{0}$$

In this case $\{(-1, 3)^T\}$ is a basis for $N(A+3I)$, and any nonzero multiple of $(-1, 3)^T$ is an eigenvector belonging to λ_2. ◀

EXAMPLE 4. Let

$$A = \begin{bmatrix} 2 & -3 & 1 \\ 1 & -2 & 1 \\ 1 & -3 & 2 \end{bmatrix}$$

Find the eigenvalues and the corresponding eigenspaces.

SOLUTION.

$$\begin{vmatrix} 2-\lambda & -3 & 1 \\ 1 & -2-\lambda & 1 \\ 1 & -3 & 2-\lambda \end{vmatrix} = -\lambda(\lambda-1)^2$$

Thus, the characteristic polynomial has roots $\lambda_1 = 0$, $\lambda_2 = \lambda_3 = 1$. The eigenspace corresponding to $\lambda_1 = 0$ is $N(A)$, which we determine in the usual manner.

$$\begin{bmatrix} 2 & -3 & 1 & | & 0 \\ 1 & -2 & 1 & | & 0 \\ 1 & -3 & 2 & | & 0 \end{bmatrix} \rightarrow \begin{bmatrix} 1 & 0 & -1 & | & 0 \\ 0 & 1 & -1 & | & 0 \\ 0 & 0 & 0 & | & 0 \end{bmatrix}$$

Setting $x_3 = \alpha$, we find that $x_1 = x_2 = x_3 = \alpha$. Thus the eigenspace corresponding to $\lambda_1 = 0$ consists of all vectors of the form $\alpha(1, 1, 1)^T$. To find the eigenspace corresponding to $\lambda = 1$, we must solve the system $(A - I)\mathbf{x} = \mathbf{0}$.

$$\begin{bmatrix} 1 & -3 & 1 & | & 0 \\ 1 & -3 & 1 & | & 0 \\ 1 & -3 & 1 & | & 0 \end{bmatrix} \rightarrow \begin{bmatrix} 1 & -3 & 1 & | & 0 \\ 0 & 0 & 0 & | & 0 \\ 0 & 0 & 0 & | & 0 \end{bmatrix}$$

Setting $x_2 = \alpha$ and $x_3 = \beta$, we get $x_1 = 3\alpha - \beta$. Thus the eigenspace corresponding to $\lambda = 1$ consists of all vectors of the form

$$\begin{bmatrix} 3\alpha - \beta \\ \alpha \\ \beta \end{bmatrix} = \alpha \begin{bmatrix} 3 \\ 1 \\ 0 \end{bmatrix} + \beta \begin{bmatrix} -1 \\ 0 \\ 1 \end{bmatrix} \qquad \blacktriangleleft$$

EXAMPLE 5. Given

$$A = \begin{bmatrix} 1 & 2 \\ -2 & 1 \end{bmatrix}$$

Compute the eigenvalues of A and find bases for the corresponding eigenspaces.

SOLUTION.

$$\begin{vmatrix} 1-\lambda & 2 \\ -2 & 1-\lambda \end{vmatrix} = (1-\lambda)^2 + 4$$

The roots of the characteristic polynomial are $\lambda_1 = 1 + 2i$, $\lambda_2 = 1 - 2i$.

$$A - \lambda_1 I = \begin{bmatrix} -2i & 2 \\ -2 & -2i \end{bmatrix} = -2 \begin{bmatrix} i & -1 \\ 1 & i \end{bmatrix}$$

It follows that $\{(1, i)^T\}$ is a basis for the eigenspace corresponding to $\lambda_1 = 1 + 2i$. Similarly,

$$A - \lambda_2 I = \begin{bmatrix} 2i & 2 \\ -2 & 2i \end{bmatrix} = 2 \begin{bmatrix} i & 1 \\ -1 & i \end{bmatrix}$$

and $\{(1, -i)^T\}$ is a basis for $N(A - \lambda_2 I)$.

◀

APPLICATION I: STRUCTURES—BUCKLING OF A BEAM

For an example of a physical eigenvalue problem, consider the case of a beam. If a force or load is applied to one end of the beam, the beam will buckle when the load reaches a critical value. If we continue increasing the load beyond the critical value, we can expect the beam to buckle again when the load reaches a second critical value, and so on. Assume that the beam has length L and that it is positioned along the x axis in the plane with the left support of the beam at $x = 0$. Let $y(x)$ represent the vertical displacement of the beam for any point x, and assume that the beam is simply supported, that is, $y(0) = y(L) = 0$. (See Figure 6.1.1.)

The physical system for the beam is modeled by the boundary value problem

$$(3) \qquad R\frac{d^2 y}{dx^2} = -Py \qquad y(0) = y(L) = 0$$

where R is the flexural rigidity of the beam and P is the load placed on the beam. A standard procedure to compute the solution $y(x)$ is to use a finite difference method to approximate the differential equation. Specifically, we partition the interval $[0, L]$ into n equal subintervals

$$0 = x_0 < x_1 < \cdots < x_n = L \qquad \left(x_j = \frac{jL}{n}, \; j = 0, \ldots, n \right)$$

FIGURE 6.1.1

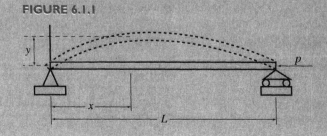

and for each j we approximate $y''(x_j)$ by a difference quotient. If we set $h = \frac{L}{n}$ and use the shorthand notation y_k for $y(x_k)$, then the standard difference approximation is given by

$$y''(x_j) \approx \frac{y_{j+1} - 2y_j + y_{j-1}}{h^2} \quad j = 1, \dots, n$$

Substituting these into equation (3), we end up with a system of n linear equations. If we multiply each equation through by $-\frac{h^2}{R}$ and set $\lambda = \frac{Ph^2}{R}$, then the system can be written as a matrix equation of the form $A\mathbf{y} = \lambda\mathbf{y}$, where

$$A = \begin{bmatrix} 2 & -1 & 0 & \cdots & 0 & 0 & 0 \\ -1 & 2 & -1 & \cdots & 0 & 0 & 0 \\ 0 & -1 & 2 & \cdots & 0 & 0 & 0 \\ \vdots & & & & & & \vdots \\ 0 & 0 & 0 & \cdots & -1 & 2 & -1 \\ 0 & 0 & 0 & \cdots & 0 & -1 & 2 \end{bmatrix}$$

The eigenvalues of this matrix will all be real and positive. (See MATLAB Exercise 24 at the end of this chapter.) For n sufficiently large, each eigenvalue λ of A can be used to approximate a critical load $P = \frac{R\lambda}{h^2}$ where buckling may occur. The most important of these critical loads is the one corresponding to the smallest eigenvalue since the beam may actually break after this load is exceeded.

Complex Eigenvalues

If A is an $n \times n$ matrix with real entries, then the characteristic polynomial of A will have real coefficients, and hence all its complex roots must occur in conjugate pairs. Thus, if $\lambda = a + bi$ $(b \neq 0)$ is an eigenvalue of A, then $\bar{\lambda} = a - bi$ must also be an eigenvalue of A. Here the symbol $\bar{\lambda}$ (read *lambda bar*) is used to denote the complex conjugate of λ. A similar notation can be used for matrices. If $A = (a_{ij})$ is a matrix with complex entries, then $\overline{A} = (\overline{a_{ij}})$ is the matrix formed from A by conjugating each of its entries. We define a *real matrix* to be one with the property that $\overline{A} = A$. In general, if A and B are matrices with complex entries and the multiplication AB is possible, then $\overline{AB} = \overline{A}\,\overline{B}$ (see Exercise 17).

Not only do the complex eigenvalues of a real matrix occur in conjugate pairs, but so do the eigenvectors. Indeed, if λ is a complex eigenvalue of a real $n \times n$ matrix A and $\mathbf{z}$ is an eigenvector belonging to λ, then

$$A\bar{\mathbf{z}} = \overline{A}\,\bar{\mathbf{z}} = \overline{A\mathbf{z}} = \overline{\lambda\mathbf{z}} = \bar{\lambda}\,\bar{\mathbf{z}}$$

Thus, $\bar{\mathbf{z}}$ is an eigenvector of A belonging to $\bar{\lambda}$. In Example 5 the eigenvector computed for the eigenvalue $\lambda = 1 + 2i$ was $\mathbf{z} = (1, i)^T$, and the eigenvector computed for $\bar{\lambda} = 1 - 2i$ was $\bar{\mathbf{z}} = (1, -i)^T$.

The Product and Sum of the Eigenvalues

It is easy to determine the sum and product of the eigenvalues of an $n \times n$ matrix A. If $p(\lambda)$ is the characteristic polynomial of A, then

$$(4) \qquad p(\lambda) = \det(A - \lambda I) = \begin{vmatrix} a_{11} - \lambda & a_{12} & \cdots & a_{1n} \\ a_{21} & a_{22} - \lambda & & a_{2n} \\ \vdots & & & \\ a_{n1} & a_{n2} & & a_{nn} - \lambda \end{vmatrix}$$

Expanding along the first column, we get

$$\det(A - \lambda I) = (a_{11} - \lambda)\det(M_{11}) + \sum_{i=2}^{n} a_{i1}(-1)^{i+1}\det(M_{i1})$$

where the minors M_{i1}, $i = 2, \ldots, n$, do not contain the two diagonal elements $(a_{11} - \lambda)$ and $(a_{ii} - \lambda)$. Expanding $\det(M_{11})$ in the same manner, we conclude that

$$(5) \qquad (a_{11} - \lambda)(a_{22} - \lambda) \cdots (a_{nn} - \lambda)$$

is the only term in the expansion of $\det(A - \lambda I)$ involving a product of more than $n - 2$ of the diagonal elements. When (5) is expanded, the coefficient of λ^n will be $(-1)^n$. Thus the lead coefficient of $p(\lambda)$ is $(-1)^n$ and hence, if $\lambda_1, \ldots, \lambda_n$ are the eigenvalues of A, then

$$(6) \qquad \begin{aligned} p(\lambda) &= (-1)^n(\lambda - \lambda_1)(\lambda - \lambda_2) \cdots (\lambda - \lambda_n) \\ &= (\lambda_1 - \lambda)(\lambda_2 - \lambda) \cdots (\lambda_n - \lambda) \end{aligned}$$

It follows from (4) and (6) that

$$\lambda_1 \cdot \lambda_2 \cdots \lambda_n = p(0) = \det(A)$$

From (5) we also see that the coefficient of $(-\lambda)^{n-1}$ is $\sum_{i=1}^{n} a_{ii}$. If we determine this same coefficient using (6), we obtain $\sum_{i=1}^{n} \lambda_i$. It follows that

$$\sum_{i=1}^{n} \lambda_i = \sum_{i=1}^{n} a_{ii}$$

The sum of the diagonal elements of A is called the *trace* of A and is denoted by $\text{tr}(A)$.

EXAMPLE 6. If

$$A = \begin{pmatrix} 5 & -18 \\ 1 & -1 \end{pmatrix}$$

then

$$\det(A) = -5 + 18 = 13 \qquad \text{and} \qquad \text{tr}(A) = 5 - 1 = 4$$

The characteristic polynomial of A is given by

$$\begin{vmatrix} 5 - \lambda & -18 \\ 1 & -1 - \lambda \end{vmatrix} = \lambda^2 - 4\lambda + 13$$

and hence the eigenvalues of A are $\lambda_1 = 2 + 3i$ and $\lambda_2 = 2 - 3i$. Note that

$$\lambda_1 + \lambda_2 = 4 = \text{tr}(A)$$

and

$$\lambda_1 \lambda_2 = 13 = \det(A) \qquad\qquad \blacktriangleleft$$

In the examples we have looked at so far, n has always been less than 4. For larger n it is more difficult to find the roots of the characteristic polynomial. In Chapter 7 we will learn numerical methods for computing eigenvalues. (These methods will not involve the characteristic polynomial at all.) If the eigenvalues of A have been computed using some numerical method, one way to check their accuracy is to compare their sum to the trace of A.

Similar Matrices

We close this section with an important result about the eigenvalues of similar matrices. Recall that a matrix B is said to be *similar* to a matrix A if there exists a nonsingular matrix S such that $B = S^{-1}AS$.

▶ **THEOREM 6.1.1** *Let A and B be $n \times n$ matrices. If B is similar to A, then the two matrices both have the same characteristic polynomial and consequently both have the same eigenvalues.*

▶ *Proof.* Let $p_A(x)$ and $p_B(x)$ denote the characteristic polynomials of A and B, respectively. If B is similar to A, then there exists a nonsingular matrix S such that $B = S^{-1}AS$. Thus

$$\begin{aligned}
p_B(\lambda) &= \det(B - \lambda I) \\
&= \det(S^{-1}AS - \lambda I) \\
&= \det(S^{-1}(A - \lambda I)S) \\
&= \det(S^{-1}) \det(A - \lambda I) \det(S) \\
&= p_A(\lambda)
\end{aligned}$$

The eigenvalues of a matrix are the roots of the characteristic polynomial. Since the two matrices have the same characteristic polynomial, they must have the same eigenvalues. ◀

EXAMPLE 7. Given

$$T = \begin{bmatrix} 2 & 1 \\ 0 & 3 \end{bmatrix} \quad \text{and} \quad S = \begin{bmatrix} 5 & 3 \\ 3 & 2 \end{bmatrix}$$

It is easily seen that the eigenvalues of T are $\lambda_1 = 2$ and $\lambda_2 = 3$. If we set $A = S^{-1}TS$, then the eigenvalues of A should be the same as those of T.

$$A = \begin{bmatrix} 2 & -3 \\ -3 & 5 \end{bmatrix} \begin{bmatrix} 2 & 1 \\ 0 & 3 \end{bmatrix} \begin{bmatrix} 5 & 3 \\ 3 & 2 \end{bmatrix} = \begin{bmatrix} -1 & -2 \\ 6 & 6 \end{bmatrix}$$

We leave it to the reader to verify that the eigenvalues of this matrix are $\lambda_1 = 2$ and $\lambda_2 = 3$. ◀

EXERCISES

1. Find the eigenvalues and the corresponding eigenspaces for each of the following matrices.

(a) $\begin{bmatrix} 3 & 2 \\ 4 & 1 \end{bmatrix}$

(b) $\begin{bmatrix} 6 & -4 \\ 3 & -1 \end{bmatrix}$

(c) $\begin{bmatrix} 3 & -1 \\ 1 & 1 \end{bmatrix}$

(d) $\begin{bmatrix} 3 & -8 \\ 2 & 3 \end{bmatrix}$

(e) $\begin{bmatrix} 1 & 1 \\ -2 & 3 \end{bmatrix}$

(f) $\begin{bmatrix} 0 & 1 & 0 \\ 0 & 0 & 1 \\ 0 & 0 & 0 \end{bmatrix}$

(g) $\begin{bmatrix} 1 & 1 & 1 \\ 0 & 2 & 1 \\ 0 & 0 & 1 \end{bmatrix}$

(h) $\begin{bmatrix} 1 & 2 & 1 \\ 0 & 3 & 1 \\ 0 & 5 & -1 \end{bmatrix}$

(i) $\begin{bmatrix} 4 & -5 & 1 \\ 1 & 0 & -1 \\ 0 & 1 & -1 \end{bmatrix}$

(j) $\begin{bmatrix} -2 & 0 & 1 \\ 1 & 0 & -1 \\ 0 & 1 & -1 \end{bmatrix}$

(k) $\begin{bmatrix} 2 & 0 & 0 & 0 \\ 0 & 2 & 0 & 0 \\ 0 & 0 & 3 & 0 \\ 0 & 0 & 0 & 4 \end{bmatrix}$

(l) $\begin{bmatrix} 3 & 0 & 0 & 0 \\ 4 & 1 & 0 & 0 \\ 0 & 0 & 2 & 1 \\ 0 & 0 & 0 & 2 \end{bmatrix}$

2. Show that the eigenvalues of a triangular matrix are the diagonal elements of the matrix.

3. Let A be an $n \times n$ matrix. Prove that A is singular if and only if $\lambda = 0$ is an eigenvalue of A.

4. Let A be a nonsingular matrix and let λ be an eigenvalue of A. Show that $1/\lambda$ is an eigenvalue of A^{-1}.

5. Let λ be an eigenvalue of A and let $\mathbf{x}$ be an eigenvector belonging to λ. Use mathematical induction to show that λ^m is an eigenvalue of A^m and $\mathbf{x}$ is an eigenvector of A^m belonging to λ^m for $m = 1, 2, \ldots$.

6. An $n \times n$ matrix A is said to be *idempotent* if $A^2 = A$. Show that if λ is an eigenvalue of an idempotent matrix, then λ must be either 0 or 1.

7. An $n \times n$ matrix is said to be *nilpotent* if $A^k = O$ for some positive integer k. Show that all eigenvalues of a nilpotent matrix are 0.

8. Let A be an $n \times n$ matrix and let $B = A - \alpha I$ for some scalar α. How do the eigenvalues of A and B compare? Explain.

9. Show that A and A^T have the same eigenvalues. Do they necessarily have the same eigenvectors? Explain.

10. Show that the matrix

$$
A = \begin{bmatrix} \cos\theta & -\sin\theta \\ \sin\theta & \cos\theta \end{bmatrix}
$$

will have complex eigenvalues if θ is not a multiple of π. Give a geometric interpretation of this result.

11. Let A be a 2×2 matrix. If $\operatorname{tr}(A) = 8$ and $\det(A) = 12$, what are the eigenvalues of A?

12. Let $A = (a_{ij})$ be an $n \times n$ matrix with eigenvalues $\lambda_1, \ldots, \lambda_n$. Show that

$$
\lambda_j = a_{jj} + \sum_{i \neq j} (a_{ii} - \lambda_i) \qquad \text{for} \quad j = 1, \ldots, n
$$

13. Let A be a 2×2 matrix and let $p(\lambda) = \lambda^2 + b\lambda + c$ be the characteristic polynomial of A. Show that $b = -\operatorname{tr}(A)$ and $c = \det(A)$.

14. Let λ be a nonzero eigenvalue of A and let $\mathbf{x}$ be an eigenvector belonging to λ. Show that $A^m \mathbf{x}$ is also an eigenvector belonging to λ for $m = 1, 2, \ldots$.

15. Let A be an $n \times n$ matrix and let λ be an eigenvalue of A. If $A - \lambda I$ has rank k, what is the dimension of the eigenspace corresponding to λ? Explain.

16. Let A be an $n \times n$ matrix. Show that a vector $\mathbf{x}$ in R^n is an eigenvector belonging to A if and only if the subspace S of R^n spanned by $\mathbf{x}$ and $A\mathbf{x}$ has dimension 1.

17. Let $\alpha = a + bi$ and $\beta = c + di$ be complex scalars and let A and B be matrices with complex entries.

    (a) Show that

$$
\overline{\alpha + \beta} = \overline{\alpha} + \overline{\beta} \qquad \text{and} \qquad \overline{\alpha\beta} = \overline{\alpha}\,\overline{\beta}
$$

    (b) Show that the (i, j) entries of $\overline{AB}$ and $\overline{A}\,\overline{B}$ are equal and hence that

$$
\overline{AB} = \overline{A}\,\overline{B}
$$

18. Let $x_1, \ldots, x_r$ be eigenvectors of an $n \times n$ matrix A and let S be the subspace of R^n spanned by $x_1, x_2, \ldots, x_r$. Show that S is invariant under A (i.e., show that $Ax \in S$ whenever $x \in S$).

19. Let $B = S^{-1}AS$ and let x be an eigenvector of B belonging to an eigenvalue λ. Show that Sx is an eigenvector of A belonging to λ.

20. Show that if two $n \times n$ matrices A and B have a common eigenvector x (but not necessarily a common eigenvalue), then x will also be an eigenvector of any matrix of the form $C = \alpha A + \beta B$.

21. Let A be an $n \times n$ matrix and let λ be a nonzero eigenvalue of A. Show that if x is an eigenvector belonging to λ, then x is in the column space of A. Hence the eigenspace corresponding to λ is a subspace of the column space of A.

22. Let $\{u_1, u_2, \ldots, u_n\}$ be an orthonormal basis for R^n and let A be a linear combination of the rank 1 matrices $u_1 u_1^T, u_2 u_2^T, \ldots, u_n u_n^T$. If

$$A = c_1 u_1 u_1^T + c_2 u_2 u_2^T + \cdots + c_n u_n u_n^T$$

show that A is a symmetric matrix with eigenvalues $c_1, c_2, \ldots, c_n$ and that u_i is an eigenvector belonging to c_i for each i.

23. Let A be a matrix whose columns all add up to a fixed constant δ. Show that δ is an eigenvalue of A.

24. Let λ_1 and λ_2 be distinct eigenvalues of A. Let x be an eigenvector of A belonging to λ_1 and let y be an eigenvector of A^T belonging to λ_2. Show that x and y are orthogonal.

25. Let A and B be $n \times n$ matrices. Show that:

(a) If λ is a nonzero eigenvalue of AB, then it is also an eigenvalue of BA.

(b) If $\lambda = 0$ is an eigenvalue of AB, then $\lambda = 0$ is also an eigenvalue of BA.

26. Prove that there do not exist $n \times n$ matrices A and B such that

$$AB - BA = I$$

[*Hint:* See Exercises 8 and 25.]

27. Let $p(\lambda) = (-1)^n(\lambda^n - a_{n-1}\lambda^{n-1} - \cdots - a_1\lambda - a_0)$ be a polynomial of degree $n \geq 1$, and let

$$C = \begin{bmatrix} a_{n-1} & a_{n-2} & \cdots & a_1 & a_0 \\ 1 & 0 & \cdots & 0 & 0 \\ 0 & 1 & \cdots & 0 & 0 \\ \vdots & & & & \\ 0 & 0 & \cdots & 1 & 0 \end{bmatrix}$$

(a) Show that if λ_i is a root of $p(\lambda) = 0$, then λ_i is an eigenvalue of C with eigenvector $x = (\lambda_i^{n-1}, \lambda_i^{n-2}, \ldots, \lambda_i, 1)^T$.

(b) Use part (a) to show that if $p(\lambda)$ has n distinct roots, then $p(\lambda)$ is the characteristic polynomial of C.

The matrix C is called the *companion matrix* of $p(\lambda)$.

28. The result given in Exercise 27(b) holds even if all the eigenvalues of $p(\lambda)$ are not distinct. Prove this as follows:

(a) Let

$$D_m(\lambda) = \begin{bmatrix} a_m & a_{m-1} & \cdots & a_1 & a_0 \\ 1 & -\lambda & \cdots & 0 & 0 \\ \vdots & & & & \\ 0 & 0 & \cdots & 1 & -\lambda \end{bmatrix}$$

and use mathematical induction to prove that

$$\det(D_m(\lambda)) = (-1)^m (a_m \lambda^m + a_{m-1}\lambda^{m-1} + \cdots + a_1\lambda + a_0)$$

(b) Show that

$$\det(C - \lambda I) = (a_{n-1} - \lambda)(-\lambda)^{n-1} - \det(D_{n-2}) = p(\lambda)$$

2 SYSTEMS OF LINEAR DIFFERENTIAL EQUATIONS

Eigenvalues play an important role in the solution of systems of linear differential equations. In this section we see how they are used in the solution of systems of linear differential equations with constant coefficients. We begin by considering systems of first-order equations of the form

$$y_1' = a_{11}y_1 + a_{12}y_2 + \cdots + a_{1n}y_n$$
$$y_2' = a_{21}y_1 + a_{22}y_2 + \cdots + a_{2n}y_n$$
$$\vdots$$
$$y_n' = a_{n1}y_1 + a_{n2}y_2 + \cdots + a_{nn}y_n$$

where $y_i = f_i(t)$ is a function in $C^1[a, b]$ for each i. If we let

$$\mathbf{Y} = \begin{bmatrix} y_1 \\ y_2 \\ \vdots \\ y_n \end{bmatrix} \quad \text{and} \quad \mathbf{Y}' = \begin{bmatrix} y_1' \\ y_2' \\ \vdots \\ y_n' \end{bmatrix}$$

then the system can be written in the form

$$\mathbf{Y}' = A\mathbf{Y}$$

$\mathbf{Y}$ and $\mathbf{Y}'$ are both vector functions of t. Let us consider the simplest case first. When $n = 1$, the system is simply

(1) $$y' = ay$$

Clearly, any function of the form

$$y(t) = ce^{at} \qquad (c \text{ an arbitrary constant})$$

satisfies equation (1). A natural generalization of this solution for the case $n > 1$ is to take

$$\mathbf{Y} = \begin{pmatrix} x_1 e^{\lambda t} \\ x_2 e^{\lambda t} \\ \vdots \\ x_n e^{\lambda t} \end{pmatrix} = e^{\lambda t} \mathbf{x}$$

where $\mathbf{x} = (x_1, x_2, \ldots, x_n)^T$. To verify that a vector function of this form does work, we compute the derivative

$$\mathbf{Y}' = \lambda e^{\lambda t} \mathbf{x} = \lambda \mathbf{Y}$$

Now, if we choose λ to be an eigenvalue of A and $\mathbf{x}$ to be an eigenvector belonging to λ, then

$$A\mathbf{Y} = e^{\lambda t} A\mathbf{x} = \lambda e^{\lambda t} \mathbf{x} = \lambda \mathbf{Y} = \mathbf{Y}'$$

Hence $\mathbf{Y}$ is a solution to the system. Thus, if λ is an eigenvalue of A and $\mathbf{x}$ is an eigenvector belonging to λ, then $e^{\lambda t}\mathbf{x}$ is a solution of the system $\mathbf{Y}' = A\mathbf{Y}$. This will be true whether λ is real or complex. Note that if $\mathbf{Y}_1$ and $\mathbf{Y}_2$ are both solutions to $\mathbf{Y}' = A\mathbf{Y}$, then $\alpha\mathbf{Y}_1 + \beta\mathbf{Y}_2$ is also a solution, since

$$(\alpha\mathbf{Y}_1 + \beta\mathbf{Y}_2)' = \alpha\mathbf{Y}_1' + \beta\mathbf{Y}_2'$$
$$= \alpha A\mathbf{Y}_1 + \beta A\mathbf{Y}_2$$
$$= A(\alpha\mathbf{Y}_1 + \beta\mathbf{Y}_2)$$

It follows by induction that if $\mathbf{Y}_1, \ldots, \mathbf{Y}_n$ are solutions to $\mathbf{Y}' = A\mathbf{Y}$, then any linear combination $c_1\mathbf{Y}_1 + \cdots + c_n\mathbf{Y}_n$ will also be a solution.

In general, the solutions to an $n \times n$ first-order system of the form

$$\mathbf{Y}' = A\mathbf{Y}$$

will form an n-dimensional subspace of the vector space of all continuous vector-valued functions. If, in addition, we require that $\mathbf{Y}(t)$ take on a prescribed value $\mathbf{Y}_0$ when $t = 0$, the problem will have a unique solution (see [34], p. 228). A problem of the form

$$\mathbf{Y}' = A\mathbf{Y}, \qquad \mathbf{Y}(0) = \mathbf{Y}_0$$

is called an *initial value problem*.

EXAMPLE I. Solve the system

$$y_1' = 3y_1 + 4y_2$$
$$y_2' = 3y_1 + 2y_2$$

SOLUTION.

$$A = \begin{bmatrix} 3 & 4 \\ 3 & 2 \end{bmatrix}$$

The eigenvalues of A are $\lambda_1 = 6$ and $\lambda_2 = -1$. Solving $(A - \lambda I)\mathbf{x} = \mathbf{0}$ with $\lambda = \lambda_1$ and $\lambda = \lambda_2$, we see that $\mathbf{x}_1 = (4, 3)^T$ is an eigenvector belonging to λ_1 and $\mathbf{x}_2 = (1, -1)^T$ is an eigenvector belonging to λ_2. Thus any vector function of the form

$$\mathbf{Y} = c_1 e^{\lambda_1 t} \mathbf{x}_1 + c_2 e^{\lambda_2 t} \mathbf{x}_2$$
$$= \begin{bmatrix} 4c_1 e^{6t} + c_2 e^{-t} \\ 3c_1 e^{6t} - c_2 e^{-t} \end{bmatrix}$$

is a solution to the system. ◀

In Example 1, suppose that we require that $y_1 = 6$ and $y_2 = 1$ when $t = 0$. Thus

$$\mathbf{Y}(0) = \begin{bmatrix} 4c_1 + c_2 \\ 3c_1 - c_2 \end{bmatrix} = \begin{bmatrix} 6 \\ 1 \end{bmatrix}$$

and it follows that $c_1 = 1$ and $c_2 = 2$. Hence the solution to the initial value problem is given by

$$\mathbf{Y} = e^{6t} \mathbf{x}_1 + 2e^{-t} \mathbf{x}_2$$
$$= \begin{bmatrix} 4e^{6t} + 2e^{-t} \\ 3e^{6t} - 2e^{-t} \end{bmatrix}$$

APPLICATION I: MIXTURES

Two tanks are connected as shown in Figure 6.2.1. Initially, tank A contains 200 liters of water in which 60 grams of salt has been dissolved, and tank B contains 200 liters of pure water. Liquid is pumped in and out of the two tanks at rates shown in the diagram. Determine the amount of salt in each tank at time t.

SOLUTION. Let $y_1(t)$ and $y_2(t)$ be the number of grams of salt in tanks A and B, respectively, at time t. Initially,

$$\mathbf{Y}(0) = \begin{bmatrix} y_1(0) \\ y_2(0) \end{bmatrix} = \begin{bmatrix} 60 \\ 0 \end{bmatrix}$$

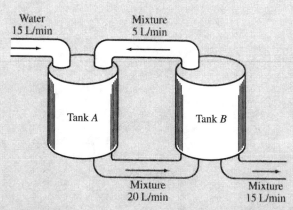

Water
15 L/min

Mixture
5 L/min

Tank A

Tank B

Mixture
20 L/min

Mixture
15 L/min

FIGURE 6.2.1

The total amount of liquid in each tank will remain at 200 liters since the amount being pumped in equals the amount being pumped out. The rate of change in the amount of salt for each tank is equal to the rate at which it is being added minus the rate at which it is being pumped out. For tank A the rate at which the salt is added is given by

$$(5 \text{ L/min}) \cdot \left(\frac{y_2(t)}{200} \text{g/L} \right) = \frac{y_2(t)}{40} \text{g/min}$$

and the rate at which the salt is being pumped out is

$$(20 \text{ L/min}) \cdot \left(\frac{y_1(t)}{200} \text{g/L} \right) = \frac{y_1(t)}{10} \text{g/min}$$

Thus the rate of change for tank A is given by

$$y_1'(t) = \frac{y_2(t)}{40} - \frac{y_1(t)}{10}$$

Similarly, for tank B, the rate of change is given by

$$y_2'(t) = \frac{20y_1(t)}{200} - \frac{20y_2(t)}{200} = \frac{y_1(t)}{10} - \frac{y_2(t)}{10}$$

To determine $y_1(t)$ and $y_2(t)$, we must solve the initial value problem

$$\mathbf{Y}' = A\mathbf{Y}, \quad \mathbf{Y}(0) = \mathbf{Y}_0$$

where

$$A = \begin{bmatrix} -\frac{1}{10} & \frac{1}{40} \\ \frac{1}{10} & -\frac{1}{10} \end{bmatrix}, \quad \mathbf{Y}_0 = \begin{bmatrix} 60 \\ 0 \end{bmatrix}$$

The eigenvalues of A are $\lambda_1 = -\frac{3}{20}$, $\lambda_2 = -\frac{1}{20}$ with corresponding eigenvectors

$$\mathbf{x}_1 = \begin{bmatrix} 1 \\ -2 \end{bmatrix} \quad \text{and} \quad \mathbf{x}_2 = \begin{bmatrix} 1 \\ 2 \end{bmatrix}$$

The solution must then be of the form

$$\mathbf{Y} = c_1 e^{-3t/20} \mathbf{x}_1 + c_2 e^{-t/20} \mathbf{x}_2$$

When $t = 0$, $\mathbf{Y} = \mathbf{Y}_0$. Thus

$$c_1 \mathbf{x}_1 + c_2 \mathbf{x}_2 = \mathbf{Y}_0$$

and we can find c_1 and c_2 by solving

$$\begin{bmatrix} 1 & 1 \\ -2 & 2 \end{bmatrix} \begin{bmatrix} c_1 \\ c_2 \end{bmatrix} = \begin{bmatrix} 60 \\ 0 \end{bmatrix}$$

The solution to this system is $c_1 = c_2 = 30$. Therefore, the solution to the initial value problem is

$$\mathbf{Y}(t) = \begin{bmatrix} y_1(t) \\ y_2(t) \end{bmatrix} = \begin{bmatrix} 30e^{-3t/20} + 30e^{-t/20} \\ -60e^{-3t/20} + 60e^{-t/20} \end{bmatrix} \quad \triangleleft$$

Complex Eigenvalues

Let A be a real $n \times n$ matrix with a complex eigenvalue $\lambda = a + bi$, and let $\mathbf{x}$ be an eigenvector belonging to λ. The vector $\mathbf{x}$ can be split up into its real and imaginary parts.

$$\mathbf{x} = \begin{bmatrix} \operatorname{Re} x_1 + i \operatorname{Im} x_1 \\ \operatorname{Re} x_2 + i \operatorname{Im} x_2 \\ \vdots \\ \operatorname{Re} x_n + i \operatorname{Im} x_n \end{bmatrix} = \begin{bmatrix} \operatorname{Re} x_1 \\ \operatorname{Re} x_2 \\ \vdots \\ \operatorname{Re} x_n \end{bmatrix} + i \begin{bmatrix} \operatorname{Im} x_1 \\ \operatorname{Im} x_2 \\ \vdots \\ \operatorname{Im} x_n \end{bmatrix} = \operatorname{Re} \mathbf{x} + i \operatorname{Im} \mathbf{x}$$

Since entries of A are all real, it follows that $\overline{\lambda} = a - bi$ is also an eigenvalue of A with eigenvector

$$\overline{\mathbf{x}} = \begin{bmatrix} \operatorname{Re} x_1 - i \operatorname{Im} x_1 \\ \operatorname{Re} x_2 - i \operatorname{Im} x_2 \\ \vdots \\ \operatorname{Re} x_n - i \operatorname{Im} x_n \end{bmatrix} = \operatorname{Re} \mathbf{x} - i \operatorname{Im} \mathbf{x}$$

and hence $e^{\lambda t} \mathbf{x}$ and $e^{\overline{\lambda} t} \overline{\mathbf{x}}$ are both solutions to the first-order system $\mathbf{Y}' = A\mathbf{Y}$. Any linear combination of these two solutions will also be a solution. Thus, if we set

$$\mathbf{Y}_1 = \frac{1}{2}(e^{\lambda t} \mathbf{x} + e^{\overline{\lambda} t} \overline{\mathbf{x}}) = \operatorname{Re}(e^{\lambda t} \mathbf{x})$$

and

$$\mathbf{Y}_2 = \frac{1}{2i}(e^{\lambda t}\mathbf{x} - e^{\bar{\lambda}t}\bar{\mathbf{x}}) = \text{Im}\,(e^{\lambda t}\mathbf{x})$$

then the vector functions $\mathbf{Y}_1$ and $\mathbf{Y}_2$ are real-valued solutions to $\mathbf{Y}' = A\mathbf{Y}$. Taking the real and imaginary parts of

$$e^{\lambda t}\mathbf{x} = e^{(a+ib)t}\mathbf{x}$$
$$= e^{at}(\cos bt + i\sin bt)(\text{Re}\,\mathbf{x} + i\text{Im}\,\mathbf{x})$$

we see that

$$\mathbf{Y}_1 = e^{at}\,[(\cos bt)\text{Re}\,\mathbf{x} - (\sin bt)\text{Im}\,\mathbf{x}]$$
$$\mathbf{Y}_2 = e^{at}\,[(\cos bt)\text{Im}\,\mathbf{x} + (\sin bt)\text{Re}\,\mathbf{x}]$$

EXAMPLE 2.   Solve the system

$$\begin{aligned} y_1' &= y_1 + y_2 \\ y_2' &= -2y_1 + 3y_2 \end{aligned}$$

SOLUTION.   Let

$$A = \begin{bmatrix} 1 & 1 \\ -2 & 3 \end{bmatrix}$$

The eigenvalues of A are $\lambda = 2+i$ and $\bar{\lambda} = 2-i$ with eigenvectors $\mathbf{x} = (1, 1+i)^T$ and $\bar{\mathbf{x}} = (1, 1-i)^T$, respectively.

$$e^{\lambda t}\mathbf{x} = \begin{bmatrix} e^{2t}(\cos t + i\sin t) \\ e^{2t}(\cos t + i\sin t)(1+i) \end{bmatrix}$$

$$= \begin{bmatrix} e^{2t}\cos t + ie^{2t}\sin t \\ e^{2t}(\cos t - \sin t) + ie^{2t}(\cos t + \sin t) \end{bmatrix}$$

Let

$$\mathbf{Y}_1 = \text{Re}\,(e^{\lambda t}\mathbf{x}) = \begin{bmatrix} e^{2t}\cos t \\ e^{2t}(\cos t - \sin t) \end{bmatrix}$$

and

$$\mathbf{Y}_2 = \text{Im}\,(e^{\lambda t}\mathbf{x}) = \begin{bmatrix} e^{2t}\sin t \\ e^{2t}(\cos t + \sin t) \end{bmatrix}$$

Any linear combination

$$\mathbf{Y} = c_1\mathbf{Y}_1 + c_2\mathbf{Y}_2$$

will be a solution to the system.

If the $n \times n$ coefficient matrix A of the system $\mathbf{Y}' = A\mathbf{Y}$ has n linearly independent eigenvectors, the general solution can be obtained by the methods that have been presented. The case when A has less than n linearly independent eigenvectors is more complicated and consequently will not be covered in this book.

Higher-Order Systems

Given a second-order system of the form

$$\mathbf{Y}'' = A_1\mathbf{Y} + A_2\mathbf{Y}'$$

we may translate it into a first-order system by setting

$$y_{n+1}(t) = y_1'(t)$$
$$y_{n+2}(t) = y_2'(t)$$
$$\vdots$$
$$y_{2n}(t) = y_n'(t)$$

If we let

$$\mathbf{Y}_1 = \mathbf{Y} = (y_1, y_2, \dots, y_n)^T$$

and

$$\mathbf{Y}_2 = \mathbf{Y}' = (y_{n+1}, \dots, y_{2n})^T$$

then

$$\mathbf{Y}_1' = O\mathbf{Y}_1 + I\mathbf{Y}_2$$

and

$$\mathbf{Y}_2' = A_1\mathbf{Y}_1 + A_2\mathbf{Y}_2$$

The equations can be combined to give the $2n \times 2n$ first-order system

$$\begin{bmatrix} \mathbf{Y}_1' \\ \mathbf{Y}_2' \end{bmatrix} = \begin{bmatrix} O & I \\ A_1 & A_2 \end{bmatrix} \begin{bmatrix} \mathbf{Y}_1 \\ \mathbf{Y}_2 \end{bmatrix}$$

If the values of $\mathbf{Y}_1 = \mathbf{Y}$ and $\mathbf{Y}_2 = \mathbf{Y}'$ are specified when $t = 0$, then the initial value problem will have a unique solution.

EXAMPLE 3.   Solve the initial value problem

$$y_1'' = 2y_1 + y_2 + y_1' + y_2'$$
$$y_2'' = -5y_1 + 2y_2 + 5y_1' - y_2'$$
$$y_1(0) = y_2(0) = y_1'(0) = 4, \qquad y_2'(0) = -4$$

SOLUTION. Set $y_3 = y_1'$ and $y_4 = y_2'$. This gives the first-order system

$$
\begin{aligned}
y_1' &= \quad\qquad\qquad\qquad\quad y_3 \\
y_2' &= \quad\qquad\qquad\qquad\qquad\qquad y_4 \\
y_3' &= \;\;2y_1 + \;\;y_2 + \;\;y_3 + y_4 \\
y_4' &= -5y_1 + 2y_2 + 5y_3 - y_4
\end{aligned}
$$

The coefficient matrix for this system,

$$
A = \begin{bmatrix}
0 & 0 & 1 & 0 \\
0 & 0 & 0 & 1 \\
2 & 1 & 1 & 1 \\
-5 & 2 & 5 & -1
\end{bmatrix}
$$

has eigenvalues

$$
\lambda_1 = 1, \qquad \lambda_2 = -1, \qquad \lambda_3 = 3, \qquad \lambda_4 = -3
$$

Corresponding to these eigenvalues are the eigenvectors

$$
\begin{aligned}
\mathbf{x}_1 &= (1, -1, 1, -1)^T, & \mathbf{x}_2 &= (1, 5, -1, -5)^T \\
\mathbf{x}_3 &= (1, 1, 3, 3)^T, & \mathbf{x}_4 &= (1, -5, -3, 15)^T
\end{aligned}
$$

Thus, the solution will be of the form

$$
c_1\mathbf{x}_1 e^t + c_2\mathbf{x}_2 e^{-t} + c_3\mathbf{x}_3 e^{3t} + c_4\mathbf{x}_4 e^{-3t}
$$

We can use the initial conditions to find c_1, c_2, c_3, and c_4. For $t = 0$, we have

$$
c_1\mathbf{x}_1 + c_2\mathbf{x}_2 + c_3\mathbf{x}_3 + c_4\mathbf{x}_4 = (4, 4, 4, -4)^T
$$

or, equivalently,

$$
\begin{bmatrix}
1 & 1 & 1 & 1 \\
-1 & 5 & 1 & -5 \\
1 & -1 & 3 & -3 \\
-1 & -5 & 3 & 15
\end{bmatrix}
\begin{bmatrix}
c_1 \\ c_2 \\ c_3 \\ c_4
\end{bmatrix}
=
\begin{bmatrix}
4 \\ 4 \\ 4 \\ -4
\end{bmatrix}
$$

The solution to this system is $\mathbf{c} = (2, 1, 1, 0)^T$, and hence the solution to the initial value problem is

$$
\mathbf{Y} = 2\mathbf{x}_1 e^t + \mathbf{x}_2 e^{-t} + \mathbf{x}_3 e^{3t}
$$

Therefore,

$$
\begin{bmatrix}
y_1 \\ y_2 \\ y_1' \\ y_2'
\end{bmatrix}
=
\begin{bmatrix}
2e^t + e^{-t} + e^{3t} \\
-2e^t + 5e^{-t} + e^{3t} \\
2e^t - e^{-t} + 3e^{3t} \\
-2e^t - 5e^{-t} + 3e^{3t}
\end{bmatrix}
$$

In general, if we have an mth-order system of the form

$$\mathbf{Y}^{(m)} = A_1 \mathbf{Y} + A_2 \mathbf{Y}' + \cdots + A_m \mathbf{Y}^{(m-1)}$$

where each A_i is an $n \times n$ matrix, we can transform it into a first-order system by setting

$$\mathbf{Y}_1 = \mathbf{Y}, \mathbf{Y}_2 = \mathbf{Y}'_1, \ldots, \mathbf{Y}_m = \mathbf{Y}'_{m-1}$$

We will end up with a system of the form

$$
\begin{Bmatrix} \mathbf{Y}'_1 \\ \mathbf{Y}'_2 \\ \vdots \\ \mathbf{Y}'_{m-1} \\ \mathbf{Y}'_m \end{Bmatrix}
=
\begin{bmatrix}
O & I & O & \cdots & O \\
O & O & I & \cdots & O \\
\vdots & & & & \\
O & O & O & \cdots & I \\
A_1 & A_2 & A_3 & \cdots & A_m
\end{bmatrix}
\begin{Bmatrix} \mathbf{Y}_1 \\ \mathbf{Y}_2 \\ \vdots \\ \mathbf{Y}_{m-1} \\ \mathbf{Y}_m \end{Bmatrix}
$$

If, in addition, we require that $\mathbf{Y}, \mathbf{Y}', \ldots, \mathbf{Y}^{(m-1)}$ take on specific values when $t = 0$, there will be exactly one solution to the problem.

If the system is simply of the form $\mathbf{Y}^{(m)} = A\mathbf{Y}$, it is usually not necessary to introduce new variables. In this case we need only calculate the mth roots of the eigenvalues of A. If λ is an eigenvalue of A, $\mathbf{x}$ is an eigenvector belonging to λ, σ is an mth root of λ, and $\mathbf{Y} = e^{\sigma t} \mathbf{x}$, then

$$\mathbf{Y}^{(m)} = \sigma^m e^{\sigma t} \mathbf{x} = \lambda \mathbf{Y}$$

and

$$A\mathbf{Y} = e^{\sigma t} A\mathbf{x} = \lambda e^{\sigma t} \mathbf{x} = \lambda \mathbf{Y}$$

Therefore, $\mathbf{Y} = e^{\sigma t} \mathbf{x}$ is a solution to the system.

APPLICATION 2: HARMONIC MOTION

In Figure 6.2.2 two masses are adjoined by springs and the ends A and B are fixed. The masses are free to move horizontally. We will assume that the three springs are uniform and that initially the system is in the equilibrium position. A force is exerted on the system to set the masses in motion. The horizontal displacements of the masses at time t will be denoted by $x_1(t)$ and $x_2(t)$, respectively. We will assume that there are no retarding forces such as friction. Then the only forces acting on mass m_1 at time t will be from the springs 1 and 2. The force from spring 1 will be

FIGURE 6.2.2

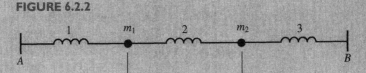

$-kx_1$ and the force from spring 2 will be $k(x_2 - x_1)$. By Newton's second law,

$$m_1 x_1''(t) = -kx_1 + k(x_2 - x_1)$$

Similarly, the only forces acting on the second mass will be from springs 2 and 3. Using Newton's second law again, we get

$$m_2 x_2''(t) = -k(x_2 - x_1) - kx_2$$

Thus we end up with the second-order system

$$x_1'' = -\frac{k}{m_1}(2x_1 - x_2)$$

$$x_2'' = -\frac{k}{m_2}(-x_1 + 2x_2)$$

Suppose now that $m_1 = m_2 = 1$, $k = 1$, and that the initial velocity of both masses is $+2$ units per second. To determine the displacements x_1 and x_2 as functions of t, we write the system in the form

(2)
$$\mathbf{X}'' = A\mathbf{X}$$

The coefficient matrix

$$A = \begin{bmatrix} -2 & 1 \\ 1 & -2 \end{bmatrix}$$

has eigenvalues $\lambda_1 = -1$ and $\lambda_2 = -3$. Corresponding to λ_1, we have the eigenvector $\mathbf{v}_1 = (1, 1)^T$ and $\sigma_1 = \pm i$. Thus $e^{it}\mathbf{v}_1$ and $e^{-it}\mathbf{v}_1$ are both solutions to (2). It follows that

$$\frac{1}{2}(e^{it} + e^{-it})\mathbf{v}_1 = (\operatorname{Re} e^{it})\mathbf{v}_1 = (\cos t)\mathbf{v}_1$$

and

$$\frac{1}{2i}(e^{it} - e^{-it})\mathbf{v}_1 = (\operatorname{Im} e^{it})\mathbf{v}_1 = (\sin t)\mathbf{v}_1$$

are both solutions to (2). Similarly, for $\lambda_2 = -3$, we have the eigenvector $\mathbf{v}_2 = (1, -1)^T$ and $\sigma_2 = \pm\sqrt{3}i$. It follows that

$$(\operatorname{Re} e^{\sqrt{3}it})\mathbf{v}_2 = (\cos\sqrt{3}t)\mathbf{v}_2$$

and

$$(\operatorname{Im} e^{\sqrt{3}it})\mathbf{v}_2 = (\sin\sqrt{3}t)\mathbf{v}_2$$

are also solutions to (2). Thus the general solution will be of the form

$$\mathbf{X}(t) = c_1(\cos t)\mathbf{v}_1 + c_2(\sin t)\mathbf{v}_1 + c_3(\cos\sqrt{3}t)\mathbf{v}_2 + c_4(\sin\sqrt{3}t)\mathbf{v}_2$$

$$= \begin{bmatrix} c_1\cos t + c_2\sin t + c_3\cos\sqrt{3}t + c_4\sin\sqrt{3}t \\ c_1\cos t + c_2\sin t - c_3\cos\sqrt{3}t - c_4\sin\sqrt{3}t \end{bmatrix}$$

At time $t = 0$, we have

$$x_1(0) = x_2(0) = 0 \quad \text{and} \quad x_1'(0) = x_2'(0) = 2$$

It follows that

$$
\begin{aligned}
c_1 + c_3 &= 0 \\
c_1 - c_3 &= 0
\end{aligned}
\quad \text{and} \quad
\begin{aligned}
c_2 + \sqrt{3}c_4 &= 2 \\
c_2 - \sqrt{3}c_4 &= 2
\end{aligned}
$$

and hence

$$c_1 = c_3 = c_4 = 0 \quad \text{and} \quad c_2 = 2$$

Therefore, the solution to the initial value problem is simply

$$\mathbf{X}(t) = \begin{bmatrix} 2\sin t \\ 2\sin t \end{bmatrix}$$

The masses will oscillate with frequency 1 and amplitude 2.

APPLICATION 3: VIBRATIONS OF A BUILDING

For another example of a physical system, we consider the vibrations of a building. If the building has k stories, we can represent the horizontal deflections of the stories at time t by the vector function $\mathbf{Y}(t) = (y_1(t), y_2(t), \ldots, y_k(t))^T$. The motion of a building can be modeled by a second-order system of differential equations of the form

$$M\mathbf{Y}''(t) = K\mathbf{Y}(t)$$

The *mass matrix* M is a diagonal matrix whose entries correspond to the concentrated weights of each level. The entries of the *stiffness matrix* K are determined by the spring constants of the supporting structures. Solutions to the equation are of the form $\mathbf{Y}(t) = e^{i\sigma t}\mathbf{x}$, where $\mathbf{x}$ is an eigenvector of $A = M^{-1}K$ belonging to an eigenvalue λ, and σ is a square root of λ.

EXERCISES

1. Find the general solution to each of the following systems.

(a) $\begin{aligned} y_1' &= y_1 + y_2 \\ y_2' &= -2y_1 + 4y_2 \end{aligned}$

(b) $\begin{aligned} y_1' &= 2y_1 + 4y_2 \\ y_2' &= -y_1 - 3y_2 \end{aligned}$

(c) $\begin{aligned} y_1' &= y_1 - 2y_2 \\ y_2' &= -2y_1 + 4y_2 \end{aligned}$

(d) $\begin{aligned} y_1' &= y_1 - y_2 \\ y_2' &= y_1 + y_2 \end{aligned}$

(e) $\begin{aligned} y_1' &= 3y_1 - 2y_2 \\ y_2' &= 2y_1 + 3y_2 \end{aligned}$

(f) $\begin{aligned} y_1' &= y_1 + y_3 \\ y_2' &= 2y_2 + 6y_3 \\ y_3' &= y_2 + 3y_3 \end{aligned}$

2. Solve each of the following initial value problems.

(a) $y_1' = -y_1 + 2y_2$ $y_1(0) = 3, y_2(0) = 1$

      $y_2' = 2y_1 - y_2$

(b) $y_1' = y_1 - 2y_2$ $y_1(0) = 1, y_2(0) = -2$

      $y_2' = 2y_1 + y_2$

(c) $y_1' = 2y_1 - 6y_3$ $y_1(0) = y_2(0) = y_3(0) = 2$

      $y_2' = y_1 - 3y_3$

      $y_3' = y_2 - 2y_3$

(d) $y_1' = y_1 + 2y_3$ $y_1(0) = y_2(0) = 1, y_3(0) = 4$

      $y_2' = y_2 - y_3$

      $y_3' = y_1 + y_2 + y_3$

3. Given

$$\mathbf{Y} = c_1 e^{\lambda_1 t} \mathbf{x}_1 + c_2 e^{\lambda_2 t} \mathbf{x}_2 + \cdots + c_n e^{\lambda_n t} \mathbf{x}_n$$

is the solution to the initial value problem

$$\mathbf{Y}' = A\mathbf{Y}, \qquad \mathbf{Y}(0) = \mathbf{Y}_0$$

(a) Show that

$$\mathbf{Y}_0 = c_1 \mathbf{x}_1 + c_2 \mathbf{x}_2 + \cdots + c_n \mathbf{x}_n$$

(b) Let $X = (\mathbf{x}_1, \ldots, \mathbf{x}_n)$ and $\mathbf{c} = (c_1, \ldots, c_n)^T$. Assuming that the vectors $\mathbf{x}_1, \ldots, \mathbf{x}_n$ are linearly independent, show that $\mathbf{c} = X^{-1} \mathbf{Y}_0$.

4. Two tanks each contain 100 liters of a mixture. Initially, the mixture in tank A contains 40 grams of salt while tank B contains 20 grams of salt. Liquid is pumped in and out of the tanks as shown in the figure. Determine the amount of salt in each tank at time t.

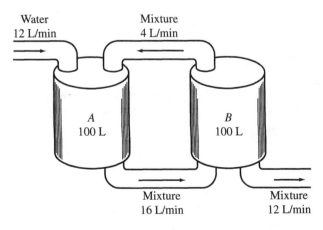

Water
12 L/min

Mixture
4 L/min

A
100 L

B
100 L

Mixture
16 L/min

Mixture
12 L/min

5. Find the general solution to each of the following:

(a) $y_1'' = -2y_2$ (b) $y_1'' = 2y_1 + y_2'$

      $y_2'' = y_1 + 3y_2$ $y_2'' = 2y_2 + y_1'$

6. Solve the initial value problem

$$y_1'' = -2y_2 + \; y_1' + 2y_2'$$
$$y_2'' = \quad 2y_1 + 2y_1' - \; y_2'$$
$$y_1(0) = 1, \qquad y_2(0) = 0, \qquad y_1'(0) = -3, \qquad y_2'(0) = 2$$

7. In the second application problem, assume that the solutions are of the form $x_1 = a_1 \sin \sigma t$, $x_2 = a_2 \sin \sigma t$. Substitute these expressions into the system and solve for the frequency σ and the amplitudes a_1 and a_2.

8. Solve the second application problem with the initial conditions

$$x_1(0) = x_2(0) = 1, \qquad x_1'(0) = 4, \qquad \text{and} \qquad x_2'(0) = 2$$

9. Two masses are connected by springs as shown in the diagram. Both springs have the same spring constant, and the end of the first spring is fixed. If x_1 and x_2 represent the displacements from the equilibrium position, derive a system of second-order differential equations that describes the motion of the system.

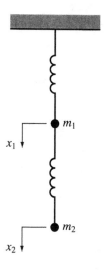

10. Three masses are connected by a series of springs between two fixed points as shown in the figure. Assume that the springs all have the same spring constant, and let $x_1(t)$, $x_2(t)$, and $x_3(t)$ represent the displacements of the respective masses at time t.

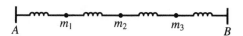

(a) Derive a system of second-order differential equations that describes the motion of this system.

(b) Solve the system if $m_1 = m_3 = \frac{1}{3}$, $m_2 = \frac{1}{4}$, $k = 1$, and

$$x_1(0) = x_2(0) = x_3(0) = 1$$

$$x_1'(0) = x_2'(0) = x_3'(0) = 0$$

11. Transform the nth-order equation

$$y^{(n)} = a_0 y + a_1 y' + \cdots + a_{n-1} y^{(n-1)}$$

into a system of first-order equations by setting $y_1 = y$ and $y_j = y'_{j-1}$ for $j = 2, \ldots, n$. Determine the characteristic polynomial of the coefficient matrix of this system.

3 DIAGONALIZATION

In this section we consider the problem of factoring an $n \times n$ matrix A into a product of the form XDX^{-1}, where D is diagonal. We will give a necessary and sufficient condition for the existence of such a factorization and look at a number of examples. We begin by showing that eigenvectors belonging to distinct eigenvalues are linearly independent.

▶ **THEOREM 6.3.1** *If $\lambda_1, \lambda_2, \ldots, \lambda_k$ are distinct eigenvalues of an $n \times n$ matrix A with corresponding eigenvectors $\mathbf{x}_1, \mathbf{x}_2, \ldots, \mathbf{x}_k$, then $\mathbf{x}_1, \ldots, \mathbf{x}_k$ are linearly independent.*

▶ *Proof.* Let r be the dimension of the subspace of R^n spanned by $\mathbf{x}_1, \ldots, \mathbf{x}_k$ and suppose that $r < k$. We may assume (reordering the $\mathbf{x}_i$'s and λ_i's if necessary) that $\mathbf{x}_1, \ldots, \mathbf{x}_r$ are linearly independent. Since $\mathbf{x}_1, \mathbf{x}_2, \ldots, \mathbf{x}_r, \mathbf{x}_{r+1}$ are linearly dependent, there exist scalars $c_1, \ldots, c_r, c_{r+1}$ not all zero such that

$$(1) \qquad c_1 \mathbf{x}_1 + \cdots + c_r \mathbf{x}_r + c_{r+1} \mathbf{x}_{r+1} = \mathbf{0}$$

Note that c_{r+1} must be nonzero; otherwise, $\mathbf{x}_1, \ldots, \mathbf{x}_r$ would be dependent. So $c_{r+1} \mathbf{x}_{r+1} \neq \mathbf{0}$ and hence $c_1, \ldots, c_r$ cannot all be zero. Multiplying (1) by A, we get

$$c_1 A \mathbf{x}_1 + \cdots + c_r A \mathbf{x}_r + c_{r+1} A \mathbf{x}_{r+1} = \mathbf{0}$$

or

$$(2) \qquad c_1 \lambda_1 \mathbf{x}_1 + \cdots + c_r \lambda_r \mathbf{x}_r + c_{r+1} \lambda_{r+1} \mathbf{x}_{r+1} = \mathbf{0}$$

Subtracting λ_{r+1} times (1) from (2) gives

$$c_1 (\lambda_1 - \lambda_{r+1}) \mathbf{x}_1 + \cdots + c_r (\lambda_r - \lambda_{r+1}) \mathbf{x}_r = \mathbf{0}$$

This contradicts the independence of $\mathbf{x}_1, \ldots, \mathbf{x}_r$. Therefore, r must equal k. ◀

▶ **DEFINITION** An $n \times n$ matrix A is said to be **diagonalizable** if there exists a nonsingular matrix X and a diagonal matrix D such that

$$X^{-1} A X = D$$

We say that X **diagonalizes** A. ◀

▶ **THEOREM 6.3.2** *An $n \times n$ matrix A is diagonalizable if and only if A has n linearly independent eigenvectors.*

▶*Proof.* Suppose that the matrix A has n linearly independent eigenvectors $\mathbf{x}_1, \mathbf{x}_2, \ldots, \mathbf{x}_n$. Let λ_i be the eigenvalue of A corresponding to $\mathbf{x}_i$ for each i. (Some of the λ_i's may be equal.) Let X be the matrix whose jth column vector is $\mathbf{x}_j$ for $j = 1, \ldots, n$. It follows that $A\mathbf{x}_j = \lambda_j \mathbf{x}_j$ is the jth column vector of AX. Thus

$$AX = (A\mathbf{x}_1, A\mathbf{x}_2, \ldots, A\mathbf{x}_n)$$

$$= (\lambda_1 \mathbf{x}_1, \lambda_2 \mathbf{x}_2, \ldots, \lambda_n \mathbf{x}_n)$$

$$= (\mathbf{x}_1, \mathbf{x}_2, \ldots, \mathbf{x}_n) \begin{bmatrix} \lambda_1 & & & \\ & \lambda_2 & & \\ & & \ddots & \\ & & & \lambda_n \end{bmatrix}$$

$$= XD$$

Since X has n linearly independent column vectors, it follows that X is nonsingular and hence

$$D = X^{-1}XD = X^{-1}AX$$

Conversely, suppose that A is diagonalizable. Then there exists a nonsingular matrix X such that $AX = XD$. If $\mathbf{x}_1, \mathbf{x}_2, \ldots, \mathbf{x}_n$ are the column vectors of X, then

$$A\mathbf{x}_j = \lambda_j \mathbf{x}_j \qquad (\lambda_j = d_{jj})$$

for each j. Thus, for each j, λ_j is an eigenvalue of A and $\mathbf{x}_j$ is an eigenvector belonging to λ_j. Since the column vectors of X are linearly independent, it follows that A has n linearly independent eigenvectors.   ◀

Remarks

1. If A is diagonalizable, then the column vectors of the diagonalizing matrix X are eigenvectors of A, and the diagonal elements of D are the corresponding eigenvalues of A.

2. The diagonalizing matrix X is not unique. Reordering the columns of a given diagonalizing matrix X or multiplying them by nonzero scalars will produce a new diagonalizing matrix.

3. If A is $n \times n$ and A has n distinct eigenvalues, then A is diagonalizable. If the eigenvalues are not distinct, then A may or may not be diagonalizable depending on whether A has n linearly independent eigenvectors.

4. If A is diagonalizable, then A can be factored into a product XDX^{-1}.   ◀

It follows from remark 4 that

$$A^2 = (XDX^{-1})(XDX^{-1}) = XD^2X^{-1}$$

and, in general,

$$A^k = XD^k X^{-1}$$

$$= X \begin{pmatrix} (\lambda_1)^k & & & \\ & (\lambda_2)^k & & \\ & & \ddots & \\ & & & (\lambda_n)^k \end{pmatrix} X^{-1}$$

Once we have a factorization $A = XDX^{-1}$, it is easy to compute powers of A.

EXAMPLE 1. Let

$$A = \begin{bmatrix} 2 & -3 \\ 2 & -5 \end{bmatrix}$$

The eigenvalues of A are $\lambda_1 = 1$ and $\lambda_2 = -4$. Corresponding to λ_1 and λ_2, we have the eigenvectors $\mathbf{x}_1 = (3, 1)^T$ and $\mathbf{x}_2 = (1, 2)^T$. Let

$$X = \begin{bmatrix} 3 & 1 \\ 1 & 2 \end{bmatrix}$$

It follows that

$$X^{-1}AX = \frac{1}{5} \begin{bmatrix} 2 & -1 \\ -1 & 3 \end{bmatrix} \begin{bmatrix} 2 & -3 \\ 2 & -5 \end{bmatrix} \begin{bmatrix} 3 & 1 \\ 1 & 2 \end{bmatrix}$$

$$= \begin{bmatrix} 1 & 0 \\ 0 & -4 \end{bmatrix}$$

and

$$XDX^{-1} = \begin{bmatrix} 3 & 1 \\ 1 & 2 \end{bmatrix} \begin{bmatrix} 1 & 0 \\ 0 & -4 \end{bmatrix} \begin{bmatrix} \frac{2}{5} & -\frac{1}{5} \\ -\frac{1}{5} & \frac{3}{5} \end{bmatrix} = \begin{bmatrix} 2 & -3 \\ 2 & -5 \end{bmatrix} = A \qquad \blacktriangleleft$$

EXAMPLE 2. Let

$$A = \begin{bmatrix} 3 & -1 & -2 \\ 2 & 0 & -2 \\ 2 & -1 & -1 \end{bmatrix}$$

It is easily seen that the eigenvalues of A are $\lambda_1 = 0$, $\lambda_2 = 1$, $\lambda_3 = 1$. Corresponding to $\lambda_1 = 0$, we have the eigenvector $(1, 1, 1)^T$, and corresponding to $\lambda = 1$, we have the eigenvectors $(1, 2, 0)^T$ and $(0, -2, 1)^T$. Let

$$X = \begin{pmatrix} 1 & 1 & 0 \\ 1 & 2 & -2 \\ 1 & 0 & 1 \end{pmatrix}$$

It follows that

$$XDX^{-1} = \begin{pmatrix} 1 & 1 & 0 \\ 1 & 2 & -2 \\ 1 & 0 & 1 \end{pmatrix} \begin{pmatrix} 0 & 0 & 0 \\ 0 & 1 & 0 \\ 0 & 0 & 1 \end{pmatrix} \begin{pmatrix} -2 & 1 & 2 \\ 3 & -1 & -2 \\ 2 & -1 & -1 \end{pmatrix}$$

$$= \begin{pmatrix} 3 & -1 & -2 \\ 2 & 0 & -2 \\ 2 & -1 & -1 \end{pmatrix}$$

$$= A$$

Even though $\lambda = 1$ is a multiple eigenvalue, the matrix can still be diagonalized since there are three linearly independent eigenvectors. Note also that

$$A^k = XD^kX^{-1} = XDX^{-1} = A$$

for any $k \geq 1$. ◀

If an $n \times n$ matrix A has fewer than n linearly independent eigenvectors, we say that A is *defective*. It follows from Theorem 6.3.2 that a defective matrix is not diagonalizable.

EXAMPLE 3. Let

$$A = \begin{pmatrix} 1 & 1 \\ 0 & 1 \end{pmatrix}$$

The eigenvalues of A are both equal to 1. Any eigenvector corresponding to $\lambda = 1$ must be a multiple of $\mathbf{x}_1 = (1, 0)^T$. Thus A is defective and cannot be diagonalized. ◀

EXAMPLE 4. Let

$$A = \begin{pmatrix} 2 & 0 & 0 \\ 0 & 4 & 0 \\ 1 & 0 & 2 \end{pmatrix} \quad \text{and} \quad B = \begin{pmatrix} 2 & 0 & 0 \\ -1 & 4 & 0 \\ -3 & 6 & 2 \end{pmatrix}$$

A and B both have the same eigenvalues

$$\lambda_1 = 4, \qquad \lambda_2 = \lambda_3 = 2$$

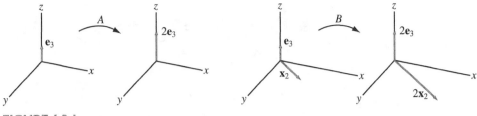

The eigenspace of A corresponding to $\lambda_1 = 4$ is spanned by $\mathbf{e}_2$, and the eigenspace corresponding to $\lambda = 2$ is spanned by $\mathbf{e}_3$. Since A has only two linearly independent eigenvectors, it is defective. On the other hand, the matrix B has eigenvector $\mathbf{x}_1 = (0, 1, 3)^T$ corresponding to $\lambda_1 = 4$ and eigenvectors $\mathbf{x}_2 = (2, 1, 0)^T$ and $\mathbf{e}_3$ corresponding to $\lambda = 2$. Thus B has three linearly independent eigenvectors and consequently is not defective. Even though $\lambda = 2$ is an eigenvalue of multiplicity 2, the matrix B is nondefective since the corresponding eigenspace has dimension 2.

Geometrically, the matrix B has the effect of stretching two linearly independent vectors by a factor of 2. We can think of the eigenvalue $\lambda = 2$ as having *geometric multiplicity* 2. On the other hand, the matrix A only stretches vectors along the z axis by a factor of 2. In this case the eigenvalue $\lambda = 2$ has algebraic multiplicity 2, but its geometric multiplicity is only 1 (see Figure 6.3.1).   ◀

APPLICATION 1: MARKOV CHAINS

In Section 1 of this chapter we studied a simple matrix model for predicting the number of married and single women in a certain town each year. Given an initial vector $\mathbf{x}_0$ whose coordinates represent the current number of married and single women, we were able to predict the number of married and single women in future years by computing

$$\mathbf{x}_1 = A\mathbf{x}_0, \ \mathbf{x}_2 = A\mathbf{x}_1, \ \mathbf{x}_3 = A\mathbf{x}_2, \ldots$$

If we scale the initial vector so that its entries indicate the proportions of the population that are married and single, then the coordinates of $\mathbf{x}_n$ will indicate the proportions of married and single women after n years. The sequence of vectors that we generate in this manner is an example of a *Markov chain*. Markov chain models occur in a wide variety of applied fields.

▶ **DEFINITION** A **stochastic process** is any sequence of experiments for which the outcome at any stage depends on chance. A **Markov process** is a stochastic process with the following properties:

  (i) The set of possible outcomes or states is finite.
  (ii) The probability of the next outcome depends only on the previous outcome.
  (iii) The probabilities are constant over time.   ◀

The following is an example of a Markov process.

TABLE I

TRANSITION PROBABILITIES FOR VEHICLE
LEASING

	Current Lease			
Sedan	Sports Car	Minivan	Sport Utility	Next Lease
0.80	0.10	0.05	0.05	**Sedan**
0.10	0.80	0.05	0.05	**Sports Car**
0.05	0.05	0.80	0.10	**Minivan**
0.05	0.05	0.10	0.80	**Four-wheel**

EXAMPLE 5. [Automobile Leasing] An automobile dealer leases four types of vehicles: four-door sedans, sports cars, minivans, and sport utility vehicles. The term of the lease is 2 years. At the end of the term, customers must renegotiate the lease and choose a new vehicle.

The automobile leasing can be viewed as a process with four possible outcomes. The probability of each outcome can be estimated by reviewing records of previous leases. These records indicate that 80 percent of the customers currently leasing sedans will continue doing so in the next lease. Furthermore, 10 percent of the customers currently leasing sports cars will switch to sedans. In addition, 5 percent of the customers driving minivans or sport utility vehicles will also switch to sedans. These results are summarized in the first row of Table 1. The second row indicates the percentages of customers that will lease sports cars the next time, and the final two rows give the percentages that will lease minivans and four-wheel vehicles, respectively.

Suppose that initially there are 200 sedans leased and 100 of each of the other three types of vehicles. If we set

$$
A = \begin{bmatrix} 0.80 & 0.10 & 0.05 & 0.05 \\ 0.10 & 0.80 & 0.05 & 0.05 \\ 0.05 & 0.05 & 0.80 & 0.10 \\ 0.05 & 0.05 & 0.10 & 0.80 \end{bmatrix} \qquad \mathbf{x}_0 = \begin{bmatrix} 200 \\ 100 \\ 100 \\ 100 \end{bmatrix}
$$

then we can determine how many people will lease each type of vehicle 2 years later by setting

$$
\mathbf{x}_1 = A\mathbf{x}_0 = \begin{bmatrix} 0.80 & 0.10 & 0.05 & 0.05 \\ 0.10 & 0.80 & 0.05 & 0.05 \\ 0.05 & 0.05 & 0.80 & 0.10 \\ 0.05 & 0.05 & 0.10 & 0.80 \end{bmatrix} \begin{bmatrix} 200 \\ 100 \\ 100 \\ 100 \end{bmatrix} = \begin{bmatrix} 180 \\ 110 \\ 105 \\ 105 \end{bmatrix}
$$

We can predict the numbers for future leases by setting

$$
\mathbf{x}_{n+1} = A\mathbf{x}_n \quad \text{for} \quad n = 1, 2, \ldots
$$

The vectors x_i produced in this manner are referred to as *state vectors*, and the sequence of state vectors is called a *Markov chain*. The matrix A is referred to as a transition matrix. The entries of each column of A are nonnegative numbers that add up to 1. Each column can be viewed as a *probability vector*. For example, the first column of A corresponds to individuals currently leasing sedans. The entries in this column are the probabilities of choosing each type of vehicle when the lease is renewed.

In general, a matrix is said to be *stochastic* if its entries are nonnegative and the entries in each column add up to 1. The columns of a stochastic matrix can be viewed as probability vectors.

If we divide the entries of the initial vector by 500 (the total number of customers), then the entries of the new initial state vector $x_0 = (0.40, 0.20, 0.20, 0.20)^T$ represent the proportions of the population that rent each type of vehicle. The entries of x_1 will represent the proportions for the next lease. Thus x_0 and x_1 are probability vectors, and it is easily seen that the succeeding state vectors in the chain will all be probability vectors.

The long-range behavior of the process is determined by the eigenvalues and eigenvectors of the transition matrix A. The eigenvalues of A are $\lambda_1 = 1$, $\lambda_2 = 0.8$, $\lambda_3 = \lambda_4 = 0.7$ Even though A has a multiple eigenvalue, it does have four linearly independent eigenvectors and hence it can be diagonalized. If the eigenvectors are used to form a diagonalizing matrix Y, then

$$A = YDY^{-1}$$

$$= \begin{bmatrix} 1 & -1 & 0 & 1 \\ 1 & -1 & 0 & -1 \\ 1 & 1 & 1 & 0 \\ 1 & 1 & -1 & 0 \end{bmatrix} \begin{bmatrix} 1 & 0 & 0 & 0 \\ 0 & \frac{8}{10} & 0 & 0 \\ 0 & 0 & \frac{7}{10} & 0 \\ 0 & 0 & 0 & \frac{7}{10} \end{bmatrix} \begin{bmatrix} \frac{1}{4} & \frac{1}{4} & \frac{1}{4} & \frac{1}{4} \\ -\frac{1}{4} & -\frac{1}{4} & \frac{1}{4} & \frac{1}{4} \\ 0 & 0 & \frac{1}{2} & -\frac{1}{2} \\ \frac{1}{2} & -\frac{1}{2} & 0 & 0 \end{bmatrix}$$

The state vectors are computed by setting

$$x_n = YD^nY^{-1}x_0$$
$$= YD^n(0.25, -0.05, 0, 0.10)^T$$
$$= Y(0.25, -0.05(0.8)^n, 0, 0.10(0.7)^n)^T$$

$$= 0.25 \begin{bmatrix} 1 \\ 1 \\ 1 \\ 1 \end{bmatrix} - 0.05(0.8)^n \begin{bmatrix} -1 \\ -1 \\ 1 \\ 1 \end{bmatrix} + 0.10(0.7)^n \begin{bmatrix} 1 \\ -1 \\ 0 \\ 0 \end{bmatrix}$$

As n increases, x_n approaches the steady-state vector

$$x = (0.25, 0.25, 0.25, 0.25)^T$$

Thus the Markov chain model predicts that in the long run the leases will be divided equally among the four types of vehicles. ◁

Not all Markov chains converge to a steady-state vector. However, if all the entries of the transition matrix A are positive, then it can be shown that there is a unique steady-state vector $\mathbf{x}$ and that $A^n\mathbf{x}_0$ will converge to $\mathbf{x}$ for any initial probability vector $\mathbf{x}_0$. In fact, this result will hold if A^k has strictly positive entries even though A may have some 0 entries. A Markov process with transition matrix A is said to be *regular* if all the entries of some power of A are positive.

The steady-state vector $\mathbf{x}$ of a regular Markov chain is both a probability vector and also an eigenvector belonging to the eigenvalue $\lambda = 1$. The existence of such a vector is guaranteed by Perron's Theorem (see Section 8 of this chapter).

APPLICATION 2: SEX-LINKED GENES

Sex-linked genes are genes that are located on the X chromosome. For example, the gene for blue-green color blindness is a recessive sex-linked gene. To devise a mathematical model to describe color blindness in a given population, it is necessary to divide the population into two classes, males and females. Let $x_1^{(0)}$ be the proportion of genes for color blindness in the male population, and let $x_2^{(0)}$ be the proportion in the female population. [Since color blindness is recessive, the actual proportion of color-blind females will be less than $x_2^{(0)}$.] Since the male receives one X chromosome from the mother and none from the father, the proportion $x_1^{(1)}$ of color-blind males in the next generation will be the same as the proportion of recessive genes in the present generation of females. Since the female receives an X chromosome from each parent, the proportion $x_2^{(1)}$ of recessive genes in the next generation of females will be the average of $x_1^{(0)}$ and $x_2^{(0)}$. Thus

$$x_2^{(0)} = x_1^{(1)}$$
$$\tfrac{1}{2}x_1^{(0)} + \tfrac{1}{2}x_2^{(0)} = x_2^{(1)}$$

If $x_1^{(0)} = x_2^{(0)}$, the proportion will not change in future generations. Let us assume that $x_1^{(0)} \neq x_2^{(0)}$ and write the system as a matrix equation.

$$\begin{bmatrix} 0 & 1 \\ \tfrac{1}{2} & \tfrac{1}{2} \end{bmatrix} \begin{bmatrix} x_1^{(0)} \\ x_2^{(0)} \end{bmatrix} = \begin{bmatrix} x_1^{(1)} \\ x_2^{(1)} \end{bmatrix}$$

Let A denote the coefficient matrix, and let $\mathbf{x}^{(n)} = (x_1^{(n)}, x_2^{(n)})^T$ denote the proportion of color-blind genes in the male and female populations of the $(n+1)$st generation. Thus

$$\mathbf{x}^{(n)} = A^n\mathbf{x}^{(0)}$$

To compute A^n, we note that A has eigenvalues 1 and $-\tfrac{1}{2}$ and consequently can be factored into a product

$$A = \begin{bmatrix} 1 & -2 \\ 1 & 1 \end{bmatrix} \begin{bmatrix} 1 & 0 \\ 0 & -\tfrac{1}{2} \end{bmatrix} \begin{bmatrix} \tfrac{1}{3} & \tfrac{2}{3} \\ -\tfrac{1}{3} & \tfrac{1}{3} \end{bmatrix}$$

Thus

$$\mathbf{x}^{(n)} = \begin{bmatrix} 1 & -2 \\ 1 & 1 \end{bmatrix} \begin{bmatrix} 1 & 0 \\ 0 & -\frac{1}{2} \end{bmatrix}^n \begin{bmatrix} \frac{1}{3} & \frac{2}{3} \\ -\frac{1}{3} & \frac{1}{3} \end{bmatrix} \begin{bmatrix} x_1^{(0)} \\ x_2^{(0)} \end{bmatrix}$$

$$= \frac{1}{3} \begin{bmatrix} 1-(-\frac{1}{2})^{n-1} & 2+(-\frac{1}{2})^{n-1} \\ 1-(-\frac{1}{2})^n & 2+(-\frac{1}{2})^n \end{bmatrix} \begin{bmatrix} x_1^{(0)} \\ x_2^{(0)} \end{bmatrix}$$

and hence

$$\lim_{n \to \infty} \mathbf{x}^{(n)} = \frac{1}{3} \begin{bmatrix} 1 & 2 \\ 1 & 2 \end{bmatrix} \begin{bmatrix} x_1^{(0)} \\ x_2^{(0)} \end{bmatrix}$$

$$= \begin{bmatrix} \dfrac{x_1^{(0)} + 2x_2^{(0)}}{3} \\ \dfrac{x_1^{(0)} + 2x_2^{(0)}}{3} \end{bmatrix}$$

The proportions of genes for color blindness in the male and female populations will tend to the same value as the number of generations increases. If the proportion of color-blind men is p and over a number of generations no outsiders have entered the population, there is justification for assuming that the proportion of genes for color blindness in the female population is also p. Since color blindness is recessive, we would expect the proportion of color-blind women to be about p^2. Thus, if 1 percent of the male population is color-blind, we would expect about 0.01 percent of the female population to be color-blind.

The Exponential of a Matrix

Given a scalar a, the exponential e^a can be expressed in terms of a power series

$$e^a = 1 + a + \frac{1}{2!}a^2 + \frac{1}{3!}a^3 + \cdots$$

Similarly, for any $n \times n$ matrix A, we can define the *matrix exponential* e^A in terms of the convergent power series

(3) $$e^A = I + A + \frac{1}{2!}A^2 + \frac{1}{3!}A^3 + \cdots$$

The matrix exponential (3) occurs in a wide variety of applications. In the case of a diagonal matrix

$$D = \begin{bmatrix} \lambda_1 & & & \\ & \lambda_2 & & \\ & & \ddots & \\ & & & \lambda_n \end{bmatrix}$$

the matrix exponential is easy to compute:

$$e^D = \lim_{m \to \infty} \left(I + D + \frac{1}{2!}D^2 + \cdots + \frac{1}{m!}D^m \right)$$

$$= \lim_{m \to \infty} \begin{bmatrix} \sum_{k=1}^{m} \frac{1}{k!}\lambda_1^k & & \\ & \ddots & \\ & & \sum_{k=1}^{m} \frac{1}{k!}\lambda_n^k \end{bmatrix}$$

$$= \begin{bmatrix} e^{\lambda_1} & & & \\ & e^{\lambda_2} & & \\ & & \ddots & \\ & & & e^{\lambda_n} \end{bmatrix}$$

It is more difficult to compute the matrix exponential for a general $n \times n$ matrix A. If, however, A is diagonalizable, then

$$A^k = XD^kX^{-1} \quad \text{for} \quad k = 1, 2, \ldots$$

$$e^A = X\left(I + D + \frac{1}{2!}D^2 + \frac{1}{3!}D^3 + \cdots \right) X^{-1}$$

$$= Xe^DX^{-1}$$

EXAMPLE 6. Compute e^A for

$$A = \begin{bmatrix} -2 & -6 \\ 1 & 3 \end{bmatrix}$$

SOLUTION. The eigenvalues of A are $\lambda_1 = 1$ and $\lambda_2 = 0$ with eigenvectors $\mathbf{x}_1 = (-2, 1)^T$ and $\mathbf{x}_2 = (-3, 1)^T$. Thus

$$A = XDX^{-1} = \begin{bmatrix} -2 & -3 \\ 1 & 1 \end{bmatrix} \begin{bmatrix} 1 & 0 \\ 0 & 0 \end{bmatrix} \begin{bmatrix} 1 & 3 \\ -1 & -2 \end{bmatrix}$$

and

$$e^A = Xe^DX^{-1} = \begin{bmatrix} -2 & -3 \\ 1 & 1 \end{bmatrix} \begin{bmatrix} e^1 & 0 \\ 0 & e^0 \end{bmatrix} \begin{bmatrix} 1 & 3 \\ -1 & -2 \end{bmatrix}$$

$$= \begin{bmatrix} 3 - 2e & 6 - 6e \\ e - 1 & 3e - 2 \end{bmatrix}$$

◀

The matrix exponential can be applied to the initial value problem

(4) $$\mathbf{Y}' = A\mathbf{Y}, \qquad \mathbf{Y}(0) = \mathbf{Y}_0$$

studied in Section 2. In the case of one equation in one unknown,

$$y' = ay, \quad y(0) = y_0$$

the solution is

(5) $$y = e^{at} y_0$$

We can generalize this and express the solution to (4) in terms of the matrix exponential e^{At}, where $At = tA$ (i.e., t times the matrix A). In general, a power series can be differentiated term by term within its radius of convergence. Since the expansion of e^{At} has infinite radius of convergence, we have

$$\frac{d}{dt}e^{At} = \frac{d}{dt}\left(I + tA + \frac{1}{2!}t^2A^2 + \frac{1}{3!}t^3A^3 + \cdots\right)$$

$$= \left(A + tA^2 + \frac{1}{2!}t^2A^3 + \cdots\right)$$

$$= A\left(I + tA + \frac{1}{2!}t^2A^2 + \cdots\right)$$

$$= Ae^{At}$$

If, as in (5), we set

$$\mathbf{Y}(t) = e^{At}\mathbf{Y}_0$$

then

$$\mathbf{Y}' = Ae^{At}\mathbf{Y}_0 = A\mathbf{Y}$$

and

$$\mathbf{Y}(0) = \mathbf{Y}_0$$

Thus, the solution to

$$\mathbf{Y}' = A\mathbf{Y}, \qquad \mathbf{Y}(0) = \mathbf{Y}_0$$

is simply

(6) $$\mathbf{Y} = e^{At}\mathbf{Y}_0$$

Although the form of this solution looks different from the solutions in Section 2, there is really no difference. In Section 2 the solution was expressed in the form

$$c_1 e^{\lambda_1 t}\mathbf{x}_1 + c_2 e^{\lambda_2 t}\mathbf{x}_2 + \cdots + c_n e^{\lambda_n t}\mathbf{x}_n$$

where $\mathbf{x}_i$ was an eigenvector belonging to λ_i for $i = 1, \ldots, n$. The c_i's that satisfied the initial conditions were determined by solving a system

$$X\mathbf{c} = \mathbf{Y}_0$$

with coefficient matrix $X = (\mathbf{x}_1, \ldots, \mathbf{x}_n)$.

If A is diagonalizable, we can write (6) in the form

$$\mathbf{Y} = Xe^{Dt}X^{-1}\mathbf{Y}_0$$

Thus,

$$\mathbf{Y} = Xe^{Dt}\mathbf{c}$$

$$= (\mathbf{x}_1, \mathbf{x}_2, \dots, \mathbf{x}_n) \begin{bmatrix} c_1 e^{\lambda_1 t} \\ c_2 e^{\lambda_2 t} \\ \vdots \\ c_n e^{\lambda_n t} \end{bmatrix}$$

$$= c_1 e^{\lambda_1 t} \mathbf{x}_1 + \cdots + c_n e^{\lambda_n t} \mathbf{x}_n$$

To summarize, the solution to the initial value problem (4) is given by

$$\mathbf{Y} = e^{At}\mathbf{Y}_0$$

If A is diagonalizable, this solution can be written in the form

$$\mathbf{Y} = Xe^{Dt} X^{-1}\mathbf{Y}_0$$

$$= c_1 e^{\lambda_1 t}\mathbf{x}_1 + c_2 e^{\lambda_2 t}\mathbf{x}_2 + \cdots + c_n e^{\lambda_n t}\mathbf{x}_n \quad (\mathbf{c} = X^{-1}\mathbf{Y}_0)$$

EXAMPLE 7.   Use the matrix exponential to solve the initial value problem

$$\mathbf{Y}' = A\mathbf{Y}, \qquad \mathbf{Y}(0) = \mathbf{Y}_0$$

where

$$A = \begin{bmatrix} 3 & 4 \\ 3 & 2 \end{bmatrix}, \qquad \mathbf{Y}_0 = \begin{bmatrix} 6 \\ 1 \end{bmatrix}$$

(This problem was solved in Example 1 of Section 2.)

SOLUTION.   The eigenvalues of A are $\lambda_1 = 6$ and $\lambda_2 = -1$ with eigenvectors $\mathbf{x}_1 = (4, 3)^T$ and $\mathbf{x}_2 = (1, -1)^T$. Thus

$$A = XDX^{-1} = \begin{bmatrix} 4 & 1 \\ 3 & -1 \end{bmatrix} \begin{bmatrix} 6 & 0 \\ 0 & -1 \end{bmatrix} \begin{bmatrix} \frac{1}{7} & \frac{1}{7} \\ \frac{3}{7} & -\frac{4}{7} \end{bmatrix}$$

and the solution is given by

$$\mathbf{Y} = e^{At}\mathbf{Y}_0$$

$$= Xe^{Dt} X^{-1}\mathbf{Y}_0$$

$$= \begin{bmatrix} 4 & 1 \\ 3 & -1 \end{bmatrix} \begin{bmatrix} e^{6t} & 0 \\ 0 & e^{-t} \end{bmatrix} \begin{bmatrix} \frac{1}{7} & \frac{1}{7} \\ \frac{3}{7} & -\frac{4}{7} \end{bmatrix} \begin{bmatrix} 6 \\ 1 \end{bmatrix}$$

$$= \begin{bmatrix} 4e^{6t} + 2e^{-t} \\ 3e^{6t} - 2e^{-t} \end{bmatrix}$$

Compare this to Example 1 in Section 2.

EXAMPLE 8.   Use the matrix exponential to solve the initial value problem

$$\mathbf{Y}' = A\mathbf{Y}, \qquad \mathbf{Y}(0) = \mathbf{Y}_0$$

where

$$A = \begin{bmatrix} 0 & 1 & 0 \\ 0 & 0 & 1 \\ 0 & 0 & 0 \end{bmatrix}, \qquad \mathbf{Y}_0 = \begin{bmatrix} 2 \\ 1 \\ 4 \end{bmatrix}$$

SOLUTION.   Since the matrix A is defective, we will use the definition of the matrix exponential to compute e^{At}. Note that $A^3 = O$, so

$$e^{At} = I + tA + \frac{1}{2!}t^2A^2$$

$$= \begin{bmatrix} 1 & t & t^2/2 \\ 0 & 1 & t \\ 0 & 0 & 1 \end{bmatrix}$$

The solution to the initial value problem is given by

$$\mathbf{Y} = e^{At}\mathbf{Y}_0$$

$$= \begin{bmatrix} 1 & t & t^2/2 \\ 0 & 1 & t \\ 0 & 0 & 1 \end{bmatrix} \begin{bmatrix} 2 \\ 1 \\ 4 \end{bmatrix}$$

$$= \begin{bmatrix} 2+t+2t^2 \\ 1+4t \\ 4 \end{bmatrix} \qquad \blacktriangleleft$$

EXERCISES

1. In each of the following, factor the matrix A into a product XDX^{-1}, where D is diagonal.

(a) $A = \begin{bmatrix} 0 & 1 \\ 1 & 0 \end{bmatrix}$

(b) $A = \begin{bmatrix} 5 & 6 \\ -2 & -2 \end{bmatrix}$

(c) $A = \begin{bmatrix} 2 & -8 \\ 1 & -4 \end{bmatrix}$

(d) $A = \begin{bmatrix} 2 & 2 & 1 \\ 0 & 1 & 2 \\ 0 & 0 & -1 \end{bmatrix}$

(e) $A = \begin{bmatrix} 1 & 0 & 0 \\ -2 & 1 & 3 \\ 1 & 1 & -1 \end{bmatrix}$ (f) $A = \begin{bmatrix} 1 & 2 & -1 \\ 2 & 4 & -2 \\ 3 & 6 & -3 \end{bmatrix}$

2. For each of the matrices in Exercise 1, use the XDX^{-1} factorization to compute A^6.

3. For each of the nonsingular matrices in Exercise 1, use the XDX^{-1} factorization to compute A^{-1}.

4. For each of the following, find a matrix B such that $B^2 = A$.

(a) $A = \begin{bmatrix} 2 & 1 \\ -2 & -1 \end{bmatrix}$ (b) $A = \begin{bmatrix} 9 & -5 & 3 \\ 0 & 4 & 3 \\ 0 & 0 & 1 \end{bmatrix}$

5. Let A be a nondefective $n \times n$ matrix with diagonalizing matrix X. Show that the matrix $Y = (X^{-1})^T$ diagonalizes A^T.

6. Let A be a diagonalizable matrix whose eigenvalues are all either 1 or -1. Show that $A^{-1} = A$.

7. Show that any 3×3 matrix of the form

$$\begin{bmatrix} a & 1 & 0 \\ 0 & a & 1 \\ 0 & 0 & b \end{bmatrix}$$

is defective.

8. For each of the following, find all possible values of the scalar α that make the matrix defective or show that no such values exist.

(a) $\begin{bmatrix} 1 & 1 & 0 \\ 1 & 1 & 0 \\ 0 & 0 & \alpha \end{bmatrix}$ (b) $\begin{bmatrix} 1 & 1 & 1 \\ 1 & 1 & 1 \\ 0 & 0 & \alpha \end{bmatrix}$

(c) $\begin{bmatrix} 1 & 2 & 0 \\ 2 & 1 & 0 \\ 2 & -1 & \alpha \end{bmatrix}$ (d) $\begin{bmatrix} 4 & 6 & -2 \\ -1 & -1 & 1 \\ 0 & 0 & \alpha \end{bmatrix}$

9. Let A be a 4×4 matrix and let λ be an eigenvalue of multiplicity 3. If $A - \lambda I$ has rank 1, is A defective? Explain.

10. Let A be an $n \times n$ matrix with positive real eigenvalues $\lambda_1 > \lambda_2 > \cdots > \lambda_n$. Let $\mathbf{x}_i$ be an eigenvector belonging to λ_i for each i, and let $\mathbf{x} = \alpha_1 \mathbf{x}_1 + \cdots + \alpha_n \mathbf{x}_n$.

(a) Show that $A^m \mathbf{x} = \sum_{i=1}^{n} \alpha_i \lambda_i^m \mathbf{x}_i$.

(b) If $\lambda_1 = 1$, show that $\lim_{m \to \infty} A^m \mathbf{x} = \alpha_1 \mathbf{x}_1$.

11. Let A be an $n \times n$ matrix with an eigenvalue λ of multiplicity n. Show that A is diagonalizable if and only if $A = \lambda I$.

12. Show that a nonzero nilpotent matrix is defective.

13. Let A be a diagonalizable matrix and let X be the diagonalizing matrix. Show that the column vectors of X that correspond to nonzero eigenvalues of A form a basis for $R(A)$.

14. It follows from Exercise 13 that for a diagonalizable matrix the number of nonzero eigenvalues (counted according to multiplicity) equals the rank of the matrix. Give an example of a defective matrix whose rank is not equal to the number of nonzero eigenvalues.

15. Let A be an $n \times n$ matrix and let λ be an eigenvalue of A whose eigenspace has dimension k, where $1 < k < n$. Any basis $\{\mathbf{x}_1, \dots, \mathbf{x}_k\}$ for the eigenspace can be extended to a basis $\{\mathbf{x}_1, \dots, \mathbf{x}_n\}$ for R^n. Let $X = (\mathbf{x}_1, \dots, \mathbf{x}_n)$ and $B = X^{-1}AX$.

(a) Show that B is of the form

$$\begin{bmatrix} \lambda I & B_{12} \\ O & B_{22} \end{bmatrix}$$

where I is the $k \times k$ identity matrix.

(b) Use Theorem 6.1.1 to show that λ is an eigenvalue of A with multiplicity at least k.

16. Let $\mathbf{x}, \mathbf{y}$ be nonzero vectors in R^n, $n \geq 2$, and let $A = \mathbf{x}\mathbf{y}^T$. Show that:

(a) Zero is an eigenvalue of A with $n - 1$ linearly independent eigenvectors and consequently has multiplicity at least $n - 1$ (see Exercise 15).

(b) The remaining eigenvalue of A is

$$\lambda_n = \operatorname{tr} A = \mathbf{x}^T \mathbf{y}$$

and $\mathbf{x}$ is an eigenvector belonging to λ_n.

(c) If $\lambda_n = \mathbf{x}^T \mathbf{y} \neq 0$, then A is diagonalizable.

17. Let A be a diagonalizable $n \times n$ matrix. Prove that if B is any matrix that is similar to A, then B is diagonalizable.

18. Show that if A and B are two $n \times n$ matrices that both have the same diagonalizing matrix X, then $AB = BA$.

19. Each year employees at a company are given the option of donating to a local charity as part of a payroll deduction plan. In general, 80 percent of the employees enrolled in the plan in any one year will choose to sign up again the following year, and 30 percent of the unenrolled will choose to enroll the

following year. Determine the transition matrix for the Markov process and find the steady-state vector. What percentage of employees would you expect to find enrolled in the program in the long run?

20. The city of Mawtookit maintains a constant population of 300,000 people from year to year. A political science study estimated that there were 150,000 Independents, 90,000 Democrats, and 60,000 Republicans in the town. It was also estimated that each year 20 percent of the Independents become Democrats and 10 percent become Republicans. Similarly, 20 percent of the Democrats become Independents and 10 percent become Republicans, while 10 percent of the Republicans defect to the Democrats and 10 percent become Independents each year. Let

$$\mathbf{x} = \begin{bmatrix} 150{,}000 \\ 90{,}000 \\ 60{,}000 \end{bmatrix}$$

and let $\mathbf{x}^{(1)}$ be a vector representing the number of people in each group after 1 year.

(a) Find a matrix A such that $A\mathbf{x} = \mathbf{x}^{(1)}$.

(b) Show that $\lambda_1 = 1.0$, $\lambda_2 = 0.5$, and $\lambda_3 = 0.7$ are the eigenvalues of A, and factor A into a product XDX^{-1}, where D is diagonal.

(c) Which group will dominate in the long run? Justify your answer by computing $\lim_{n \to \infty} A^n \mathbf{x}$.

21. Show that if A is a stochastic matrix then $\lambda = 1$ is an eigenvalue of A.

22. A matrix A is said to be *doubly stochastic* if both A and A^T are stochastic. Show that if A is an $n \times n$ doubly stochastic matrix then $\mathbf{x} = \left(\frac{1}{n}, \frac{1}{n}, \dots, \frac{1}{n} \right)^T$ is an eigenvector belonging to $\lambda = 1$.

23. Use the definition of the matrix exponential to compute e^A for each of the following matrices:

(a) $A = \begin{bmatrix} 1 & 1 \\ -1 & -1 \end{bmatrix}$ (b) $A = \begin{bmatrix} 1 & 1 \\ 0 & 1 \end{bmatrix}$ (c) $A = \begin{bmatrix} 1 & 0 & -1 \\ 0 & 1 & 0 \\ 0 & 0 & 1 \end{bmatrix}$

24. Compute e^A for each of the following matrices:

(a) $A = \begin{bmatrix} -2 & -1 \\ 6 & 3 \end{bmatrix}$ (b) $A = \begin{bmatrix} 3 & 4 \\ -2 & -3 \end{bmatrix}$ (c) $A = \begin{bmatrix} 1 & 1 & 1 \\ -1 & -1 & -1 \\ 1 & 1 & 1 \end{bmatrix}$

25. In each of the following, solve the initial value problem $\mathbf{Y}' = A\mathbf{Y}$, $\mathbf{Y}(0) = \mathbf{Y}_0$ by computing $e^{At}\mathbf{Y}_0$.

(a) $A = \begin{bmatrix} 1 & -2 \\ 0 & -1 \end{bmatrix}$, $\quad \mathbf{Y}_0 = \begin{bmatrix} 1 \\ 1 \end{bmatrix}$

(b) $A = \begin{bmatrix} 2 & 3 \\ -1 & -2 \end{bmatrix}$, $\quad \mathbf{Y}_0 = \begin{bmatrix} -4 \\ 2 \end{bmatrix}$

(c) $A = \begin{bmatrix} 1 & 1 & 1 \\ 0 & 0 & 1 \\ 0 & 0 & -1 \end{bmatrix}$, $\quad \mathbf{Y}_0 = \begin{bmatrix} 1 \\ 1 \\ 1 \end{bmatrix}$

(d) $A = \begin{bmatrix} 1 & 1 & 1 \\ 1 & 0 & 1 \\ -1 & -1 & -1 \end{bmatrix}$, $\quad \mathbf{Y}_0 = \begin{bmatrix} 1 \\ 1 \\ -1 \end{bmatrix}$

26. Let λ be an eigenvalue of an $n \times n$ matrix A, and let $\mathbf{x}$ be an eigenvector belonging to λ. Show that e^λ is an eigenvalue of e^A and $\mathbf{x}$ is an eigenvector of e^A belonging to e^λ.

27. Show that e^A is nonsingular for any diagonalizable matrix A.

28. Let A be a diagonalizable matrix with characteristic polynomial

$$p(\lambda) = a_1 \lambda^n + a_2 \lambda^{n-1} + \cdots + a_{n+1}$$

(a) If D is a diagonal matrix whose diagonal entries are the eigenvalues of A, show that

$$p(D) = a_1 D^n + a_2 D^{n-1} + \cdots + a_{n+1} I = O$$

(b) Show that $p(A) = O$.

(c) Show that if $a_{n+1} \neq 0$, then A is nonsingular and $A^{-1} = q(A)$ for some polynomial q of degree less than n.

ANSWERS TO SELECTED EXERCISES

Chapter 1

1. (a) $(11, 3)$;   (b) $(4, 1, 3)$;   (c) $(-2, 0, 3, 1)$;   (d) $(-2, 3, 0, 3, 1)$

2. (a) $\begin{bmatrix} 1 & -3 \\ 0 & 2 \end{bmatrix}$;   (b) $\begin{bmatrix} 1 & 1 & 1 \\ 0 & 2 & 1 \\ 0 & 0 & 3 \end{bmatrix}$;   (c) $\begin{bmatrix} 1 & 2 & 2 & 1 \\ 0 & 3 & 1 & -2 \\ 0 & 0 & -1 & 2 \\ 0 & 0 & 0 & 4 \end{bmatrix}$

3. (a) One solution. The two lines intersect at the point $(3, 1)$.
   (b) No solution. The lines are parallel.
   (c) Infinitely many solutions. Both equations represent the same line.
   (d) No solution. Each pair of lines intersect in a point; however, there is no point that is on all three lines.

4. (a) $\left[\begin{array}{cc|c} 1 & 1 & 4 \\ 1 & -1 & 2 \end{array} \right]$;   (b) $\left[\begin{array}{cc|c} 1 & 2 & 4 \\ -2 & -4 & 4 \end{array} \right]$;   (c) $\left[\begin{array}{cc|c} 2 & -1 & 3 \\ -4 & 2 & -6 \end{array} \right]$;   (d) $\left[\begin{array}{cc|c} 1 & 1 & 1 \\ 1 & -1 & 1 \\ -1 & 3 & 3 \end{array} \right]$

6. (a) $(1, -2)$;   (b) $(3, 2)$;   (c) $(\frac{1}{2}, \frac{2}{3})$;   (d) $(1, 1, 2)$;   (e) $(-3, 1, 2)$;   (f) $(-1, 1, 1)$;
   (g) $(1, 1, -1)$;   (h) $(4, -3, 1, 2)$

7. (a) $(2, -1)$;   (b) $(-2, 3)$ 8. (a) $(-1, 2, 1)$;   (b) $(3, 1, -2)$

SECTION 2

1. Row echelon form: (a), (c), (d), (g), and (h); reduced row echelon form: (c), (d), and (g)

2. (a) Inconsistent; (b) consistent $(4, -1)$; (c) consistent, infinitely many solutions; (d) consistent $(4, 5, 2)$; (e) inconsistent; (f) consistent, $(5, 3, 2)$

3. (a) $(-2, 5, 3)$; (b) Ø; (c) $\{(2+3\alpha, \alpha, -2) \mid \alpha \text{ real}\}$; (d) $\{(5-2\alpha-\beta, \alpha, 4-3\beta, \beta) \mid \alpha, \beta \text{ real}\}$; (e) $\{(3 - 5\alpha + 2\beta, \alpha, \beta, 6) \mid \alpha, \beta \text{ real}\}$; (f) $\{(\alpha, 2, -1) \mid \alpha \text{ real}\}$

4. (a) x_1, x_2, x_3 are lead variables. (c) x_1, x_3 are lead variables and x_2 is a free variable. (e) x_1, x_4 are lead variables and x_2, x_3 are free variables.

5. (a) $(5, 1)$; (b) inconsistent; (c) $(0, 0)$; (d) $\left\{\left(\dfrac{5-\alpha}{4}, \dfrac{1+7\alpha}{8}, \alpha\right) \bigg| \alpha \text{ real}\right\}$; (e) $\{(8 - 2\alpha, \alpha - 5, \alpha)\}$; (f) inconsistent; (g) inconsistent; (h) inconsistent; (i) $(0, \frac{3}{2}, 1)$; (j) $\{(2 - 6\alpha, 4 + \alpha, 3 - \alpha, \alpha)\}$; (k) $\{(\frac{15}{4} - \frac{5}{8}\alpha - \beta, -\frac{1}{4} - \frac{1}{8}\alpha, \alpha, \beta)\}$; (l) $\{(1 + \frac{2}{7}\alpha, \frac{3}{7}\alpha, \alpha)\}$

6. (a) $(0, -1)$; (b) $\{(\frac{3}{4} - \frac{5}{8}\alpha, -\frac{1}{4} - \frac{1}{8}\alpha, \alpha, 3) \mid \alpha \text{ is real}\}$; (c) $\{(0, \alpha, -\alpha)\}$; (d) $\{\alpha(-\frac{4}{3}, 0, \frac{1}{3}, 1)\}$

8. $a \neq -2$ 9. $\beta = 2$ 10. (a) $a = 5, b = 4$; (b) $a = 5, b \neq 4$

11. (a) $(-2, 2)$; (b) $(-7, 4)$ 12. (a) $(-3, 2, 1)$; (b) $(2, -2, 1)$

13. $x_1 = 280, x_2 = 230, x_3 = 350, x_4 = 590$ 17. $x_1 = 1, \; x_2 = 3, \; x_3 = 6, \; x_4 = 6$

18. 6 moles N_2, 18 moles H_2, 21 moles O_2

19. All three should be equal, i.e., $x_1 = x_2 = x_3$.

20. (a) $(5, 3, -2)$; (b) $(2, 4, 2)$; (c) $(2, 0, -2, -2, 0, 2)$

SECTION 3

1. (a) $\begin{bmatrix} 6 & 2 & 8 \\ -4 & 0 & 2 \\ 2 & 4 & 4 \end{bmatrix}$; (b) $\begin{bmatrix} 4 & 1 & 6 \\ -5 & 1 & 2 \\ 3 & -2 & 3 \end{bmatrix}$; (c) $\begin{bmatrix} 3 & 2 & 2 \\ 5 & -3 & -1 \\ -4 & 16 & 1 \end{bmatrix}$;

   (d) $\begin{bmatrix} 3 & 5 & -4 \\ 2 & -3 & 16 \\ 2 & -1 & 1 \end{bmatrix}$; (f) $\begin{bmatrix} 5 & 5 & 8 \\ -10 & -1 & -9 \\ 15 & 4 & 6 \end{bmatrix}$; (h) $\begin{bmatrix} 5 & -10 & 15 \\ 5 & -1 & 4 \\ 8 & -9 & 6 \end{bmatrix}$

2. (a) $\begin{bmatrix} 15 & 19 \\ 4 & 0 \end{bmatrix}$; (c) $\begin{bmatrix} 19 & 21 \\ 17 & 21 \\ 8 & 10 \end{bmatrix}$; (d) $\begin{bmatrix} 36 & 10 & 56 \\ 10 & 3 & 16 \end{bmatrix}$; (f) $\begin{bmatrix} 6 & 4 & 8 & 10 \\ -3 & -2 & -4 & -5 \\ 9 & 6 & 12 & 15 \end{bmatrix}$
   (b) and (e) are not possible.

3. (a) 3×3; (b) 1×2

4. (a) $\begin{bmatrix} 3 & 2 \\ 2 & -3 \end{bmatrix} \begin{bmatrix} x_1 \\ x_2 \end{bmatrix} = \begin{bmatrix} 1 \\ 5 \end{bmatrix}$; (b) $\begin{bmatrix} 1 & 1 & 0 \\ 2 & 1 & -1 \\ 3 & -2 & 2 \end{bmatrix} \begin{bmatrix} x_1 \\ x_2 \\ x_3 \end{bmatrix} = \begin{bmatrix} 5 \\ 6 \\ 7 \end{bmatrix}$;

   (c) $\begin{bmatrix} 2 & 1 & 1 \\ 1 & -1 & 2 \\ 3 & -2 & -1 \end{bmatrix} \begin{bmatrix} x_1 \\ x_2 \\ x_3 \end{bmatrix} = \begin{bmatrix} 4 \\ 2 \\ 0 \end{bmatrix}$

10. $A = A^2 = A^3 = A^n$ 11. $A^{2n} = I$, $A^{2n+1} = A$ 13. (a) $\mathbf{b} = 2\mathbf{a}_1 + \mathbf{a}_2$

14. (a) inconsistent; (b) consistent; (c) inconsistent

28. Monday, 575; Tuesday, 936; Wednesday, 457.8; Thursday, 1105; Friday, 457.8

29. 4500 married, 5500 single

31. (b) 0 walks of length 2 from V_2 to V_3 and 3 walks of length 2 from V_2 to V_5;
    (c) 6 walks of length 3 from V_2 to V_3 and 2 walks of length 3 from V_2 to V_5

32. (a) $A = \begin{bmatrix} 0 & 1 & 0 & 1 & 0 \\ 1 & 0 & 1 & 1 & 0 \\ 0 & 1 & 0 & 0 & 0 \\ 1 & 1 & 0 & 0 & 1 \\ 0 & 0 & 0 & 1 & 0 \end{bmatrix}$;

(c) 5 walks of length 3 from V_2 to V_4 and 7 walks of length 3 or less

33. $b = a_{22} - \dfrac{a_{12}a_{21}}{a_{11}}$

SECTION 4

1. (a) Type I;   (b) not an elementary matrix;   (c) type III;   (d) type II

3. (a) $\begin{bmatrix} -2 & 0 \\ 0 & 1 \end{bmatrix}$;   (b) $\begin{bmatrix} 1 & 0 & 0 \\ 0 & 0 & 1 \\ 0 & 1 & 0 \end{bmatrix}$;   (c) $\begin{bmatrix} 1 & 0 & 0 \\ 0 & 1 & 0 \\ 0 & 2 & 1 \end{bmatrix}$

4. (a) $\begin{bmatrix} 0 & 0 & 1 \\ 0 & 1 & 0 \\ 1 & 0 & 0 \end{bmatrix}$;   (b) $\begin{bmatrix} 1 & -3 \\ 0 & 1 \end{bmatrix}$;   (c) $\begin{bmatrix} \frac{1}{2} & 0 & 0 \\ 0 & 1 & 0 \\ 0 & 0 & 1 \end{bmatrix}$

5. (a) $E = \begin{bmatrix} 1 & 0 & 0 \\ 0 & 1 & 0 \\ 1 & 0 & 1 \end{bmatrix}$;   (b) $F = \begin{bmatrix} 1 & 0 & 0 \\ 0 & 1 & -1 \\ 0 & 0 & 1 \end{bmatrix}$

6. (a) $E_1 = \begin{bmatrix} 1 & 0 & 0 \\ -3 & 1 & 0 \\ 0 & 0 & 1 \end{bmatrix}$;   (b) $E_2 = \begin{bmatrix} 1 & 0 & 0 \\ 0 & 1 & 0 \\ -2 & 0 & 1 \end{bmatrix}$;   (c) $E_3 = \begin{bmatrix} 1 & 0 & 0 \\ 0 & 1 & 0 \\ 0 & 1 & 1 \end{bmatrix}$

7. (a) $\begin{bmatrix} 1 & 0 \\ 3 & 1 \end{bmatrix} \begin{bmatrix} 3 & 1 \\ 0 & 2 \end{bmatrix}$,   (c) $\begin{bmatrix} 1 & 0 & 0 \\ 3 & 1 & 0 \\ -2 & 2 & 1 \end{bmatrix} \begin{bmatrix} 1 & 1 & 1 \\ 0 & 2 & 3 \\ 0 & 0 & 3 \end{bmatrix}$

8. (b) (i) $(0, -1, 1)^T$,   (ii) $(-4, -2, 5)^T$,   (iii) $(0, 3, -2)^T$

9. (a) $\begin{bmatrix} 0 & 1 \\ 1 & 1 \end{bmatrix}$; (b) $\begin{bmatrix} 3 & -5 \\ -1 & 2 \end{bmatrix}$; (c) $\begin{bmatrix} -4 & 3 \\ \frac{3}{2} & -1 \end{bmatrix}$; (d) $\begin{bmatrix} \frac{1}{3} & 0 \\ -1 & \frac{1}{3} \end{bmatrix}$;

(e) $\begin{bmatrix} 1 & -1 & 0 \\ 0 & 1 & -1 \\ 0 & 0 & 1 \end{bmatrix}$; (f) $\begin{bmatrix} 3 & 0 & -5 \\ 0 & \frac{1}{3} & 0 \\ -1 & 0 & 2 \end{bmatrix}$; (g) $\begin{bmatrix} 2 & -3 & 3 \\ -\frac{3}{5} & \frac{6}{5} & -1 \\ -\frac{2}{5} & -\frac{1}{5} & 0 \end{bmatrix}$; (h) $\begin{bmatrix} -\frac{1}{2} & -1 & -\frac{1}{2} \\ -2 & -1 & -1 \\ \frac{3}{2} & 1 & \frac{1}{2} \end{bmatrix}$

10. (a) $\begin{bmatrix} -1 & 0 \\ 4 & 2 \end{bmatrix}$; (b) $\begin{bmatrix} -8 & 5 \\ -14 & 9 \end{bmatrix}$ 11. (a) $\begin{bmatrix} 20 & -5 \\ -34 & 7 \end{bmatrix}$; (c) $\begin{bmatrix} 0 & -2 \\ -2 & 2 \end{bmatrix}$

SECTION 5

1. (a) $\begin{bmatrix} I & A^{-1} \end{bmatrix}$; (b) $\begin{bmatrix} I \\ A^{-1} \end{bmatrix}$; (c) $\begin{bmatrix} A^T A & A^T \\ A & I \end{bmatrix}$; (d) $AA^T + I$; (e) $\begin{bmatrix} I & A^{-1} \\ A & I \end{bmatrix}$

3. (a) $A\mathbf{b}_1 = \begin{bmatrix} 3 \\ 3 \end{bmatrix}$, $A\mathbf{b}_2 = \begin{bmatrix} 4 \\ -1 \end{bmatrix}$;

(b) $\begin{bmatrix} 1 & 1 \end{bmatrix} B = \begin{bmatrix} 3 & 4 \end{bmatrix}$, $\begin{bmatrix} 2 & -1 \end{bmatrix} B = \begin{bmatrix} 3 & -1 \end{bmatrix}$; (c) $AB = \begin{bmatrix} 3 & 4 \\ 3 & -1 \end{bmatrix}$

4. (a) $\begin{bmatrix} 3 & 1 & 1 & 1 \\ 3 & 2 & 1 & 2 \\ \hline 1 & 1 & 1 & 1 \\ 1 & 2 & 1 & 1 \end{bmatrix}$; (b) $\begin{bmatrix} 1 & 1 & 1 & 1 \\ 0 & 1 & 0 & 0 \\ \hline 3 & 1 & 1 & 1 \\ 0 & 1 & 0 & 1 \end{bmatrix}$; (c) $\begin{bmatrix} 2 & 2 & 2 & 2 \\ 2 & 4 & 2 & 2 \\ \hline 3 & 1 & 1 & 1 \\ 3 & 2 & 1 & 2 \end{bmatrix}$; (d) $\begin{bmatrix} 1 & 2 & 1 & 1 \\ 1 & 1 & 1 & 1 \\ \hline 3 & 2 & 1 & 2 \\ 3 & 1 & 1 & 1 \end{bmatrix}$

5. (b) $\begin{bmatrix} 0 & 2 & 0 & -2 \\ 8 & 5 & 8 & -5 \\ \hline 3 & 2 & 3 & -2 \\ 5 & 3 & 5 & -3 \end{bmatrix}$; (d) $\begin{bmatrix} 3 & -3 \\ 2 & -2 \\ 1 & -1 \\ \hline 5 & -5 \\ 4 & -4 \end{bmatrix}$

12. $A^2 = \begin{bmatrix} B & O \\ O & B \end{bmatrix}$, $A^4 = \begin{bmatrix} B^2 & O \\ O & B^2 \end{bmatrix}$

13. (a) $\begin{bmatrix} O & I \\ I & O \end{bmatrix}$; (b) $\begin{bmatrix} I & O \\ -B & I \end{bmatrix}$

CHAPTER TEST

1. False 2. True 3. True 4. False 5. False 6. False 7. False 8. False 9. True 10. True

Chapter 2

SECTION I

1. (a) $\det(M_{21}) = -8$, $\det(M_{22}) = -2$, $\det(M_{23}) = 5$; (b) $A_{21} = 8$, $A_{22} = -2$, $A_{23} = -5$

2. (a) and (c) are nonsingular.

3. (a) 1;   (b) 4;   (c) 0;   (d) 58;   (e) -39;   (f) 0;   (g) 8;   (h) 20

4. (a) 2;   (b) -4;   (c) 0;   (d) 0

5. $-x^3 + ax^2 + bx + c$ 6. $\lambda = 6$ or -1

SECTION 2

1. (a) -24;   (b) 30;   (c) -1 2. (a) 10;   (b) 20

3. (a), (e), and (f) are singular while (b), (c), and (d) are nonsingular.

4. $c = 5$ or -3 7. (a) 20;   (b) 108;   (c) 160;   (d) $\frac{5}{4}$

8. (a) -6;   (c) 6;   (e) 1   11. $\det(A) = u_{11}u_{22}u_{33}$

Chapter 6

SECTION I

1. (a) $\lambda_1 = 5$, the eigenspace is spanned by $(1, 1)^T$,
$\lambda_2 = -1$, the eigenspace is spanned by $(1, -2)^T$;

(b) $\lambda_1 = 3$, the eigenspace is spanned by $(4, 3)^T$,
$\lambda_2 = 2$, the eigenspace is spanned by $(1, 1)^T$;

(c) $\lambda_1 = \lambda_2 = 2$, the eigenspace is spanned by $(1, 1)^T$,

(d) $\lambda_1 = 3 + 4i$, the eigenspace is spanned by $(2i, 1)^T$,
$\lambda_2 = 3 - 4i$, the eigenspace is spanned by $(-2i, 1)^T$;

(e) $\lambda_1 = 2 + i$, the eigenspace is spanned by $(1, 1 + i)^T$,
$\lambda_2 = 2 - i$, the eigenspace is spanned by $(1, 1 - i)^T$;

(f) $\lambda_1 = \lambda_2 = \lambda_3 = 0$, the eigenspace is spanned by $(1, 0, 0)^T$;

(g) $\lambda_1 = 2$, the eigenspace is spanned by $(1, 1, 0)^T$,
$\lambda_2 = 1$, the eigenspace is spanned by $(1, 0, 0)^T$, $(0, 1, -1)^T$;

(h) $\lambda_1 = 1$, the eigenspace is spanned by $(1, 0, 0)^T$,
$\lambda_2 = 4$, the eigenspace is spanned by $(1, 1, 1)^T$,
$\lambda_3 = -2$, the eigenspace is spanned by $(-1, -1, 5)^T$;

(i) $\lambda_1 = 2$, the eigenspace is spanned by $(7, 3, 1)^T$,
$\lambda_2 = 1$, the eigenspace is spanned by $(3, 2, 1)^T$,
$\lambda_3 = 0$, the eigenspace is spanned by $(1, 1, 1)^T$;

(j) $\lambda_1 = \lambda_2 = \lambda_3 = -1$, the eigenspace is spanned by $(1, 0, 1)^T$;

(k) $\lambda_1 = \lambda_2 = 2$, the eigenspace is spanned by e_1 and e_2,
$\lambda_3 = 3$, the eigenspace is spanned by e_3,
$\lambda_4 = 4$, the eigenspace is spanned by e_4;

(l) $\lambda_1 = 3$, the eigenspace is spanned by $(1, 2, 0, 0)^T$,
$\lambda_2 = 1$, the eigenspace is spanned by $(0, 1, 0, 0)^T$,
$\lambda_3 = \lambda_4 = 2$, the eigenspace is spanned by $(0, 0, 1, 0)^T$

8. β is an eigenvalue of B if and only if $\beta = \lambda - \alpha$ for some eigenvalue λ of A.

11. $\lambda_1 = 6$, $\lambda_2 = 2$

24. $\lambda_1 x^T y = (Ax)^T y = x^T A^T y = \lambda_2 x^T y$

SECTION 2

1. (a) $\begin{bmatrix} c_1 e^{2t} + c_2 e^{3t} \\ c_1 e^{2t} + 2c_2 e^{3t} \end{bmatrix}$;   (b) $\begin{bmatrix} -c_1 e^{-2t} - 4c_2 e^t \\ c_1 e^{-2t} + c_2 e^t \end{bmatrix}$;   (c) $\begin{bmatrix} 2c_1 + c_2 e^{5t} \\ c_1 - 2c_2 e^{5t} \end{bmatrix}$;

(d) $\begin{bmatrix} -c_1 e^t \sin t + c_2 e^t \cos t \\ c_1 e^t \cos t + c_2 e^t \sin t \end{bmatrix}$;   (e) $\begin{bmatrix} -c_1 e^{3t} \sin 2t + c_2 e^{3t} \cos 2t \\ c_1 e^{3t} \cos 2t + c_2 e^{3t} \sin 2t \end{bmatrix}$;

(f) $\begin{bmatrix} -c_1 + c_2 e^{5t} + c_3 e^t \\ -3c_1 + 8c_2 e^{5t} \\ c_1 + 4c_2 e^{5t} \end{bmatrix}$

2. (a) $\begin{bmatrix} e^{-3t} + 2e^t \\ -e^{-3t} + 2e^t \end{bmatrix}$;   (b) $\begin{bmatrix} e^t \cos 2t + 2e^t \sin 2t \\ e^t \sin 2t - 2e^t \cos 2t \end{bmatrix}$;   (c) $\begin{bmatrix} -6e^t + 2e^{-t} + 6 \\ -3e^t + e^{-t} + 4 \\ -e^t + e^{-t} + 2 \end{bmatrix}$;

(d) $\begin{bmatrix} -2 - 3e^t + 6e^{2t} \\ 1 + 3e^t - 3e^{2t} \\ 1 + 3e^{2t} \end{bmatrix}$

4. $y_1(t) = 15e^{-0.24t} + 25e^{-0.08t}$, $y_2(t) = -30e^{-0.24t} + 50e^{-0.08t}$

5. (a) $\begin{bmatrix} -2c_1 e^t - 2c_2 e^{-t} + c_3 e^{\sqrt{2}t} + c_4 e^{-\sqrt{2}t} \\ c_1 e^t + c_2 e^{-t} - c_3 e^{\sqrt{2}t} - c_4 e^{-\sqrt{2}t} \end{bmatrix}$; (b) $\begin{bmatrix} c_1 e^{2t} + c_2 e^{-2t} - c_3 e^t - c_4 e^{-t} \\ c_1 e^{2t} - c_2 e^{-2t} + c_3 e^t - c_4 e^{-t} \end{bmatrix}$

6. $y_1(t) = -e^{2t} + e^{-2t} + e^t$; $y_2(t) = -e^{2t} - e^{-2t} + 2e^t$

8. $x_1(t) = \cos t + 3 \sin t + \dfrac{1}{\sqrt{3}} \sin \sqrt{3}t$, $x_2(t) = \cos t + 3 \sin t - \dfrac{1}{\sqrt{3}} \sin \sqrt{3}t$

10. (a) $m_1 x_1''(t) = -kx_1 + k(x_2 - x_1)$, $m_2 x_2''(t) = -k(x_2 - x_1) + k(x_3 - x_2)$, $m_3 x_3''(t) = -k(x_3 - x_2) - kx_3$;

(b) $\begin{bmatrix} 0.1 \cos 2\sqrt{3}t + 0.9 \cos \sqrt{2}t \\ -0.2 \cos 2\sqrt{3}t + 1.2 \cos \sqrt{2}t \\ 0.1 \cos 2\sqrt{3}t + 0.9 \cos \sqrt{2}t \end{bmatrix}$

11. $p(\lambda) = (-1)^n (\lambda^n - a_{n-1} \lambda^{n-1} - \cdots - a_1 \lambda - a_0)$

8. (b) $\alpha = 2$;   (c) $\alpha = 3$ or $\alpha = -1$;   (d) $\alpha = 1$

19. The transition matrix and steady-state vector for the Markov chain are

$$\begin{bmatrix} 0.80 & 0.30 \\ 0.20 & 0.70 \end{bmatrix} \qquad \mathbf{x} = \begin{bmatrix} 0.60 \\ 0.40 \end{bmatrix}$$

In the long run we would expect 60% of the employees to be enrolled.

20. (a) $A = \begin{bmatrix} 0.70 & 0.20 & 0.10 \\ 0.20 & 0.70 & 0.10 \\ 0.10 & 0.10 & 0.80 \end{bmatrix}$

(c) The membership of all three groups will approach $100,000$ as n gets large.

23. (b) $\begin{bmatrix} e & e \\ 0 & e \end{bmatrix}$

24. (a) $\begin{bmatrix} 3 - 2e & 1 - e \\ -6 + 6e & -2 + 3e \end{bmatrix}$;   (c) $\begin{bmatrix} e & -1 + e & -1 + e \\ 1 - e & 2 - e & 1 - e \\ -1 + e & -1 + e & e \end{bmatrix}$

25. (a) $\begin{bmatrix} e^{-t} \\ e^{-t} \end{bmatrix}$;   (b) $\begin{bmatrix} -3e^t - e^{-t} \\ e^t + e^{-t} \end{bmatrix}$;   (c) $\begin{bmatrix} 3e^t - 2 \\ 2 - e^{-t} \\ e^{-t} \end{bmatrix}$

INDEX